D1376399

# RHUS DERMATITIS

## ITS PATHOLOGY AND CHEMOTHERAPY

THE UNIVERSITY OF CHICAGO PRESS
CHICAGO, ILLINOIS

THE BAKER & TAYLOR COMPANY
NEW YORK

THE CAMBRIDGE UNIVERSITY PRESS
LONDON

THE MARUZEN-KABUSHIKI-KAISHA
TOKYO, OSAKA, KYOTO, FUKUOKA, SENDAI

THE MISSION BOOK COMPANY
SHANGHAI

# RHUS DERMATITIS

FROM RHUS TOXICODENDRON, RADICANS
AND DIVERSILOBA

## (POISON IVY)

ITS PATHOLOGY *and* CHEMOTHERAPY

*By*

JAMES B. McNAIR

THE UNIVERSITY OF CHICAGO PRESS
CHICAGO, ILLINOIS

Published June 1923

Composed and Printed By
The University of Chicago Press
Chicago, Illinois, U.S.A.

# PREFACE

Of all the cutaneous eruptions caused accidentally by plant substances, that produced by the different species of *Rhus* is probably the most common in this country. The common occurrence of poisoning with poison ivy and poison oak, and the lack of any rational treatment, led me to try to isolate the principal skin irritant of this plant, in the hope that a knowledge of its characteristic properties might serve as a basis for such treatment.

The investigation of this poison has been carried on from the standpoint of pharmacology, of botany, and of chemistry. It is hoped evidence has thus been secured from these three which will help to eliminate error and converge toward a true understanding of the poison. The study of the morphology of the plant gives the method of formation, location, and means of transmission of the poison. The study of pathology has shown its manner of action on the body. Botany and pathology combined with a chemical knowledge of the structure of the poison have yielded a rational remedy for Rhus dermatitis.

It is my pleasant duty to gratefully acknowledge the many helpful suggestions and assistance in bacteriology from Professor Ivan C. Hall, in botany from Professor T. H. Goodspeed, in chemistry from professors H. C. Biddle and T. Brailsford Robertson, all of the University of California. The splendid co-operation of Dr. R. T. Legge, Dr. Ruby L. Cunningham, Dr. Paroni-Meads, Dr. C. L. McVey, Miss E. Sherman, Mrs. E. M. Calder, and the rest of the Infirmary Staff of the University of California has resulted in a collection of many statistics of diagnostic value.

I wish to thank Professor W. R. Bloor for the use of his laboratory at the University of California, where much of the work in chapter x was done.

I am indebted to the publishers of the *American Journal of Botany*, the *Archives of Dermatology and Syphilology*, the *Botanical Gazette*, the *Journal of Infectious Diseases*, the *Journal of the American*

*Chemical Society*, and the *Medical Record* for permission to reprint material from their journals.

Much of the appended bibliography was given to me by Leslie E. Warren, of the American Medical Association, Chicago, Illinois.

The above-mentioned persons are in no way responsible for any errors which may appear in the text.

The publication of a book involves editing, composition, proof-reading, printing, and publishing. For the successful co-operation of everyone from the errand boys to the managers, the author extends his grateful appreciation.

JAMES B. MCNAIR

UNIVERSITY OF CHICAGO
CHICAGO, ILLINOIS
1923

## CONTENTS

# LIST OF ILLUSTRATIONS

# CHAPTER I

## HISTORY AND DISTRIBUTION OF RHUS TOXICODENDRON, RADICANS, AND DIVERSILOBA[1]

*Rhus Toxicodendron* L., *Rhus radicans* L., and *Rhus diversiloba* T. and G. form a triad of plants equally regarded with aversion. The general recognition of their deleterious character is shown in the application of the names *poison ivy*, *poison vine*, and *poison oak*, given to them in various parts of the United States.

Perhaps the earliest mention of these plants in North America is the following description by Captain John Smith in 1609:

> The poisonous weed, being in shape but little different from our English yvie; but being touched causeth reddness, itchinge, and lastly blysters, the which howsoever, after a while they passe awaye of themselves without further harme; yet because for the time they are somewhat painefull, and in aspect dangerous, it hath gotten itselfe an ill name, although questionlesse of noe very ill nature.

Long before the birth of Linnaeus, Cornutus in 1635 described the plant as a species of ivy in his work on the plants of Canada (*Hedera trifolia Canadensis* Corn. 96 from Carolina in the British Herbarium).

About 1736 Linnaeus classified this plant as *Toxicodendron triphyllum glabrum*. At the same time he described and named *Rhus radicans*.

In an entry dated October 9, 1748, Peter Kalm gave an extensive and interesting description in his travels in North America of the *R. radicans* of Linnaeus. Since that time there have been many accounts of these plants and of their toxic nature.[2]

In 1820, Bigelow described *R. radicans* of Linnaeus as having

> Ternate leaves, that grow on long semicylindrical petioles. Leaflets ovate or rhomboidal, acute, smooth and shining on both sides, and veins sometimes

[1] Reprinted from the *American Journal of Botany*, VIII (March, 1921), 127–37.

[2] In 1719 in what is now New Mexico a Spanish expedition under Governor Valverde suffered severely from poison ivy (De Aguilar, 1719, cited by Bancroft, 1889, and Saunders, 1920).

a little hairy beneath. The margin is sometimes entire and sometimes variously toothed and lobed, in the same plant. The flowers are small and greenish white. They grow in panicles or compound racemes on the sides of the new shoots and are chiefly axillary. The barren [male] flowers have a calyx of five erect, acute segments, and a corolla of five oblong recurved petals. Stamens erect with oblong anthers. In the center is a rudiment of a style. The fertile [female] flowers, situated on a different plant, are about half the size of the preceding. The calyx and corolla are similar but more erect. They have five small, abortive stamens and a roundish germ [ovule] surmounted with a short, erect style ending in three stigmas. The berries are roundish and of a pale green color, approaching to white.

A plant has long appeared in the Pharmacopoeias under the name of *Rhus Toxicodendron.* Botanists are not agreed whether this plant is a separate species from the one under consideration, or whether they are varieties of the same. Linnaeus made them different with the distinction of the leaves being naked and entire in *Rhus radicans*, while they are pubescent and angular in *Rhus Toxicodendron.* Michaux and Pursh, whose opportunities of observation have been more extensive, consider the two as mere local varieties; while Elliott and Nuttall still hold them to be distinct species. Among the plants which grow abundantly around Boston, I have frequently observed individual shoots from the same stock having the characters of both varieties. I have also observed that young plants of *Rhus radicans* frequently do not put out rooting fibers until they are several years old and that they seem, in this respect, to be considerably influenced by the contiguity of supporting objects.

The attitude taken by Bigelow has been sustained by later botanists, among them Torrey and Gray (1839) who consider *R. radicans* a variety of *R. Toxicodendron.*

*Rhus diversiloba* was discovered by Douglas at Fort Vancouver on the Columbia River about 1830. Upon examination of this specimen, W. J. Hooker (1831), although he considered it "nearly allied, as this assuredly is, to the two preceding species [*R. Toxicodendron* and *R. radicans*]," nevertheless "ventured to consider it distinct." He therefore gave it botanical significance as *Rhus lobata.* To support his conclusion he advances the following reasons:

Its general habit is very different, having erect straight *stems* and numerous small leafy *branches.* The leaflets besides being deeply lobed with acute sinuses are truly ovate, very obtuse, and greatly smaller than in any state of *R. Toxicodendron*, or *R. radicans*, which I have seen; the *panicles*, too, are exceedingly numerous.

A free translation of Hooker's Latin description of the plant is as follows:

> Bush erect, 3–4 feet, branches round with the youngest ones pubescent, branches numerous, short, spreading, leafy. *Leaves* long-petiolate, trifoliate, with little leaves ovate, 1–2 inches long, very obtuse, membranaceous, at the base sometimes acute, sometimes rotund or truncate, beneath especially pubescent, deeply and variously lobate, terminate one sub-long-petiolate, each side sub-equally lobate with lobes generally less than 3, with little lateral leaves at the exterior margin more deeply lobate. *Flowers* (male) yellow, in loose racemes, shorter than leaf, longer than petiole. *Bracts* at the base of the branches oblong, ciliate. *Calyx* deeply parted with oblong lappets. *Petals* 5, much longer than the lappets of the calyx, obovate into a tongue evidently with attenuated base, at the back veined. *Stamens* 5, erect, little shorter than petals. *Filaments* subulate. *Anthers* 5, somewhat more greatly ovate, pale yellow, with cells sub-opposite. *Style* small, extending from the center of a platter-shaped disc situated in the bottom of the calyx, margin of the disc elevated, curled.

The next known discovery of *R. lobata* was that of Captain Beechy (Hooker and Arnott, 1832) at San Francisco and Monterey Bay about 1832. These specimens differed in no respect from the more northern ones discovered by Mr. Douglas. The observations of Nuttall (Torrey and Gray, 1839) furthered the botanical knowledge of the plant. He noticed:

> The sterile and fertile flowers of this species (which is very near *R. Toxicodendron*) present some notable differences. The sterile, which is figured by Hooker, has rather deeply lobed leaflets, sometimes in fives and larger flowers; in the fertile the leaflets are almost entire or slightly lobed and the flowers considerably smaller, so that it might readily be taken for a distinct species. The fruit is white, somewhat pubescent and gibbous.

Torrey and Gray (1839) summed up the previous knowledge of the plant and renamed it *Rhus diversiloba*, the name by which it is now more commonly known.

The difference between *R. diversiloba* and *R. Toxicodendron* is so small that their proper classification forms a bone of contention between botanists. Those botanists who believe in innumerable species are in favor of their separation, while the more conservative are opposed to it. Greene (1903) considers *R. diversiloba* "a peculiar type of *Toxicodendron* belonging exclusively to the Pacific

Coast." Engler (1897) believes *diversiloba* a subspecies of *Toxicodendron*. The only botanical ground for the separation of the two into different species is a slight difference in the shape of their leaflet (Gray, 1826). A three years' study of *R. diversiloba* and a recent study of *R. Toxicodendron* in Pennsylvania and Maryland for a year have enabled me to make a personal comparison of the two plants. The tracings of the outlines of mature leaves of both

FIG. 1.—Tracings of mature leaves of *Rhus Toxicodendron* (reduced $6\frac{3}{4}\times$)

plants (Figs. 1, 2) and a tabular account of the flowers of both plants will permit the reader to decide whether or not there is sufficient difference to constitute a separation into species.

### GEOGRAPHICAL DISTRIBUTION OF R. DIVERSILOBA

The distribution of poison oak includes Lower California north of latitude 29° (Brandegee, 1889), Santa Barbara and Santa Catalina Islands (Brandegee, 1890), California, Oregon, Washington,

Vancouver Island, and British Columbia. The region inhabited by the plant has been approximately defined by citations from botanical literature, sources of herbarium specimens, and places where birds were found that had poison oak seeds in their stomachs. From these data, the territory inhabited by poison oak embraces the Sonoran and lower transition life-zones, and excludes the desert

FIG. 2.—Tracings of mature leaves of *Rhus diversiloba* (reduced $6\frac{3}{4}\times$)

and central valley regions of California together with the upper transition and boreal zones.

The inhabited area has an altitude varying from sea-level to 6,000 feet above sea-level. Hall's (1912) observations in the Yosemite Valley make it an inhabitant of the Hetch Hetchy and the low foothills with a maximum altitude of about 4,000 feet. In southern California he noticed it in the San Jacinto Mountains along the North Fork of the San Jacinto River at an altitude of

TABLE I

COMPARISON OF FLOWERS OF RHUS TOXICODENDRON (POISON IVY) AND RHUS DIVERSILOBA (POISON OAK)*

| | Male | | Female | |
|---|---|---|---|---|
| | *Rhus diversiloba* | *Rhus Toxicodendron* | *Rhus diversiloba* | *Rhus Toxicodendron* |
| Panicles: | | | | |
| Color | Light green | Light green | Light green | Light green |
| Number | As many as leaves on flowering shoot, except none in highest or lowest axils | As many as leaves on flowering shoot, except none in highest or lowest axils | ½ as many as leaves. Total number about the same as in male (3 to 5) | |
| Length | 7 cm. | 3–5 cm. | 3–6 cm. | 3–4 cm. |
| Angle with stem | Sharp. 45° | Sharp. 45° | Obtuse, limp | Obtuse, limp |
| Number of side twigs of first order | 12 | 12 | 12 | 5 |
| Length | 3 lowest, 2 cm. | 3 lowest, 2 cm. | 2.5 cm. | 1.5–2 cm. |
| Phyllotaxy | Same as leaf | Same as leaf (3/9) | | |
| Flowers: | | | | |
| Number | | | | |
| Pedicel length | 4–7 mm. | 2–3 mm. | 5–10 mm. | 1.5–2 mm. |
| Flower width | 5–7 mm. | 9 mm. | 5 mm. | 4 mm. |
| Calyx leaves: | | | | |
| Number | 5 | 5 | 5 | 5 |
| Length | 2 mm. | 2 mm. | 2 mm. | 1 mm. |
| Width | | 1 mm. | | |
| Shape | Tongue-shaped | Tongue-shaped | Tongue-shaped | Tongue-shaped |
| Color | Dark green | Dark green | Dark green | Dark green |
| Petals: | | | | |
| Number | 5 | 5 | 5 | 5 |
| Length | 4 mm. | 4 mm. | 3 mm. | 2 mm. |
| Width | 1.5 mm. | 2 mm. | 1.5 mm. | 1 mm. |
| Shape | Elliptical, curved down | Elliptical, curved down | Not curved down as much as male | Not curved down as much as male |
| Color | Light green | Light green | | |

* Specimens of *R. Toxicodendron* collected in the Botanical Garden of the University of Pennsylvania; specimens of *R. diversiloba* collected at Berkeley, California.

TABLE I—*Continued*

| | Male | | Female | |
|---|---|---|---|---|
| | *Rhus diversiloba* | *Rhus Toxicodendron* | *Rhus diversiloba* | *Rhus Toxicodendron* |
| Stamens: | | | | |
| Number | 5 | 5 | 5 | 5 |
| Length | 2.5 mm. | | 1.5 mm. | |
| Anther: | | | | |
| Variety | Introrse, shrunken | Introrse | Introrse, shrunken | Introrse, shrunken |
| Filament | Dirty yellow color | | Dirty yellow color | Dirty yellow color |
| Length | 2 times as long as anther | | | |
| Pollen: | | | | |
| Size | 1/800 sq. mm. in horizontal area | | | |
| Shape | Wide $\frac{1}{3}$–$\frac{1}{2}$ of length | | | |
| Color | Yellow | | Absent | |
| Condition | Rough with sharp-pointed cells, adhesive | | | |
| Ovules: | | | | |
| Number | | | | |
| Size | 1 mm. high | | | |
| Shape | Keg | | Egg-shaped | |
| Color | | | | |
| Condition | Rudimentary | Rudimentary | Fully developed | Fully developed |
| Carpels | | | 3, of which 2 are rudimentary | 3, of which 2 are rudimentary |
| Stigmas: | | | | |
| Number | 3 | | | |
| Size | | | | |
| Shape | | | | |
| Color | | | | |
| Condition | | | | |

approximately 3,000 feet. I have found it in Cold Water Canyon on the southwest side of Mount San Antonio in the San Gabriel Range in southern California at an altitude of 4,500 feet. The lowest and highest regions of California are therefore free from poison oak.

From rainfall data compiled by the United States government the plant requires an annual rainfall of at least 10 inches.

TABLE II

GEOGRAPHICAL DISTRIBUTION OF RHUS DIVERSILOBA (POISON OAK) ACCORDING TO LITERATURE AND CORRESPONDENCE

| Date | Author | Location |
|---|---|---|
| 1831 | Douglas | Common on the outskirts of woods in dry soils in northwest America. Plentiful at Fort Vancouver |
| 1832 | Hooker and Arnott | San Francisco and Monterey Bay |
| 1845 | Lindley and Lyon | Common everywhere in California. An inhabitant of Santa Catalina Island |
| 1855 | Newberry | Common throughout Northern California; more rare in the Klamath Basin |
| 1856 | Torrey | Plains and mountains near San Gabriel; Martinez |
| 1876 | Brewer and Watson | From southern California to British Columbia in California most abundant in the Coast Range. |
| 1878 | Wheeler | Common on the Pacific Coast |
| 1886 | Greene | On the north side of Santa Cruz Island |
| 1886 | Lyon | An inhabitant of Santa Catalina Island |
| 1889 | Brandegee | In Lower California, very abundant about El Rosario |
| 1890 | Brandegee | Common on San Miguel, Santa Rosa, Santa Cruz, and Santa Catalina Island |
| 1893 | Coville | Found at several points on rocky hillsides in the foothill belt of the western slopes of the Sierra Nevada |
| 1894 | Greene | Copious in the Coast Range hills, preferring cool northward slopes and the banks of streams; absent from the more elevated portions of the Sierra |
| 1895 | Gray | Common throughout California, north to the borders of Washington |
| 1897 | Jepson | Fort Bragg to Sherwood Valley in redwood belt |
| 1898 | Howell | In forests and rocky hillsides, British Columbia to California |
| 1898 | Jepson | Mitchell Canyon, Mount Diablo |
| 1899 | Jepson | Crane Creek and Rosewood, Stiver's ranch |

| Date | Author | Location |
|---|---|---|
| 1900 | Jepson | Cedar Creek |
| 1901 | Jepson | Smith Mountains, Palomar, 6,000 feet |
| 1901 | Jepson | Kaweah Range, north slopes and moist places |
| 1901 | Jepson | St. Helena, climbing redwood |
| 1901 | Jepson | Pine Canyon, Mount Diablo, shrubs 6 feet high |
| 1902 | Chestnut | Common in valleys and on hillsides everywhere throughout Mendocino County |
| 1902 | Jepson | Givin Mine, Calaveras County, 1,100 feet altitude. Shrubs 12 and 13 feet high |
| | | Schoolhouse Creek, Fort Bragg, Cahto |
| | | Redstone Park |
| | | Hawley School, Willits. Fort Seward, Ranch Ridge, Humboldt County, 3,000 feet. Abundant |
| | | Idolwild (near Camp Grant), Humboldt County Climbs up redwood trunks 90–100 feet |
| | | Hawkins Bar (Dyer's ranch) |
| | | Usal to Cottonaby Creek |
| 1903 | Greene | A peculiar type of *Toxicodendron* belonging exclusively to the Pacific Coast |
| 1903 | Jepson | Along fences in Vacaville |
| | | Vacaville to Twin Sister's Peak. Vacaville Rock Peak |
| 1906 | Piper | Washington to California in the coast regions. Humid transition zone |
| 1907 | Jepson | Cudahay Trail to Dutch Henry's on Klamath River, 2,500–4,000 feet, below fir zone, only along river |
| 1909 | Parsons | Throughout California, save in the high Sierras |
| 1909 | Jepson | Pepperwood, Humboldt County, in redwood trees. Hetch Hetchy (3,700 feet) |
| 1910 | Jepson | Belden, 2,000 (approximate) feet. Half Moon Bay |
| 1911 | Jepson | Arroyo Seco, Monterey County, altitude 100–500 feet. Napa Range near Atlas Peak |
| 1911 | Abrams | Frequent in chaparral belt throughout southern California |
| 1911 | Muir | Common throughout the foothill region up to a height of at least 3,000 feet above sea-level |
| 1911 | Jepson | Found in Coast Range and foothills of the Sierra Nevada, widely distributed and often abundant |
| 1912 | Hall | Confined to lower end of Yosemite Valley, and to the Hetch Hetchy and low foothills |
| 1912 | Jepson | Nelson, middle Tule River, altitude 4,760 feet |
| | | Saratoga, Santa Clara County, altitude 600 feet |

| Date | Author | Location |
|---|---|---|
| 1916 | Hall............... | Merced Canyon, not rare to 3,200 feet altitude. West of Wawona at 4,500 feet. Small<br>In Santa Cruz Mountains, dominant shrub Alma to summit, especially in redwood belt |
| 1916 | Sanborn............ | Abundant in the hills about Eugene, and all through the western part of Oregon |
| 1916 | Crawford........... | In mountain canyons and valleys from sea-level to about 7,000–7,500 feet elevation<br>Very common throughout Pomona Valley and all valley regions between San Bernardino and the coast |
| 1916 | Parish............. | Grows to some extent in damp soil in San Bernardino Valley, altitude 1,000 feet, and abundantly in the canyons of the southern slope of the San Bernardino Mountains up to 3,500 feet altitude at least. Does not grow in the higher mountains nor in either the Mojave or the Colorado Desert |
| 1919 | Jepson............. | Dunsmuir to Castle Rock Station along Sacramento River, 2,200 feet altitude |

The following is a list[1] of locations where birds which had eaten *R. diversiloba* fruit were collected:

CALIFORNIA

Alhambra
Arroyo Valley Creek
Berkeley
Berryessa
Camp Meeker
Chico, Tehama County
Claremont
Cull Canyon
Guadalupe
Haywards
Mount Diablo
Northwest of Pasadena
Palo Alto
Pasadena
Payne P.O., Tehama County
Petrolia
Pinte Mountains
Rio Dell, 15 miles southwest
San Antonio Canyon
San Fernando
San Jose
Santa Clara County
Santa Monica Mountains
Santa Rosa
Sierra Morena, 6 miles
Simol
Smith Creek
South of Palo Alto
Stewart's Ranch
Voltas
Watsonville

[1] Communicated to the author by Dr. E. W. Nelson, acting chief, Biological Survey, United States Department of Agriculture.

### Oregon

Ashland
Bybee's Bridge
Coquille
Los Gatos

### Washington

Garfield County

The following shows the distribution of *R. diversiloba* according to sources of herbarium specimens:

### California

Alpine, San Diego County, Mearns 4019
Alum Rock Springs, vicinity, Santa Clara County
Big Chico Creek Canyon, Butte County, altitude 250 feet, A. A. Heller
Black Mountain, Santa Clara County, Elmer 4785
Blochman's Ranch, Mariposa County, Alice Eastwood
Cantara, Siskiyou County, Alice Eastwood
Carmel, Monterey County
Casitas Pass, Ventura County, altitude 1,000 feet
Chico, near, Palmer 2060
Clayton, Contra Costa County, Brewer 1068
Cow Creek Mounts, Shasta County
Folsom
Forest Ranch, 1897, Mrs. R. M. Austin, 1901
Fort Tejon, vicinity, Kern County
Foster Park, Ventura County, Alice Eastwood
Gasquet, Del Norte County, Alice Eastwood
Havilah, Grinnell 362
Healdsburg, Sonoma County
Kings Canyon, Lieber Mounts, Los Angeles County
Little Chico Creek, Austin 749
Los Gatos foothills, 1904, A. A. Heller 7327
Los Tronus Creek, San Mateo County
Mendocino, near, H. E. Brown 750
Monterey, Bailey
Monterey, Botta in Mus. Herb., Paris
Mount Diablo, Alice Eastwood
Mutair Flat, Ventura County
New York Falls, Amador County, altitude 2,000 feet
North Fork and vicinity, Griffiths 4531
Oroville, Table Mount, 8 miles north of, Butte County
Pacific Grove
Petrified Forest, Alice Eastwood
Palo Alto, foothills near, Santa Clara County

Pasadena, Jones 3206
Red Reed Canyon, Ventura County
Round Valley, Mendocino County
St. Helena, vicinity
San Clemente Island, Mearns 4048
San Diego, canyons near, J. J. Hernleer
San Francisco, Lone Mount Cemetery
San Franciquito Creek, San Mateo County
San Jacinto Mountains, shade along north fork of San Jacinto River, altitude 3,000 feet, H. M. Hall
Santa Barbara, Elmer 3940
Santa Clara County, J. J. Hernleer
Santa Cruz, Marcus E. Jones
Santa Cruz Island, Stanford Herbarium
Santa Cruz Mountains, 1903, N. L. Gardner
Sausalito Hills, Kellogg and Herford 332
Savage Hill, Amador County, altitude 2,200 feet, Hansen 53
Shasta River, near mouth, Siskiyou County
Stanford University, Santa Clara County, Rutter 163
Stanford foothills, Baker's collection No. 547
Sulphur Banks, Lake County
Sulphur Mountain Spring, Sulphur Mountains, Abrams and McGregor 46
Sulphur Mountain Spring, Ventura County
Table Mount, Butte County, altitude 600 feet
Tamalpais
Tassajara Hot Springs, Elmer 3178
Topsajoin (?) Hot Springs, Monterey County
Vaca Valley, Solano County

### Oregon

Ashland, Stanford Herbarium
Azalea Creek, Mears
Cascade Mountains, Moseley in Kew Herbarium
Columbia River, between 46° and 49° latitude
Columbia River, rocky places, Ethel I. Sanborn
Coos Bay, House 4746
Corvallis, 1898, Moses Craig
Dallas
Deschutes River, 1885, Thomas Howell
Jackson County, along Walker Creek, altitude 3,300 feet, Applegate 2339
Lyall in Kew Herbarium
Portland, 1885, L. E. Henderson
Portland, open hillsides, Ethel I. Sanborn
Portland, Walpole 44 and 8

Portland, rocky hillsides, 1903, J. Lunell
Rocky Butte, Multnomah County, Ethel I. Sanborn
Umpqua Divide, head of Elk Creek, altitude 1,400 feet, Leiberg 4190
Umpqua River, east fork of North Fork, 6–10 miles east of Peel, altitude 1,500 feet, Applegate 2,700
Umpqua–Rogeu River Divide, dry hillsides, Ethel I. Sanborn
Wasco County, 1896, L. F. Henderson

### Washington

American Lake, south of Tacoma, F. S. Hall
Orchard Point, Kitsap County, F. L. Pickett
Seattle, F. L. Pickett
Seattle, F. S. Hall
Tacoma, seashore and bluffs, F. L. Pickett
Union City, F. L. Pickett

### Vancouver Island

Vancouver Island, Tolmic, Douglas in Kew Herbarium
Victoria, near Swan Lake and on the west side of Seanich Arm, J. R. Anderson

# CHAPTER II

## THE MORPHOLOGY AND ANATOMY OF RHUS DIVERSILOBA[1]

*Rhus diversiloba* T. and G. may be either a low deciduous shrub or a high climbing vine, as it readily adapts itself to local conditions. In sunny exposures it most frequently occurs as a low shrub 3–4 feet high. One instance is known, however, of a treelike plant, 14 feet high with a diameter at its base of 6 inches. In shady locations it more frequently assumes a vinelike form and by means of its aerial rootlets ascends the trunks of trees to a height of 15–20 feet.

The new wood has pale-grayish bark, is light in weight, brittle, and contains much pith. The ends of the young shoots and the petioles are usually red-brown in color. In the early spring groups of plants may be distinguished at a distance before fully leafing out by this red-brown of the young stems and leaves. The branches gradually become wood with the accumulation of successive annual rings, the bark thickens, roughens, and becomes the abode of many lichens and mosses. The bark on the old wood is brown-gray, furrowed lengthwise, has horizontal rows of wartlike lenticels, and on dead limbs peels off laterally, not spirally. The large branches have but few small lateral branches. In its shrubby form no difference can be observed between the height of the male and that of the female plants, nor can any noticeable difference be determined in the angles which the branches subtend to the trunk. The leaflets, too, generally have similar shapes on both plants.

Flower panicles do not develop on the ends of young shoots, but form on the sides. The apical bud makes a growth of 4–5 centimeters per year. It requires about four weeks for the full development of a leaf. The flower and leaf buds begin to expand simultaneously, but the leaves soon expand more rapidly and consequently some of the leaves reach maturity before the flowers open. The expanding leaves are very tender and turgid, and sap flows

[1] Reprinted from the *American Journal of Botany*, VIII (April, 1921), 179–91.

quickly out of injured stem or leaf areas. These leaves are arranged alternately on the stem and have a phyllotaxy of 8/21.

The leaf scars are triangular in outline. The swelling where the leaf is attached may have the function, by its growth, of turning the leaf to a better exposure.

## THE LEAF

The glossy, dark-green leaflets are deepest in color when in the sun, pale underneath, generally three in number, although sometimes five, orbicular to ovate or oblong-ovate, undulate or plane, entire or variously lobed, segmented or toothed, and from 1 to 4 inches long. The five-leaflet variety, according to Brandegee (1890) is quite common on the Santa Barbara Islands. Leaves having five leaflets are also found on plants which have a majority of the three-leaflet kind. Leaflets are singularly variable in size, outline, and segmentation, even on the same plant. This fact constitutes one of the most remarkable features of the plant and is the principal basis for its differentiation from *R. Toxicodendron* L. Leaf tracings (Fig 2, p. 5) made from mature leaves collected by the writer at Berkeley, California, on September 27, 1916, were taken from plants within a radius of 100 feet, all of which were enjoying the same soil and exposure and had no apparent cause for such marked differences in leaf shape.

Leaves in the sun differ from those in the shade, not only as regards color, but also in several structural details. The young leaves are covered with hairs, which dry out and fall off as the leaves become fully matured. These hairs are apparently more frequent on leaves exposed to the sun than on those in the shade. Other differences will be described later.

In autumn, as in spring and summer, the plant is singularly attractive, its leaves turning many shades of red, yellow, and brown. This color change may be induced in leaves mature in midsummer by certain insect injuries, by attacks of fungi, or by an interference with the flow of sap caused by twisting the stem. There is no apparent difference between the leaves of male and female plants in this respect. Some plants, however, particularly those in the shade, may have all their leaves yellow. Conversely, red leaves seem to be peculiar to plants of sunny exposure, although there are many exceptions; far more frequently the leaves are mixtures of all three colors. The oldest leaves often assume autumnal tints first.

The petiole in transverse section (Plate III, *G*, facing p. 36) has in form nearly a semi-circle for its dorsal side and a small concave arc as a ventral surface. Under the epidermis lie two or three layers of collenchyma cells. The vascular bundles, of which there are more than eighteen, are arranged in a flattened circle parallel to the outer surface of the petiole. The pith consists of large, thin-walled cells with very small triangular intercellular spaces. The vascular bundles are separated from each other by broad medullary rays. Large resin ducts are found in the phloem. The primary cortex is bordered internally by a starch sheath. The cells of the xylem have thick and lignified walls. The pith is inclosed by bast fibers and xylem and takes up the largest part of the section. There are no resin ducts in the pith or in the primary cortex.

The leaf in transverse section exhibits palisade parenchyma occupying about one-third of the entire thickness of the mesophyl (Plate I, Fig. 4). The spongy parenchyma occupies about five layers of cells. Cells with crystal clusters, presumably of calcium oxalate, occur in the palisade parenchyma. The cells of the lower epidermis are similar to those of the upper epidermis but smaller; stomata are very frequent and apparently absent from the ridges. The leaves wilt very easily; it is hardly possible to bring a cut branch from the field to the laboratory without observing wilting. There are two kinds of trichomes on the leaves, multicellular club-shaped, and unicellular or multicellular bristle-shaped (Plate III, *F*, facing p. 36).

The thick-walled bristle hairs occur mainly on the lower side on the ridges, large and small, of the leaf, although they are found also in fewer numbers on the upper side in corresponding places. The club-shaped trichomes, on the other hand, are found mostly between the ridges of the leaves. These two different forms of trichomes are similar to those found by Möbius (1899) on *R. vernicifera* L. and by Rost and Gilg (1912) on *R. Toxicodendron* L. Morphologically the club-shaped hairs seem to be glandular: first, because the upper multicellular portion is sharply marked off from the basal portion, which resembles a stalk; second, the upper portion has thinner walls than the basal portion; third, they are found mostly on the young, rapidly growing organs of the plant, especially the floral region and the leaves, less on the green stem, and hardly at all on the woody portion. Schwalbe (1902, 1903) considered the poison of *R. diversiloba* to be excreted from glandular hairs on the surface of the plant. That such is not the case is shown in chapter iv, page 34.

The club-shaped hairs are so minute as to be hardly discernible by the naked eye. They have a length of 0.071 mm. and a maximum breadth of 0.0027 mm. Under the microscope they exhibit a clear, unicellular basal portion as an outgrowth of an epidermal cell, above which are the numerous cells that go to make up the main portion of the hair. The cells of the main portion when viewed transversely radiate from a longitudinal central axis. The apex terminates in a single cell, and the entire main portion of the hair is inclosed in a thin-walled sac. The hairs appear to be of two types, which apparently correspond to different stages in development: a densely granular and a sparsely granular form. This difference in granular density is interesting. In animal glands it has long been noticed that when a serous gland has been quiescent for several hours the secretory cells are granular throughout, and the outlines of the cells are only faintly marked as clear lines bounding the granular areas. When the gland secretes, many of the granules disappear and after prolonged secretion very few granules are left; i.e., during secretion the granules normally contained by the cells are in some way or other used up, probably to form a part of the secretion. Although the diminution of zymogen granules is a normal occurrence in the secretion of the salivary, infra-orbital, lachrymal, mucous, and pancreatic glands, yet in the case of the mammary glands the opposite is true, viz., that granules begin to form with the commencement of secretion and do not occur during rest. In the mammary gland, the active growth of protoplasm, the formation of granules from the protoplasm, and the discharge of these granules in the secretion appear to go on at one and the same time. Investigation of the club-shaped hairs of *R. diversiloba* has not as yet revealed a positive glandular nature, and consequently a relation between differences in their granulation cannot be definitely connected with secretion. From a morphological standpoint, however, as above pointed out, the club-shaped hairs seem to be glandular.

Club-shaped hairs from leaves gathered in the morning before sunrise and from those secured in the heat of the day could not be differentiated. Hairs from rapidly growing leaves could not be distinguished from those of old leaves or stems. Hairs from leaves grown in sunny exposures exhibited no differences, although they were present in greater number than those on leaves continuously in the shade.

### THE STEM

A transverse section of a green stem of *R. diversiloba* shows, beginning at the outside, the following tissues (Plate I, Fig. 5): epidermis, with its trichomes and stomata; collenchyma; cortical parenchyma; pericycle, with bast fibers and thin-walled pericycle parenchyma; phloem, with resin ducts; cambium; xylem; medullary ray; pith.

As the stem increases in diameter (Plate I, Fig. 3) the cortex develops a phellogen. The continuous activity of the phellogen results in an increasing thickness of the sheet of cork. The chloroplast-containing tissue beneath the cork layer maintains connection with the air by means of lenticels which have replaced the stomata. As may be anticipated, the dead cork cells are non-poisonous, i.e., they do not cause dermatitis when rubbed on the skin of a susceptible individual, and therefore do not constitute a means of transference for the poison.

No resin ducts have been found in the pith of this plant. Engler (1881), studying *R. Toxicodendron* L., and Inui (1900), studying *R. Toxicodendron* var. *radicans*, were unable to discover resin ducts in the pith. Jadin (1893) cited eighteen species of the genus which are provided with permanent pith resin ducts, and nine species which do not have them.

At the periphery of the pith the small, outer cells acquire a thick wall and become sclerenchymatous. These thick-walled cells may assist the inner large-celled and the outer small-celled pith to maintain a circular outline. A semi-circular row of bast fibers lies external to the primary phloem and serves mechanically to protect the phloem with its resin ducts from external injury.

In the phloem of the second year, new resin ducts appear. These lie neither in radial nor in tangential rows, but are so arranged as to be very nearly equidistant. The first appear in the secondary phloem between two primary resin ducts, and more are formed in a corresponding manner. It must not be forgotten, however, that the formation of resin ducts does not occur in a regular manner.

New bast fibers do not appear to be formed in the pericycle. The epidermis has been almost wholly lost in the second year and is replaced by cork.

The histology of the pith, wood, and bark of the older stems will be treated individually.

The pith cells are polygonal and lie close together; they are generally wider than high, so that their vertical measurement is the smallest. In the specimens examined, the pith cells contained for the most part no particular substance; starch was found sparingly, and tannin sacs appeared as narrow, elongated cells. Tannin sacs, according to Engler (1881), appear abundantly in the pith of the Anacardiaceae and in all species of *Rhus* which he investigated. Pith tannin sacs are not necessarily characteristic of toxic species of *Rhus*, as Möbius (1899) was unable to find them in *R. vernicifera* L.

The bulk of the wood consists of simple, pitted wood fibers. In transverse section they are bordered at right angles, and are assembled in rows. The narrower and thicker-walled cells of the fall wood contain starch; the wider and thinner-walled ones of spring wood appear empty.

The pits of the tracheal vessels are exclusively simple with circular or elliptical outlines. The walls are relatively thick. The structure of the vessel wall, where it is in contact with wood parenchyma, is characteristic. In these places simple pits of large size are found chiefly on the vessel wall, and, side by side with them, either transitional or true bordered pits, but no separate bordered pits were noticed. The elliptical pits are transverse to the longitudinal axis of the vessel and parallel to one another, so that they remind one of scalariform perforations.

The medullary rays are, as a rule, uniseriate; sometimes, however, they are biseriate. In tangential longitudinal section they are from three to eighteen cells high; radially their cells are joined together as are the stones in a wall of plane ashlar masonry. The walls of their cells are only moderately thickened, and their lumina are often filled with starch. The medullary rays are most noticeable in the lower part of the stem and in the roots. One small root had five primary medullary rays.

The difference between fall and spring wood rests partly on the dissimilarity of the wood fiber cells and partly on that of the vessels. The first tracheals of spring are larger, thicker-walled, and stretched somewhat radially, while those toward the outer border of the annual ring are flattened to smaller, thicker-walled, and radial rings. The vessels in the spring wood are wider and more numerous, in the fall wood narrower and scarcer, as shown in Plate I, Figure 3. The breadth of the annual rings varies.

The inner wood is colored yellow or yellow-brown. A great deal of this coloring matter can be extracted with hot alcohol. This extract behaves similarly to the extract of the related species *R. Continus* L. (*Continus coggygria* Scop.) in the following treatment: an orange-yellow solution in water was made bright yellow by hydrochloric acid, yellow-red by ammonia, orange N. with alum and sodium carbonate solution, and brown N. by calcium chlorid solution. Such a behavior by no means proves that the solutes from the wood of *R. diversiloba* are identical with those from *R. vernicifera*, although such may actually be the case. The coloring matter is naturally attached to the membrane of the wood cells, which appear golden yellow under the microscope and assumed a brown color with caustic potash. Besides the yellow crystals, the wood cavities contain a reddish amorphous resinous substance which is likewise soluble in 95 per cent alcohol.

The primary cortex contains sclerosed parenchyma.

The structure of the pericycle is characteristic. It contains many bast fibers, which, in transverse section, have the form of arcs whose convex sides are on the exterior and whose inner concave surfaces surround in each case a single, usually large, resin duct (Plate I, Fig. 5).

The resin canals in the later-formed portions of the bark have a lumen, and are arranged more or less regularly in concentric circles as heretofore described. The old resin canals appear to be obliterated through a kind of tylotic growth. On one transverse section through the bark of an old stem which has already thrown off the primary covering there are many resin canals differing in form, outline, and dimensions. The innermost are open and nearly circular, but usually more strictly oval in shape, stretched tangentially, and of larger circumference than the outer ones. The outermost, particularly in old stem parts, are entirely or almost entirely obliterated through the luxuriant growth of intruding contiguous tissue. It is possible to observe at different heights of the same resin canal different states of development so that in one place it may still be open and in another closed. This occurrence of tyloses in the secretory ducts is similar to that described by Möbius (1899) in *R. vernicifera* L., by Leblois (1887) in *Brucea ferruginea*, and by Conwentz in the intercellular canals of other plants.

The secondary medullary rays, as already noted, are usually constituted of one row of cells. Where biseriate rays are found, it is sometimes noticed that they split apart tangentially while they remain intact radially. From this it would seem that adjacent cells of the two columns of the medullary ray are only loosely united, whereas those cells which constitute a radial row are more firmly attached.

Besides what has already been said regarding the phloem, it should be added that the sieve tubes and their companion cells extend tangentially and build approximately alternating bands with the layers of phloem parenchyma cells, as in the stem section of *Aristolochia Sipho* Strasburger (1898). The phloem apparently has but little starch, which is found deposited chiefly in the medullary rays. These cells also give a distinct reaction for tannin with ferric chlorid.

### MORPHOLOGY AND ANATOMY OF THE ROOT

The root system in its ramifications resembles the crown, in that comparatively few strong branch roots are formed which carry the fine, interlaced roots. The spread of roots depends largely upon the nature of the soil, and upon the supply of food and water.

There is a strong tendency to form long, lateral roots, particularly in shallow soil. Propagation by layering is very frequently made use of naturally by the plant to insure its food supply and reproduction. The fine, interlacing rootlets are dark brown in color and are covered with fine root hairs of a lighter color. The apical tips of the rootlets are light yellow or colorless for several millimeters.

As in other roots, after the secondary phloem is formed the cambium soon takes on a circular form in section, and behaves in the formation of xylem and phloem exactly as in the stem (Plate I, Fig. 2).

The wood of the root is less firm than that of the stem; there exist numerous large bundles, the fiber cells are less strongly thickened, the medullary rays are broader, being indeed commonly composed of two layers of cells.

### MORPHOLOGY AND ANATOMY OF THE FLOWERS

*Rhus diversiloba* is strictly dioecious, so far as my observations go. The male and female plants begin to bloom at about the same time. At Berkeley, California, but few of the flowers were open April 4, 1915. The next spring the plants near the Greek Theater at Berkeley bloomed mostly between March 22 and May 1. In 1917 at Pasadena I noticed some male plants at the foot of the Mount Wilson trail in bloom on January 5. On February 28, 1917, the plants of both sexes were just starting to bloom in the Arroyo Seco, south of the Colorado Street bridge, Pasadena. In spite of their yellow-green color, the flower panicles are conspicuously displayed as a result of their size and their accumulation on the ends of the twigs. The presence of the staminate flowers is made very noticeable by their fragrant jasmine or hyacinth aroma. The pistillate flowers, on the other hand, have no apparent perfume. At this point it may be well to mention that an aromatic perfume so similar as to be perhaps identical is noticed when the fresh end of a freshly broken branch is smelled, and that this perfume, unlike that of the flowers, is not confined to the male plant, but is observed also in the female. The similarity between the perfume of the sap and that of the flower becomes more marked upon purification. The "aqueous solution" as made and described in a previous paper (McNair, 1916*a*) contains this more purified sap perfume. The panicles of the male and female flowers are somewhat differentiated as to location and structure.

The flowering shoots of the male plant commonly bear as many flower panicles as leaves, in which case neither the highest nor the lowest leaves develop any panicles in their axils. The lowest leaves of the flowering shoot soon fall off and more readily expose the flower panicles to insects, while the highest leaves remain and tend to protect the blossoms from the direct sunlight, wind, and rain. The panicles are 7 cm. long and stand somewhat stiffly upright at a sharp angle to the axil of the attached twig. The longer ones bear about a dozen side twigs of the first order, of which the three lowest ones are about 2 cm. long and in their turn are again richly branched. Toward the tip the side twigs of the first order become shorter and are not further branched. They are formed like a bunch of grapes, and the end of a panicle is likewise visibly terminated by a flower. The same regularity, as nearly as could be determined, appears in the arrangement of the side twigs of the first order on the panicle stem as was noticed in the phyllotaxy. Minute woolly hairs appear on the panicles at the blooming time, particularly on the bases of the panicle stem and on those of the side twigs.

The flowers are placed singly on stalks from 4 to 7 mm. long, and have a diameter of from 5 to 7 mm. when fully opened. The flowers have five calyx leaves, five petals, five stamens, and one rudimentary ovule; only by way of exception do six or eight occur and in one flower with six stamens six petals occurred also.

The calyx leaves are tongue-shaped and have broad bases. They are about 2 mm. long and have a dark-green color.

The petals are long-ellipitical in shape, narrowed at the base and at the point, and somewhat pointed in the front. They are 4 mm. long and in the middle about 1½ mm. wide. When in bloom the flowers are strongly bent downward. The color of the petals is light green, much lighter than that of the calyx leaves.

The stamens are 2½ mm. long. The white filaments, which are nearly twice as long as the anthers, shove themselves between the anther halves, which somewhat retreat from each other underneath.

The anthers are introrse and are borne on upright but slightly curved filaments.

The rudimentary ovary forms a keg-shaped pivot about 1 mm. high, and has three discernible stigmas. Between the ovary and the anthers is a disk, which during flowering time glistens with nectar.

The flower, as viewed from above, is divided into five broad lobes, which stand in front of the petals and are separated by the insertion of the stamens; each lobe is again slightly indented in the middle. The outer and inner rims of the disk are somewhat arched toward the top; from this construction a ringlike depression appears in the middle.

While just as many inflorescences as leaves are found on the blossom shoots of the male plants, the number of panicles on the female plant is only about one-half as great as that of the leaves. The leaves, however, are more numerous on the blossom shoots of the female. The number of leaves fluctuated between seven and nine in several investigations of shoots, while the number of panicles ranged between three and five. As on the male plant, neither the lowest nor the highest leaves bear inflorescences in their axils but only the middle ones. The panicles have a length of 3 to 6 cm. They are not stiffly erect as in the male, but on the contrary only limply placed. The side twigs of the higher order than those of first order are up to 2.5 cm. in length and have about as numerous branches, but shorter side twigs of the higher order than those of the male. The entire female panicle has about the same general outline as the male panicle. The anatomical structure of the panicle axis is essentially similar to that of the vegetative twig in the first year, and there is no noticeable difference in this respect between the male and the female panicle. Particular structures for tensile strength are not noticed in the axes of the fruit panicles. The stems of the pistillate flowers are not longer than 1 cm. and are often 5 mm. long. The flower itself is smaller than that of the male; its diameter, it is true, measures about 5 mm., but the petals are less curved.

The five calyx leaves are somewhat similar to those in the staminate flower, but slightly shorter. The five petals are spread out flatter and do not have the curled side rims. They are approximately 3 mm. long and 1.5 mm. broad. Five stamens also occur in the pistillate flower; their anthers are of nearly the same length as the fertile ones of the staminate flower, but the filaments are about 1.5 mm. long and therefore much shorter than those of the male. The anthers are shrunken, of a dirty yellow color, with pollen absent, so that the entire pistillate flower and panicles appear darker. As seen from the broad side, the pistil originates in a somewhat compressed, egg-shaped ovary which is extended in a short style. Toward the top the style spreads out into three thick, brownish stigmas which are beset with papilli. The ovary is also to be considered as constituted by three carpels, of which, however, two are rudimentary so that they appear only in the stigmas. Between the stamens and the ovary is the disk, which is similar to that of the staminate flower except that it is narrower because of the greater expansion of the ovary.

As far as the growth and the finer structure of the flower are concerned the male and female flowers show a great similarity. If one investigates young inflorescences on which the individual flowers are distinguishable as small buds, it is noticed that each flower stands in the axil of a comparatively large carrying leaf which somewhat overhangs the flower. The outside of the bract, as well as the stigma and the axil, are covered with upward-bent trichomes. These trichomes are of two forms, one a single, long, bristle hair and the other a short, apparently glandular, hair with a single-celled base and many-celled ovoid head. These hairs are similar to those previously described as found on the leaves and stems. Further developed flowers, which, with their panicles, are 2 mm. long, have a hairy, carrying leaf longer than the panicle. The calyx leaves, the petals, and the stamens lie alongside each other like small enlargements and finally the carpels arise as wall-like growths. In this instance, in which one can clearly recognize the construction of the bud, the stamens are egg-shaped and are covered by the short petals and the longer calyx leaves. Finally the disk shows itself between the gynoecium and the androecium. The course of the vascular bundles may very clearly be recognized in the mounted material, as resin ducts contained in the phloem have their contents turned brown. In the calyx leaf, which is formed with a broad base, five ribs appear of which the middle one is the strongest and most branched. On the other hand, the petal, which had a small base, has only one short, weak, or unbranched rib on each side of the strongly branched midrib.

The disk appears in longitudinal section as a wide, somewhat sunken cushion. Toward the bottom its tissue is large-celled; above, on the other hand, it consists of small, closely united, plasma-rich cells, of the sort common to glandular tissues. Many small crystal clusters lie on the border of both tissues and in the upper, small-celled tissue, but are lacking in the lower, large-celled tissue. The epidermis consists of rather small polygonal cells and contains numerous stoma-like apertures whose guard cells are almost always larger than the other epidermal cells. A small space is found under the stoma-like opening. These openings apparently do not serve for gaseous interchange, but for the excretion of a glistening and strongly aromatic fragrant nectar whose existence has already been mentioned.

The development of the stamens in pistillate and staminate flowers is apparently similar to the time of the formation of pollen mother-cells. In the pistillate flower no pollen grains are formed, the anthers remain empty, and have a shrunken appearance. The filaments of the pistillate flower remain as short as those of the staminate flower until the flowers open. The stamens naturally develop farther in the latter. Pollen formation occurs in the anthers but shows nothing particularly noteworthy. The vascular bundles of the anthers contain no resin ducts, these having ended halfway up the filaments. The anther is also to a certain degree the only organ of the plant which has no resin-like or poisonous sap. It is not surprising then that the pollen has no toxic action on the human skin (McNair, 1916*b*). Similar observations have been made by Inui (1900) on the pollen of *R. vernicifera*, by Warren (1913) on that of *R. Vernix*, and by Rost and Gilg (1912) on that of *R. Toxicodendron*. The pollen sacs of *R. diversiloba* are composed of two coalesced sporangia, as is common in angiosperms. Their dehiscence occurs by a longitudinal slit, developed where the two coalesced sporangia join. According to Edgeworth (1879), the pollen of the Anacardiaceae is oval with three slits. The fresh pollen grains of *R. diversiloba* are ellipsoidal, about 1/800 sq. mm. in horizontal area, with a width one-third to one-half the length. The exine is roughened by minute, sharply pointed projections. When the pollen grains are immersed in N/4 KOH they assume a spherical form with no color change. In the material treated (which had been fixed in alcohol and xylol, stained, and mounted in balsam like the rest of the plant material), the spores assumed spherical shapes or in some instances became rounded tetrahedrons. As is common in entomophilous plants, the pollen has no surfaces so modified as to permit the wind to take hold of it, of the nature of the bladder-like appendages of the pine pollen, etc. Whereas anemophilous pollen has a dry outer covering to prevent large masses of pollen from adhering to the flower and hindering wind transportation, the entomophilous pollen of *R. diversiloba* is surrounded with a sticky substance so as to adhere to the feet and other parts of the insect. In common with other entomophilous flowers, *R. diversiloba* has perfume-secreting glands heretofore described which may serve to attract insects. The pollen itself being non-toxic and not wind-blown, the aerial transmission of the poison by the agency of pollen is quite out of the question.

As in the female flower the stamens develop to a certain advanced stage, so the ovary develops in the male flower to the extent that an almost fully developed ovule is produced. Such development of an ovule in a flower which is functionally purely staminate, borne on a purely male plant, is a phenomenon which has been but rarely observed. Each ovary contains regularly but one ovule. The funiculus becomes curved at its apex, so that the body of the ovule lies against it, and, although the axis of the body is straight, the micropyle is directed toward the surface of origin; thus the funiculus appears as a ridge along one side of the body of the ovule, and the ovule is anatropous and consequently of the form most common among angiosperms.

The ovule, in the mature female flower, fills the ovarian cavity. The outer integument, therefore, occupies considerable space. The micropyle is somewhat widely removed from the upper arching of the nucellus. The inner integument is widely tubular and lengthened outwardly over the nucellus, in which the embryo sac is again somewhat pressed back toward the inside so that a wider path is prepared for the pollen tube. The advantage of an anatropous ovule is apparent when it is remembered that the pollen tube advances along the wall of the ovary, and that the micropyle is thus brought near the wall. It is not surprising, then, that this plant with its efficient apparatus for fertilization should have large fruit production.

Numerous germinating pollen grains are found on the stigmas of open pistillate flowers. The pollen tubes grow inside between the stigma papillae and pass through four to six cells of which the upper one is longest and thickest. On the stigmas of the staminate flowers such papillae are not formed, so that here no pollen grains are found. The wall of the ovary is penetrated by numerous vascular bundles with resin ducts which continue to the upper end of the pistil where the resin ducts terminate blindly with pointed ends.

The development of the fruit, which terminates the life of the plant, has been taken up in chapter v.

## EXPLANATION OF PLATES I AND II

### PLATE I

All figures have been reduced one-half in reproduction and now show magnifications as follows: Figure 1, ×10; Figure 2, ×10; Figure 3, ×23.3; Figure 4, ×470; Figure 5, ×91.65.

FIG. 1.—Transverse section through the same stem as in Figure 3.

FIG. 2.—Transverse section through a woody root.

FIG. 3.—Transverse section through a stem older than that of Figure 5, showing annual rings with their varied formations of spring and fall growth.

FIG. 4.—Transverse section through mature leaf showing cystolith in palisade parenchyma.

FIG. 5.—Transverse section through stem showing cork cambium; tracheal tube (*T*); pericycle with sclerenchyma cells or bast fibers and thin-walled pericycle parenchyma; phloem with resin duct (*R*); cambium (*C*); pith (*P*).

### PLATE II

All figures have been reduced one-half in reproduction and now show magnifications as follows: Figure 1, ×23.3; Figure 2, ×23.3; Figure 3, ×470; Figure 4, ×23.3.

PLATE I

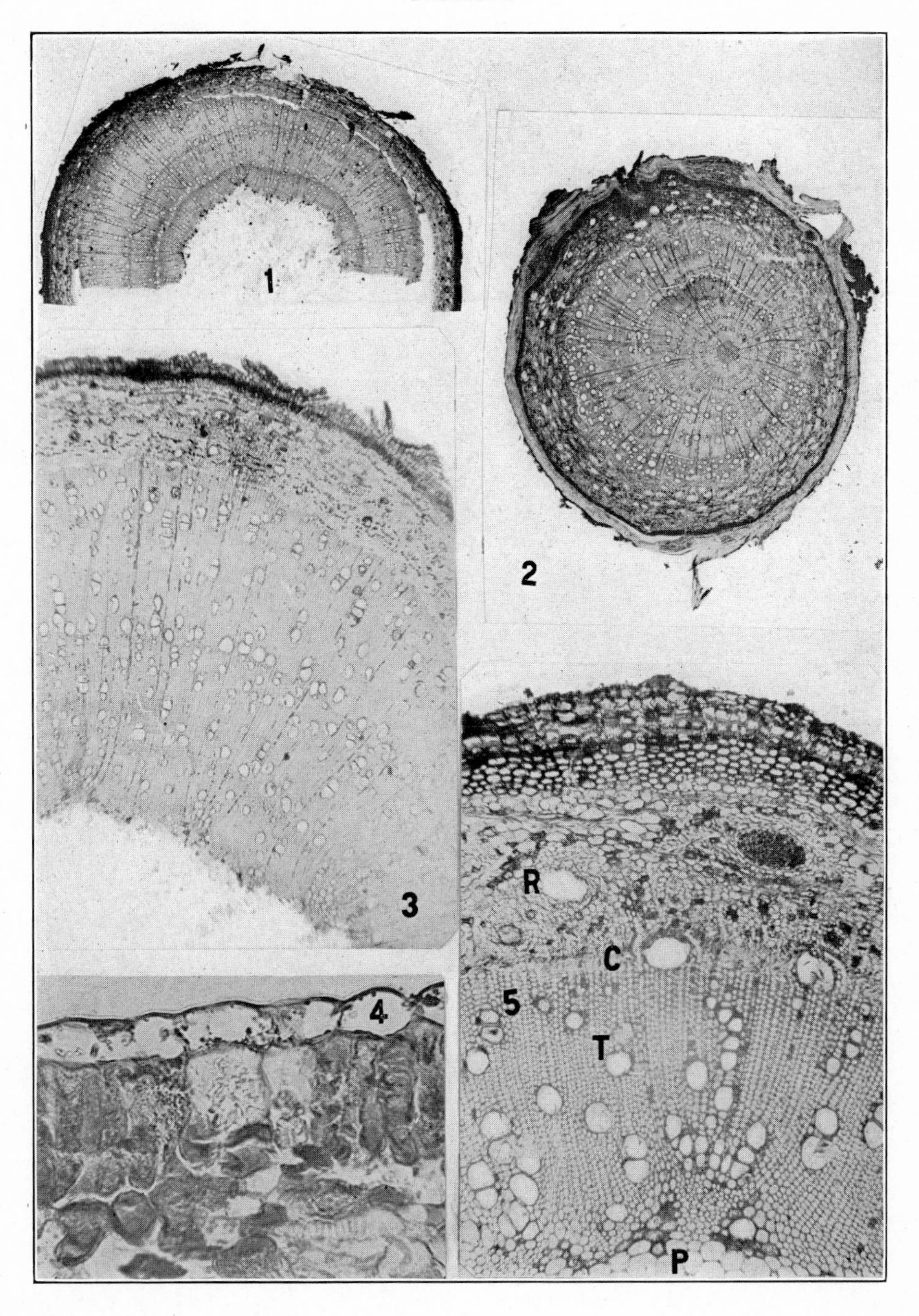

PLATE II

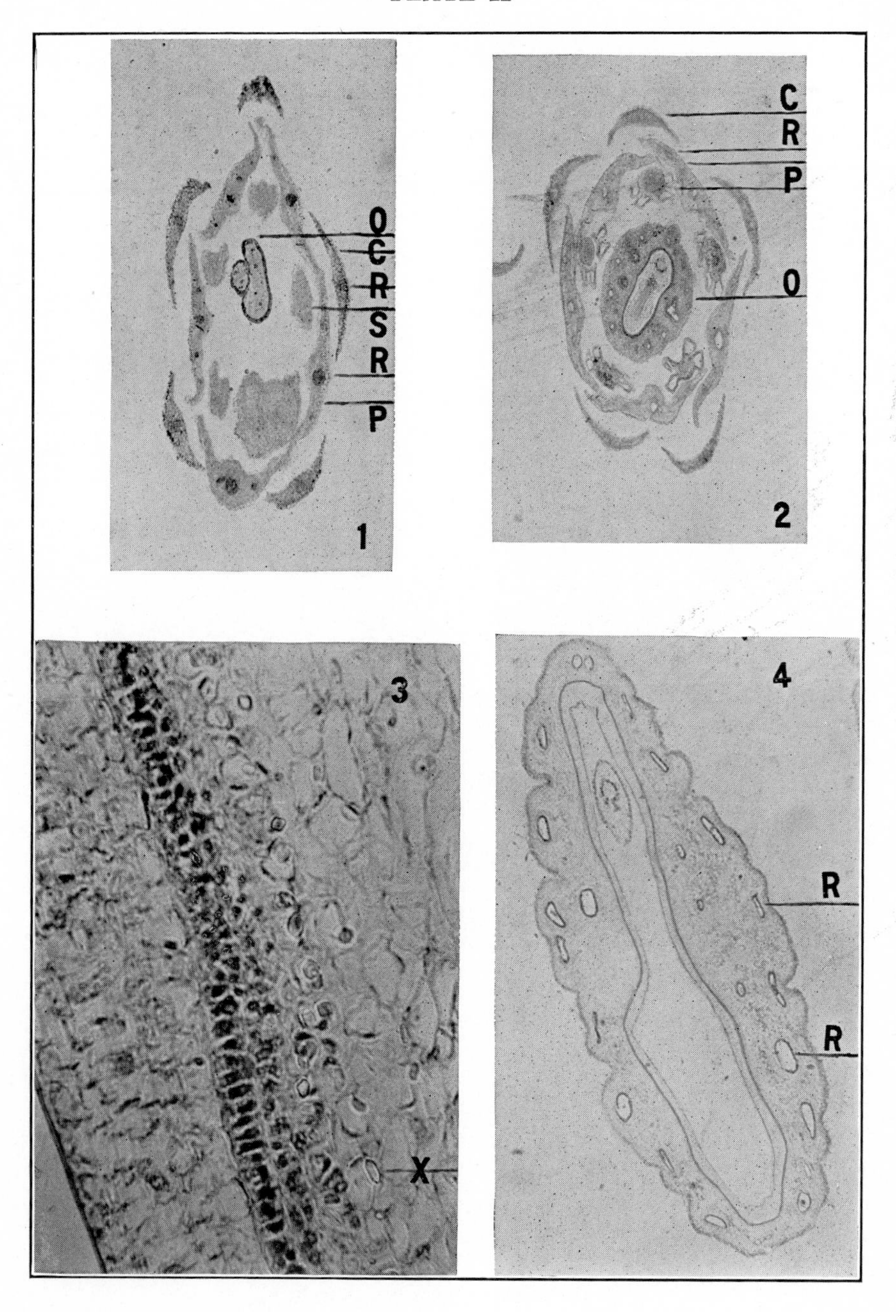

FIG. 1.—Transverse section through a male flower near its base, showing five calyx leaves (*C*) with resin ducts (*R*), five petals (*P*) with resin ducts (*R*), five stamens (*S*), and the non-fertile ovule (*O*).

FIG. 2.—Transverse section through a female flower near its apex, showing five calyx leaves (*C*) with resin ducts (*R*), five petals (*P*) with resin ducts, five rudimentary anthers with neither pollen nor resin ducts, and the fertile ovule (*O*).

FIG. 3.—Transverse section through an unripe fruit near the seed, showing numerous crystals. Size of hexagonal crystal, 0.007×0.0025 mm.

FIG. 4.—Transverse section through an unripe fruit showing an abundance of resin ducts (*RR*). Diameter of largest resin duct, 0.0085 mm.

# CHAPTER III

## RESIN CANALS OF RHUS DIVERSILOBA[1]

In *Rhus diversiloba* T. and G. the resin passages are situated in the roots, stems, leaves, and fruit in the phloem of the primary vascular bundles. In addition, there are others in the secondary bast of the stem and root.

The root contains a single, wide resin canal in each of the phloem portions of the primary bast. In the secondary bast, resin canals in concentric circles with smaller lumina are successively added. After the secondary phloem is formed in the root, the xylem and phloem are formed exactly as in the stem.

In the stem the phloem portion of the primary bundles is separated from the parenchymatous outer cortex by a strong bundle of sclerenchymatous (bast) fibers of crescent-shaped transverse section. These fibrous bundles are almost in contact with one another at their margins, and thus constitute a ring around the outer cortex. Outside of this sclerenchymatic ring no resin passages are found, but large ones are located immediately within it, one in the phloem of each vascular bundle. In the secondary cortex, which is formed later internally, new canals are formed successively in the strands of the bast. The cortical passages of the secondary bast are connected in the internodes by more or less numerous tangential anastomoses, and thus combine to form a more or less complete cylindrical network in the bark concentric with the stem cylinder. The cortical passages in the nodes anastomose with one another. The leaf passages extend up the internode to the plexus of anastomoses.

The vascular bundles which pass into the petiole are arranged in curves to follow the outline of the petiole in its transverse section. These branch when they reach the leaflets. The resin passages are arranged in the petiole as in the primary vascular bundles. The canals may be absent in the weaker bundles, however.

[1] Reprinted from the *Botanical Gazette*, LXV (March, 1918), 268–73.

In the midrib of the leaflets the fibrovascular system is divided into two parts. One, the superior, the ventral, is formed of three reunited bundles placed under the endophloem; the other, the dorsal, has five to seven bundles arranged in an arc, and has also five to seven resin passages in the phloem parts.

All lateral ribs contain at least one passage on their dorsal sides, which is in the phloem as usual. Some of the resin canals seem to end blindly in the spongy parenchyma and palisade parenchyma, while others apparently anastomose in a reticulate manner like the vascular bundles which they accompany.

Trecul (1867) noticed in *R. Toxicodendron* L., to which *R. diversiloba* is very closely allied, the obstruction of the resin canals at the base of the petiole just before the fall of the leaves. This obstruction is effected by an increase in the parietal cells of the canals, and thus constitutes an instance of tylosis, similar perhaps to the obliteration of the old canals in the bark. The enlarged cells divide and the new ones produce more of the same kind. Soon the ducts are seen on the outside of the parenchyma at the place of insertion of the leaves. At a small distance away in the leaflet the passages have a normal appearance and are filled with sap.

According to Sieck (1895), the resin canals of the Anacardiaceae are of schizolysigenous origin.[1] The first development of the intercellular cavities can readily be observed in *R. diversiloba*, which has good, clear channels. In the beginning the evolution of the resin tube in this plant is clearly schizogenous. It forms itself from a little group of cells individually much narrower than the other parenchyma cells. A short slit soon appears toward the center of the group. When this slit enlarges itself, a little of the resinous sap appears. The opening, first irregular in outline, enlarges to a channel of considerable size with a regular circular outline and is bordered by narrow cells. This is by far the form most commonly noticed and is plainly schizogenous. Some of the secreting cells may eventually break down altogether to leave their secretions in the cavity formed by their disintegration, and thus be designated

[1] It should be stated that Sieck worked with *Anacardium occidentale*, which is not very closely related to *R. diversiloba*, a fact which may explain the apparent difference in origin of the secretory canals.

lysigenous in character. Cavities so appearing in my investigations of this plant may have been due to imperfect sections. At any rate, lysigenous cavities are apparently in the minority.

If these observations be compared with previous works on other Anacardiaceae, it will be seen that there are no essential differences in the arrangement of the intercellular secretory reservoirs. Which genera should be poisonous, or why their poisons should vary, either in physiological action or in chemical composition, cannot be deduced from this part of their anatomies.

Plants other than the Anacardiaceae that secrete resin, emulsions of gum-resin, etc., in passages are as follows: Coniferae, Alismaceae, Aroideae, the tubifloral Compositae, Umbelliferae, Arliaceae, Pittosporeae, many species of *Mamillaria*, Clusiaceae, and *Ailantus* and Bruceae of the Simarubeae.

The abundance and comparatively large size of the resin ducts, together with their fusing, make an intercommunicating system. When a wound is made, the sap and its poison are quickly pressed out, either by the tension of the elastic walls of its own cells or by a combination of both. In the spring the sap is very watery, while the autumn product is much thicker, granulous, and slower in exudation. The sap, which is properly an emulsion, is, when first expressed, white or light gray in color, and as it quickly coagulates and browns in the air, it forms an efficient covering for the wound. The sap is darkened in the air, mainly by oxidation as is shown in chapter viii: first, when deprived of oxygen the sap darkens but very slowly; secondly, when in the presence of oxygen the sap darkens rapidly; and finally, ultimate chemical analyses of the sap before and after darkening show an appreciable difference only in the oxygen content.

Under the microscope the freshly exuded sap is in part a colorless liquid and in part made up of minute globules. Very soon some of these globules become dark brown, while the fewer remaining globules continue to be colorless. While this change has been taking place, oblong rectangular colorless crystals separate out. The first crystals to separate are larger than those which form later. This process of crystallization probably has its cause in the evaporation of the menstrum. If these crystals be viewed through a petrogaphic microscope, they are seen to be birefringent, similar perhaps to those noticed by Wiesner (1900) in the sap of *R. vernicifera*. On adding water the light-colored globules disappear, but the brown ones remain. The addition of alcohol, on the other hand, causes the solution of the brown globules.

## SUMMARY

1. The intercellular secretory canals of *R. diversiloba* T. and G. are found in the roots, stem, leaves, and fruit in the phloem of the primary vascular bundles. There are other secretory canals situated in the secondary bast of the stem. They are found also in the phloem of the mesocarp of the fruit and in the hypocotyl and cotyledons of the embryo.

2. Their formation may possibly be schizolysigenous. In the beginning they are clearly schizogenous.

3. There are no essential differences in the arrangement of the intercellular secretory reservoirs between the poisonous and non-poisonous Anacardiaceae.

4. From an anatomical standpoint there is no reason why the poisons of the Anacardiaceae should vary either in physiological action or in chemical composition.

# CHAPTER IV

## THE ORIGIN AND OCCURRENCE OF THE POISON[1]

The freshly exuded resinous sap of *Rhus diversiloba* has long been known to be capable of producing dermatitis when applied to the skin. With this in mind, investigations were carried out to see whether the poisonous portions of the plant are limited to those portions that contain the resin canals.

Microscopical examination of the staminate flower shows four resin ducts in the receptacle and pedicel, one in each petal, but no resin ducts more than halfway up the basal filaments of the stamens. Realizing the absence of resin canals in the anthers, it was thought perhaps the pollen might be non-toxic (see Plate III, *D*). The pollen was collected by shaking the flowers over a glass funnel to the stem of which a test tube was attached. This pollen was found to be non-poisonous when rubbed into the skin of an individual sensitive to the poison. An alcoholic extract of the pollen was non-toxic, nor did the pollen or the alcoholic solution assume a dark-brown color when treated for five minutes with potassium hydroxid as does the poison. It is concluded, therefore, that the pollen is incapable of producing dermatitis. Similar non-toxic results have been obtained with the pollen of *R. vernicifera* by Inui (1900), with that of *R. Vernix* by Warren (1913), and with that of *R. Toxicodendron* by Rost and Gilg (1912).

C. Schwalbe (1903) considered the poison of *R. diversiloba* to be excreted from glandular hairs on the surface of the plant. As the resin canals are not connected with the epidermis or with the trichomes, it was considered that these, like the stamens, might also be non-toxic. Two different forms of trichomes have been noticed on the plant, similar morphologically to those found by Möbius (1899) on *R. vernicifera* and by Rost and Gilg (1912) on *R. Toxicodendron;* namely, a unicellular or multicellular needle-shaped hair, and a multicellular club-shaped hair (Plate III, *F*). Morpho-

[1] Taken from the *American Journal of Botany*, VIII (March, 1921), 137–38.

logically the club-shaped hairs seem to be glandular; first, the upper multicellular portion is sharply marked off from the basal portion, which resembles a stalk; second, the upper portion has thinner walls than the basal portion; third, they are found mostly on the young, rapidly growing organs of the plant, especially on the floral region and the leaves, less on the green stems, and hardly at all on the woody portions.

When the green stem, pedicel, or main ribs of the leaf, which are covered with trichomes, are rubbed on skin sensitive to the poison, no dermatitis results. Care must be taken, however, that the epidermis of the plant is not broken severely enough to cause the resinous sap to exude.

The fresh, green leaves were placed in a finger bowl and soaked in room temperature in 95 per cent alcohol for ten minutes. The leaves had been examined first under a hand lens to make sure that through possible injury no resinous sap was on the surface. When placed in the finger bowl the sap was prevented from running down the pedicel from the cut end into the alcohol. The leaves when taken out of the alcohol had lost their gloss. The pale-yellowish alcoholic solution remaining was concentrated by boiling in an open beaker. It was found to be non-toxic. It was not darkened by potassium hydroxid nor did it respond to other chemical tests for the poison. These results indicate that neither the plant trichomes nor their exudate are poisonous.

The cork cells of the older stem were likewise found to be non-toxic either when the branch was rubbed on the skin or when an alcoholic solution was made of scrapings from the outermost cork cells of a branch as thick as a man's wrist.

As no resin ducts were seen on a microscopical examination of the pith of a one-year-old stem of the poison oak nor in the woody stem, experiments were undertaken to determine their toxicity. The bark was carefully removed from the pith, a clean knife being used to shave off the outermost portions of the pith. The pith was then cut up in small portions and extracted in a Soxhlet apparatus with hot 95 per cent alcohol. This alcoholic solution when concentrated gave neither a physiological test for the poison nor any of the chemical tests.

A similar experiment carried on with the woody xylem gave corresponding results.

## SUMMARY

1. The fresh sap emulsion is the only part of the plant capable of producing dermatitis.

2. Those portions of the plant that do not contain the resin canals do not normally have this kind of toxic effect.

3. The non-toxic portions are the anthers, pollen, xylem, epidermis, cork cells, and trichomes.

## EXPLANATION OF PLATE III

The material selected for the sections was fixed in a chromacetic fixative (1 per cent by weight chromic acid in water, 0.5 per cent glacial acetic acid by weight). Suitable pieces were then hardened by placing in alcohol of different concentrations in series of 6 per cent, 12 per cent, 25 per cent, 50 per cent, and 75 per cent, then in xylol and paraffin and finally in paraffin. Sections were then cut on the microtome in series, fastened to clean slides with egg albumen, stained with safranin and Delafield's haemotoxylin, and finally washed in absolute alcohol, in xylol, and mounted in balsam. By this treatment lignified and suberized walls were stained red and cellulose walls violet.

The photomicrographs were made with an electric arc as the source of light. The amount of magnification was calculated by the aid of a ruled slide on the miscoscope stage and of a rule on the ground-glass focusing screen, using the same lenses as were used in the exposure. The photomicrographs have been reduced $2\frac{2}{3}$ times.

*A*. Transverse section through a lateral leaf rib, showing a resin duct. The resin duct is 0.0053 mm. in diameter. The shortest distance to the bast ring which surrounds the resin duct is 0.0056 mm. ×168.4.

*B*. Young shoots showing simultaneous expansion of leaves and flower panicles (reduced one-fifth).

*C*. Transverse section through a woody root. ×7.5.

*D*. Transverse section through a staminate flower near the apex showing five calyx leaves with resin ducts, five petals with resin ducts, five anthers showing absence of resin ducts and presence of pollen, and the non-fertile ovule. ×40.9.

*E*. Transverse section through a green stem, showing epidermis with its trichomes, collenchyma, cortical parenchyma, pericycle with sclerenchyma cells or bast fibers, and thin-walled pericycle parenchyma. ×40.9.

*F*. Leaf epidermis with attached club-shaped trichomes. (Size of trichomes 0.071×0.0027 mm.) ×353.7.

*G*. Transverse sections of petiole. The largest resin duct has a diameter of 0.01 mm.; the smallest is 0.0044 mm. in diameter. The largest pith cells are larger than the smallest resin ducts. It is 0.02 mm. from the corner of the petiole section to the bast ring which surrounds the nearest resin duct. ×33.8.

PLATE III

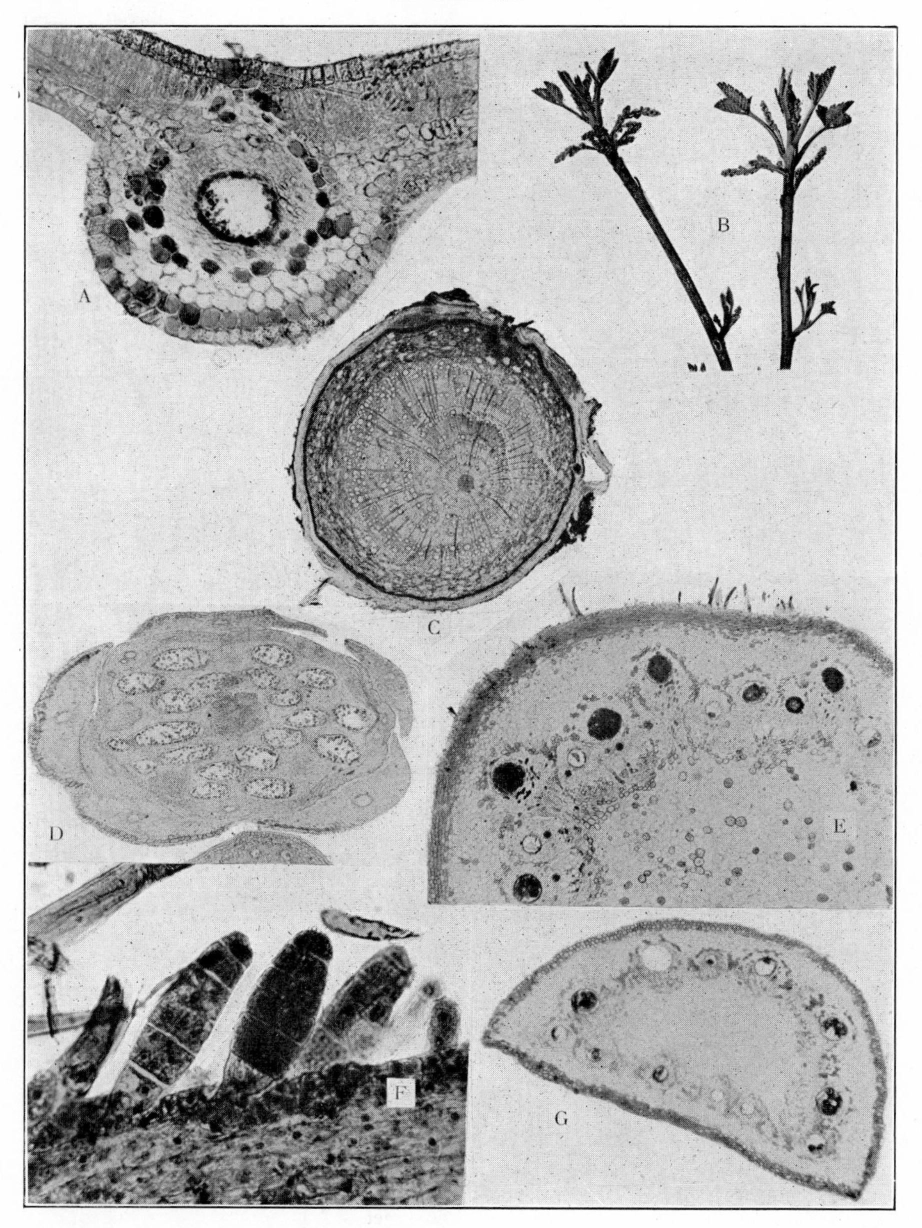

## CHAPTER V

## RESIN AND POISON VERSUS FAT FORMATION IN FRUIT[1]

Stevens (1908) has noticed that the green fruit of *Rhus radicans* is very poisonous. Stevens and Warren (1907), when investigating the fruit of *R. vernix*, found the green fruit highly toxic, while the ripe fruit is harmless. Warren (1909) attributes this interesting change in toxicity to an apparent replacement of acrid resins by wholesome and palatable fats. Besides these species of *Rhus*, a fat (Japan wax) has been found in four species of *Rhus: R. succedanea* L., *R. acuminata* DC., *R. vernicifera* DC., and *R. sylvestris* Sieb. and Zucc. (Lewkowitch, 1914). All six of these species are poisonous, and it is interesting to note that the discovery of fat in the fully matured fruit of *R. laurina* Nutt. may add a non-poisonous species to the list.

Investigations[2] were begun by me on the fats from *R. laurina* Nutt. and *R. diversiloba* T. and G. with two objects in view: (1) to discover whether or not these fats are identical with Japan wax, and (2) to determine, if possible, the connection between this fat and the poisonous property of *R. diversiloba*. This latter problem appeared all the more interesting when the fact became apparent that during the ripening of the drupes their poisonous properties simultaneously decreased with their increase in fat. When the fruits have reached full maturity (when the semi-transparent epidermis loosens and easily falls off from the waxy mesocarp) they are non-toxic. The toxicity was tested by thoroughly rubbing the pulverized fruits, as well as an alcoholic solution from them (concentrated to one-third of the original volume of the fruits), on the skin of a sensitive person.

The fats experimented with were obtained by boiling the ripe fruits in 95 per cent alcohol under a reflux condenser. The fat

[1] Reprinted from the *Botanical Gazette*, LXIV (October, 1917), 330–36.

[2] I am indebted to Professor T. Brailsford Robertson for having placed the resources of his laboratory at my disposal during this investigation.

samples were purified by repeated solution, evaporation of the solvent, and crystallization of the solid matter. The substances thus purified are pale yellow, hard, with a conchoidal and somewhat lustrous fracture. Their odor recalls that of tallow and beeswax. Under the microscope they appear to consist of small and large refractive grains. They are insoluble in water, slightly soluble in cold 95 per cent alcohol and ether, easily soluble in hot 95 per cent alcohol (separate on cooling to granular crystalline mass), warm ether, benzol, petroleum ether, and carbon bisulphid. They form grease spots when melted on filter paper. That glycerol is probably a constituent is evident from an irritating odor of acrolein evolved when the substances are mixed with powdered potassium bisulphate and heated in a dry test tube.

TABLE III

ANALYTICAL FIGURES OBTAINED

| | *R. diversiloba* | *R. laurina* |
|---|---|---|
| Specific gravity..... | 0.9872 18°.5 C. | 0.8987 18°.5 C. |
| Solubility*......... | 170 | 136 |
| Iodine absorption... | 8.79 per cent (Hübl.) | 11.44 per cent (Hübl.) |
| Saponi value†...... | 220.6 | 157.1 |
| Melting-point...... | 53° C. | 74° C. |

* Mg. per liter in 95 per cent alcohol at 20° C.
† Mg. KOH per gm.

From a consideration of their physical and chemical properties so far determined, the fats from *R. laurina* and *R. diversiloba* seem to be similar to Japan wax. This means that similar fats have been found in a non-poisonous and a poisonous species of *Rhus*.

The wide variance in the physical and chemical constants of Japan wax obtained by different experiments, and different experiments by the same investigators, may have been due to several factors, namely, adulterations of water, starch, oil of *Perilla ocimoides* Linn. (Brannt, 1896), tallow (Brannt), the fact that the fat becomes transparent below its fusing point (18–23.5° F. below m.p., Brannt), the fact that the melting-point becomes higher with the age of the sample (Brannt), impurities, and different methods of analysis.

MORPHOLOGY OF FRUIT OF R. DIVERSILOBA IN RELATION TO FAT FORMATION

The ripe fruit of *R. diversiloba* is oval, 5–9 mm. broad, 4–6 mm. high, and 4–6 mm. thick. When first formed it has a shining grass-green color and smooth texture. When dry it becomes brown and presents long, dark stripes which previously were only slightly indicated. The outer surface of these stripes is depressed because of the collapsing of the large resin ducts which lie directly beneath them. The outer layer of the fruit, which is a drupe, is something over 1 mm. thick. In the horizontal cross-section twenty to thirty large resin passages are present. These form a single outer row completely around, which conforms with the general outline of the drupe. Many smaller resin ducts are present, which alternate with the wider ones to form a row next to the seed. The arrangement on the top and bottom of the drupe is less regular. The epidermis is bordered by two or three layers of strong sclerenchymatous cells. Between these border layers and the resin passages lies the parenchymatous tissue whose cells for the most part contain solid fat. In the ripe fruit the fat appears in the principal tissue of the mesocarp. Fat is not found in the exocarp, the thin walls and the inner boundary of the mesocarp, the sclerenchymatous cells, the cells of the vascular bundles and their sheaths, and the parenchymatous sheaths of the resin passages.

The presence of solid fat in the fruit cannot be detected before July. At the beginning of August fat formation is nearly completed. The granulated layer of fat can be seen in the cell between the membrane and the protoplasm. This layer makes the lumen smaller, increases on the outside, and goes in between the already formed fat. Its granular form changes to striated masses. Before the formation of this fat in the fruit a progressive increase in the starch content is noticeable. Starch forms partly in the chromatophores in the cell and partly in the cells. When the fruit cells are rich in starch the cells contain besides only granular protoplasm and nuclei. This starch gives a positive reaction with iodine. When fat formation is near completion no starch can be detected in the fruit. In fruits which have nearly completed their growth the resin passages are everywhere constricted by the growth of parenchyma sheaths. From a consideration of these phenomena fat is apparently formed from starch and not from the resin-like poisonous sap.

This view does not seem untenable, for it has been proved that, in the storage foods of plants, carbohydrates and fats are interchangeable, and in certain cases carbohydrates are entirely replaced by fats. Starch is stored in potatoes and in the tubers of dahlia, and cane-sugar is stored in beet root; the seeds of the two former plants contain oil, while those of the beet are starchy. Although the grains of most grasses contain starch, some instances are known in which fatty oil is present instead (*Phragmites communis, Koeleria cristata*, etc.). In the cotyledons of *Impatiens Balsamina* amyloid is stored in the form of enormously thickened walls, while in other species of *Impatiens* the tissue of the cotyledon is thin-walled and oil is present instead of reserve cellulose.

The change of carbohydrates to fats in the seeds of plants has been studied by Schmidt (1891), LeClerc du Sablon (1893–97), and others. These investigators have shown clearly that as the carbohydrates decrease in seeds the fat increases. For instance, when almond seeds first begin to ripen, they are rich in carbohydrates and poor in fat; when fully matured, however, they are poor in carbohydrates and rich in fat. The seeds of *Ricinus* and *Paeonia* are also typical cases. It seems as though the oil in the mature *Ricinus* seed comes from glucose, while that of the *Paeonia* is formed from starch. As it is possible for the plant to translocate fat as such, provided it be an emulsion sufficiently fine, or in the form of fatty acids and glycerine, it might appear to some that the fats in seeds have not been formed *in situ*, but have been conveyed there by the sap. It cannot be denied that translocation of fat may occur to a certain extent; but it is a fact that fats will appear as the carbohydrates disappear in immature seeds even when removed from the parent plant. This fact, when considered with the facts known regarding the formation of fats in vegetative organs under the influence of cold, leads to the inevitable conclusion that fats are formed at the expense of carbohydrates and that this transformation may occur *in situ*.

Schmidt (1891) and LeClerc du Sablon (1893–97) have shown conclusively that during the germination of oily seeds a reversal of this process takes place, carbohydrates being formed apparently from fat.

The processes by which carbohydrates are changed to fat are still unknown. As the carbohydrates do not contain such complicated carbon chains as the fats, the formation of fat from

TABLE IV*

MONTHS IN WHICH FRUITS OF POISON OAK (RHUS DIVERSILOBA) HAVE BEEN FOUND IN STOMACHS OF CALIFORNIA BIRDS

| | Jan. | Feb. | Mar. | Apr. | May | June | July | Aug. | Sept. | Oct. | Nov. | Dec. |
|---|---|---|---|---|---|---|---|---|---|---|---|---|
| *Asyndesmus lewisi* | | | | | | | × | | | | | |
| *Baeolophus inornatus* | | × | | | | | | × | × | | | |
| *Carpodacus mexicanua* | | | | | | | | | × | | | |
| *Chamaea fasciata* | × | × | | | | | | × | × | × | × | × |
| *Colaptes cafer* | × | | | | | | | | × | × | × | × |
| *Dendroica auduboni* | × | | | | | | | | | × | × | |
| *Dendroica coronata* | | | | × | | | | | | × | × | |
| *Dryobates nuttalli* | × | | | | | | × | × | × | | × | |
| *Dryobates pubescens* | | | | | | | | × | | × | × | |
| *Heleodytes brunneicapillus* | | | | | | | | × | × | | | |
| *Hylocichla guttata* | × | × | | | | | | | | × | × | |
| *Hylocichla ustulata* | | | | | | | | | | × | × | |
| *Ixoreus naevius* | | | | | | | | | | × | | |
| *Junco hyemalia* | × | | | | | | | | × | × | × | |
| *Lanivireo solitarius* | | | | | | | | | × | × | × | |
| *Lophcrtyx californicus* | × | × | | | | | | × | × | × | × | × |
| *Melospiza melodia* | | | | | | | | | × | × | | |
| *Mimus polyglottos* | | | | | | | | | | | × | |
| *Passerella Iliaca* | | | | | | | | | | × | | |
| *Pedioesetes phasianellus* | | | | | | | | | | × | | |
| *Penthestes atricapillus* | | | | | | | | | | × | | |
| *Phloeotomus pileatus*† | | | | | | | | | | | × | |
| *Pica nuttalli* | | | | | | | | | × | | | |
| *Pica pica* | × | × | | | | | × | | | × | | |
| *Pipilo crissalis* | | | | | | | | | × | × | × | |
| *Pipilo maculatus* | | | | | | | | | × | × | × | |
| *Psaltriparus minimus* | | | | | | | | × | | × | × | × |
| *Regulus calendula* | × | × | | | | | | | | × | × | |
| *Sayornis nigricans* | | | | | | | | | × | × | | |
| *Sialia mexicana* | | | | | | | × | | | | | |
| *Sphyrapicus ruber* | | | | | | | | | | × | × | |
| *Thryomanes bewickii* | | × | | | | | | | | | | |
| *Toxostoma redivivum* | × | × | | | | | × | × | | × | | × |
| *Vireo huttoni* | | | | | | | | | × | × | | × |
| *Vireosylva gilva* | | | | | | | | × | | | | |
| *Zamelodia melanocephala* | | | | | | × | | | | × | × | |
| *Zonotrichia coronata* | | | | | | | | | × | × | × | |
| *Zonotrichia leucophrys* | | | | | | | | | | | | |
| Total | 10 | 8 | 0 | 1 | 0 | 1 | 5 | 9 | 16 | 26 | 20 | 6 |

* Table communicated to me by E. W. Nelson, Bureau of Biological Survey, United States Department of Agriculture.

† Examined by H. C. Bryant.

carbohydrates must consist of a synthesis, in which the CHOH group is converted into $CH_2$; hence a reduction must occur.

The formation of fat from carbohydrates in the plant has its parallel in the animal. The great influence of carbohydrates on fat formation in the animal was observed and proved by Lawes and

Gilbert (1859), Voit (1895), Lummert, and many others by means of a series of nutrition experiments with different animals, with foods especially rich in carbohydrates, who have apparently proved that a direct formation of fat from carbohydrates actually occurs.

The fat of the poison-oak fruit is not a reserve food supply for use of the cotyledon; this is shown by morphology and sprouting. When the drupe is planted, the growing embryo does not utilize the fat, as it remains unchanged. The fat, however, may be of service to the seed as a protection against cold on account of its low power

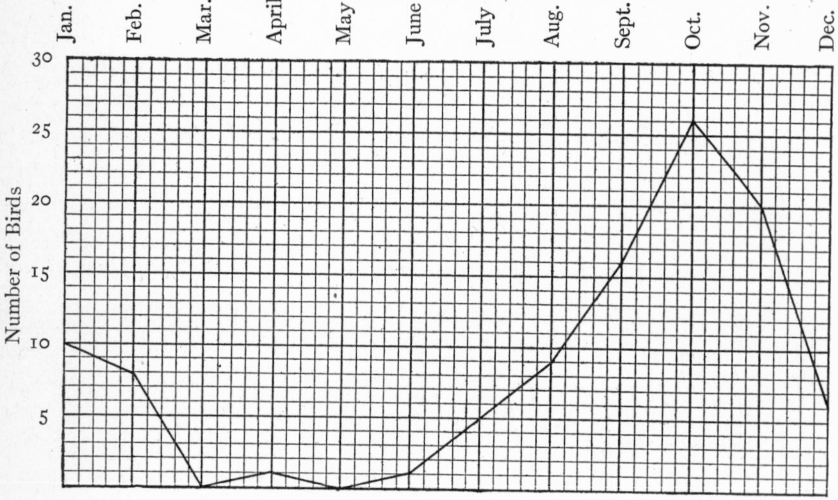


FIG. 3.—Frequency polygon showing time when and number of birds that eat *R. diversiloba* fruit. See Table IV.

for heat conduction, increasing its chance of dispersal by streams, as it is far lighter than starch (specific gravity of starch 1.56, fat 0.9872); as a protection from rain and humidity; as a protection from fungi (Pfeffer, 1900); and as an attraction to birds and therefore a factor in seed dissemination.[1] The ripe fruits persist on the plant during the winter, long after the leaves have fallen, some until May. Birds, therefore, can see them for a long distance. When eaten, the fatty covering of the drupe only is

[1] The common occurrence of the plant along fences and under trees may be due to the transportation of seeds by birds, and the prevalence of this plant along streams may be due to the fact that the ripe fruits are lighter than water and are consequently carried by streams.

digested; the ejected seeds can still germinate. Möbius (1897) has observed the fruits of *R. vernicifera* eaten by half-wild pigeons at Frankfurt. Reinecke has recorded the doves of Samoa as eating the fruit of *R. tahitensis*. Barrows (1895) speaks of the consumption of the fruit of *R. venenata* and *R. Toxicodendron* by the crow. After eating the fruits the crow rapidly digests the nutritious pulp and ejects from the mouth (in less than 40 minutes after eating) the seeds clean and devoid of pulp, together with the sand swallowed to aid in digestion. Of these ejected seeds 90 per cent germinated.

Bryant (1916) has observed that the favorite food of the road runner (*Geococcyx californianus*) during the winter season consists of the fruit and seeds of *R. integrifolia*. Unlike many birds which turn their attention to vegetable food during the winter season, the road runner appears to discriminate as to the kind of seeds taken. Of the stomachs examined, those of twenty-six (31.3 per cent) contained the seeds or fruit of *R. integrifolia*, and 8.4 per cent of the food taken by all the birds was made up of this element. The attention of the road runner is apparently attracted to this vegetable food only during the winter season, when insects, lizards, and other kinds of food are least abundant.

## SUMMARY

1. Substances more similar to Japan wax than to any other fat have been isolated from the ripe fruit of *R. laurina* and *R. diversiloba*.

2. A decrease in the poisonous properties of the fruit of *R. diversiloba* occurs simultaneously with the increase in fat content.

3. The decrease in the poisonous properties in the ripening of the fruit of *R. diversiloba* eventually results in the fruit becoming non-toxic. This phenomenon is not necessarily due to a chemical transformation of the poison into fat for: (*a*) subsequent to the formation of fat the cells in which it is deposited become filled with starch; (*b*) it is possible for the plant to transform starch into fat; (*c*) fat is not formed in the parenchymatous sheaths of the resin passages; (*d*) consequent upon the formation of fat, the resin passages are everywhere constricted by the growth of parenchyma sheaths; (*e*) a similar fat has been found in the fruit of a non-poisonous species of *Rhus*.

# CHAPTER VI

## LIABILITY TO POISONING RELATIVE TO GROWTH OF PLANT[1]

At just what stage in its life the *Rhus diversiloba* plant first contains its irritant poison has not yet been determined. After the plant has become several years old, however, all parts except the xylem, cork cells, epidermis, and trichomes are toxic. Although many persons know the sap of the stems and leaves to be poisonous, yet there are some who do not consider the sap of the roots toxic. Such is the case, however, as is attested by persons who have come in accidental contact with the broken roots of the plant while digging out other botanical specimens (Kunze, 1883; Stirling, 1913). The poisonous action of the roots might be expected from their structure, as they have numerous vertical resin canals encircling the xylem (Plate III, *C*, facing p. 36).

The resinous sap of the stems and roots retains its toxicity probably without much variation in amount or in the degree of virulency throughout the year. This is evinced not only by citations from literature (White, 1873; Beringer, 1896) and by statistics (Table V), but also by experiments conducted with the sap by the writer.

The virulency (the liability to cause poisoning) of the plant varies with the different seasons of the year in accordance with the stage of growth of the leaves, stems, and flowers. When the first leaves of the plant are unfolding in the spring they are very turgescent and easily injured. Analogously, the growing stems are less resistant than the mature stems. The mature leaves of the plant are not nearly as easily injured. Of the mature leaves, those that grow in the shade have a weaker structure than those which develop in the sun. From this fact one might expect the shade leaves to be less resistant to injury.

The amount of poison in the plant varies with the capacity of its resin canals. Of this variation in amount, that of the stems and

[1] Reprinted from the *American Journal of Botany*, VIII (March, 1921), 138–46.

TABLE V*

OCCURRENCE OF RHUS DIVERSILOBA DERMATITIS AMONG UNIVERSITY STUDENTS, BERKELEY, CALIFORNIA

| Year | Time and Frequency of Occurrence | | | | | | | | | | | | | | | | | |
|---|---|---|---|---|---|---|---|---|---|---|---|---|---|---|---|---|---|---|
| | June (Part of Month) | | July | | August (Part of Month) | | | | September | | | | October | | | |
| | Number | | Number | | Number | | Percentage | | Number | | Percentage | | Number | | Percentage | |
| 1912–13 | ... | | ... | | 2 | | 1.5 | | 13 | | 10.4 | | 6 | | 4.8 | |
| | | | | | 0 | | 2.0 | 1.5 | 11 | 24 | 9.4 | 9.9 | 4 | 10 | 3.4 | 4.1 |
| 1913–14 | ... | | ... | | ... | | ... | | 14 | | 8.9 | | 8 | | 5.0 | |
| | | | | | | | | | 21 | 35 | 13.2 | 11.0 | 13 | 21 | 8.1 | 6.5 |
| 1914–15 | ... | | ... | | 4 | | 2.2 | | 15 | | 8.4 | | 25 | | 14.1 | |
| | | | | | 3 | 7 | 1.6 | 1.4 | 16 | 31 | 8.8 | 8.6 | 22 | 47 | 12.2 | 13.1 |
| 1915–16 | ... | | ... | | 9 | | 5.4 | | 25 | | 15.2 | | 18 | | 10.9 | |
| | | | | | 4 | 13 | 3.5 | 4.4 | 15 | 40 | 13.3 | 14.2 | 9 | 27 | 8.0 | 9.4 |
| 1916–17 | ... | | ... | | 2 | | 0.8 | | 27 | | 11.5 | | 28 | | 12.4 | |
| | | | | | 4 | 6 | 2.1 | 1.4 | 16 | 43 | 8.7 | 10.1 | 19 | 47 | 10.4 | 11.4 |
| 1917–18 | 4 | | 4 | | 3 | | 3.8 | | 8 | | 10.2 | | 6 | | 7.6 | |
| | 1 | 5 | 16 | 20 | 3 | 6 | 1.9 | 2.8 | 18 | 26 | 11.6 | 10.9 | 13 | 19 | 8.3 | 7.8 |
| 1918–19 | 0 | | 0 | | 0 | | | | 0 | | | | 0 | | | |
| | 6 | 6 | 11 | 11 | 1 | 1 | | | 0 | 0 | | | 8 | 8 | | |

* The upper figures on the left of each group refer to men, the lower to women; the figures on the right side are the totals.

TABLE V—*Continued*

| Year | Time and Frequency of Occurrence | | | | | | | | | |
|---|---|---|---|---|---|---|---|---|---|---|
| | November | | December (Part of Month) | | January (Part of Month) | | February | | March | |
| | Number | Percentage | Number | Percentage | Number | Percentage | Number | Percentage | Number | Percentage |
| 1912–13..... | 13 | 10.4 | 11 | 8.8 | 9 | 7.2 | 24 | 19.3 | 19 | 16.1 |
| | 9 22 | 7.6 9 | 11 22 | 9.4 9.1 | 3 12 | 2.5 4.8 | 21 45 | 17.9 18.6 | 42 61 | 35.8 25.9 |
| 1913–14..... | 11 | 7.0 | 14 | 8.9 | 8 | 5.0 | 22 | 14.0 | 61 | 38.8 |
| | 23 34 | 14.4 10.7 | 20 34 | 12.8 10.8 | 5 13 | 3.2 4.1 | 19 41 | 12.1 13.0 | 49 110 | 31.4 35.1 |
| 1914–15..... | 20 | 11.2 | 9 | 5.0 | 12 | 6.7 | 18 | 10.1 | 30 | 16.9 |
| | 30 50 | 16.6 13.9 | 6 15 | 3.3 4.1 | 10 22 | 5.5 6.1 | 21 39 | 11.6 10.8 | 43 73 | 23.8 20.3 |
| 1915–16..... | 19 | 11.5 | 10 | 7.3 | 6 | 3.6 | 32 | 19.5 | 45 | 27.4 |
| | 14 33 | 12.5 12.0 | 4 14 | 3.5 5.4 | 3 9 | 2.6 3.1 | 40 72 | 35.7 27.5 | 23 68 | 20.5 23.9 |
| 1916–17..... | 26 | 11.1 | 12 | 5.1 | 8 | 3.4 | 34 | 14.5 | 61 | 26.1 |
| | 26 52 | 14.2 12.6 | 10 22 | 5.4 5.2 | 7 15 | 3.8 3.6 | 25 59 | 13.7 14.1 | 29 90 | 15.9 21.0 |
| 1917–18..... | 13 | 16.6 | 8 | 10.2 | 7 | 8.9 | 8 | 10.2 | 12 | 15.3 |
| | 24 37 | 15.4 16.0 | 9 17 | 5.8 8.0 | 15 22 | 9.6 9.7 | 19 27 | 12.2 11.2 | 29 41 | 18.7 17.0 |
| 1918–19..... | 2 | | | | | | | | | |
| | 11 13 | | | | | | | | | |

TABLE V—*Continued*

| YEAR | TIME AND FREQUENCY OF OCCURRENCE | | | | ANNUAL SUMMARIES | | | |
|---|---|---|---|---|---|---|---|---|
| | April | | May (Part of Month) | | Total Annual | | Total Students in Attendance at Berkeley§ | Percentage of Students Affected by *Rhus diversiloba* Treated at University Infirmary |
| | Number | Percentage | Number | Percentage | Number | Percentage | | |
| 1912–13.. | 18 | 14.5 | 9 | 7.2 | 124 | 99.4 | 2821 | 4.03 |
| | 11 29 | 9.4 11.9 | 5 14 | 4.2 5.7 | 117 241 | 96.6 100.5 | 1846 4667 | 6.33 5.18 |
| 1913–14.. | 19 | 12.1 | 0 | 0 | 157 | 99.7 | 3285 | 4.77 |
| | 6 25 | 3.8 7.9 | 0 | 0 | 156 313 | 99.0 99.1 | 2064 5349 | 7.55 6.16 |
| 1914–15.. | 35 | 19.7 | 9 | 5.0 | 177 | 99.3 | 3454 | 5.12 |
| | 27 62 | 15.0 17.3 | 2 11 | 1.1 3.0 | 180 357 | 99.5 98.6 | 2394 5848 | 7.52 6.32 |
| 1915–16†. | No record | | No record | | 164 | 100.8 | 3491 | 4.69 |
| | | | | | 112 276 | 99.6 99.9 | 2706 6197 | 4.13 4.41 |
| 1916–17.. | 28 | 12.0 | 7 | 3.0 | 233‡ | 99.9 | 3751 | 6.21 |
| | 37 65 | 20.3 16.1 | 9 16 | 4.9 3.9 | 182‡ 415‡ | 99.4 99.4 | 2944 6695 | 6.18 6.19 |
| 1917–18.. | 13 | 16.6 | 0 | 0 | 78 | 99.4 | 2765 | |
| | 23 36 | 14.8 15.7 | 2 2 | 1.2 0.6 | 155 233 | 99.5 99.8 | 3248 6013 | 4.7 |
| 1918–19.. | ........... | ........... | ........... | ........... | ........... | ........... | ........... | ........... |

† 1915–16 annual percentages would probably be greater and monthly percentages less if record were complete.
‡ Summer school excluded in order that a more true comparison may be made.
§ Figures from *Annual Report of the President of the University, 1918–19.*

leaves is most commonly effective in the index of virulency. The leaf area undoubtedly makes its greatest increase in the spring

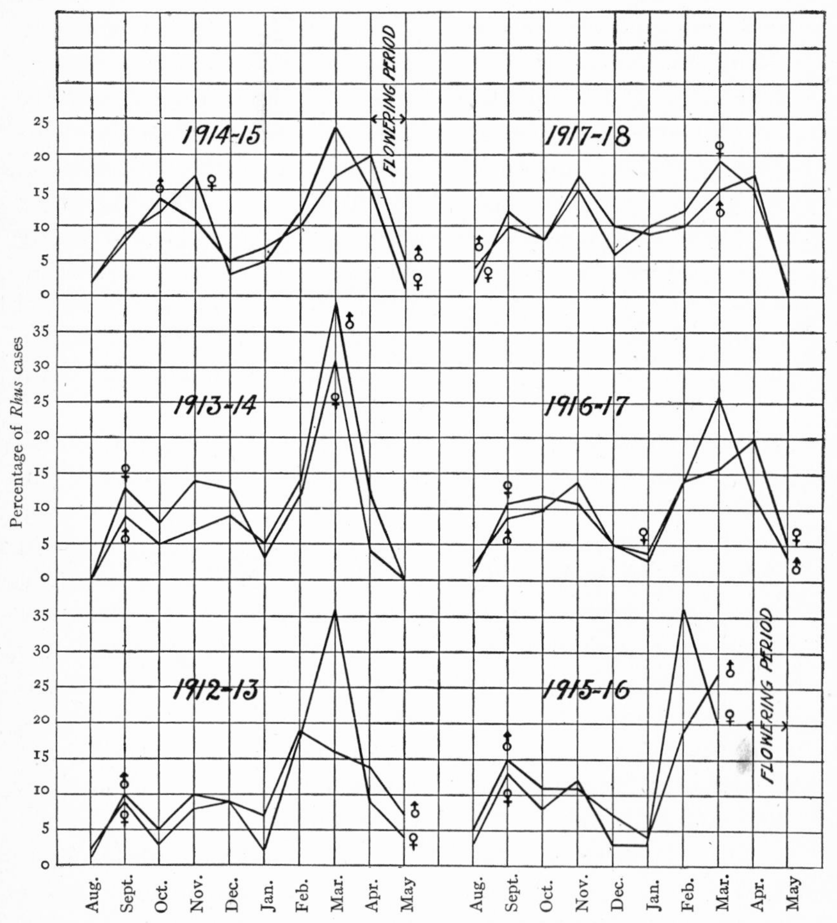


FIG. 4.—Frequency polygons showing monthly percentages of male (♂) and female (♀) cases of Rhus dermatitis treated at the University of California Dispensary. Compiled from Table V on pages 45–47.

This chart shows plainly that the percentage of cases is greatest in the spring (when the plant is budding, as indicated on Plate III, *B*) and previous to the time when the plant is in bloom. The usual seasonal drop in the percentage of cases in October may be due to the fact that the leaves of the plant have assumed bright autumn tints and are then not only more conspicuous but less poisonous. It is also evident that poisoning may occur, although less frequently, during the months (November, December, January) when the plant is leafless and dormant.

between the time when the leaves begin to unfold and the time when the flowers open. From this latter time the leaf area of the plant is nearly constant until the leaves begin to fall in autumn. Four weeks are generally required for the full development of a leaf. The flower and leaf buds begin to expand simultaneously, but the leaves soon expand more rapidly and reach maturity before the flowers open (Plate III, *B*). The staminate and pistillate plants begin to bloom at about the same time. At Berkeley, California, but few of the flowers were open April 4, 1915. The next spring the plants near the Greek Theater, at Berkeley, bloomed mostly between March 22 and May 1. Either the amount or the virulence of the poison in the autumn leaves is less than that of the normal mature leaves. Of the autumnal leaves the red are less toxic than the yellow, and when the leaves have finally withered and fallen they are non-toxic (McNair, 1917*c;* and chap. viii).

Inui (1900) has noticed that the amount of secretion of *R. vernicifera* is influenced by the conditions of light and atmospheric humidity. In potted plants the secretion lessened when carbon assimilation was hindered. Similarly, secretion was greater in damp than in dry air. This secretion therefore seems to bear a relation to transpiration and hence to turgor. As the degree of turgor varies indirectly with the amount of transpiration, other factors being equal, secretion would be least when transpiration is greatest. Turgor, too, is a necessary accompaniment of growth; flaccid tissues do not grow larger. If those influences which affect *R. vernicifera* have a similar action on *R. diversiloba*, then secretion, and consequently the plant conditions for poisoning, would be greatest during that time of the year when the growth of the plant is most active and the tissues least resistant, namely, in the spring. Obviously enough, when the plant is in full leaf and when growth has diminished, its resistance to injury will be greater and the liability of poisoning by it less.

The malignancy of the plant may also be considered in relation to its visibility or conspicuity. From this standpoint the virulency of the plant would be indirectly proportional to its conspicuity. The plant is least conspicuous when it is not in leaf, more conspicuous in the spring when the leaves and flowers are expanding, still more easily recognized when in full leaf, and most likely to be observed when its leaves have assumed their bright autumnal colors.

The virulency of the plant may be summarized according to its toxic portions, the virulency of the resinous sap, the turgescence and ease of fracture of its parts, the conditions of light and atmospheric humidity, and its conspicuity. The liability of poisoning, then, by *R. diversiloba* tissues decreases as follows: immature leaves and flower parts (except anthers and pollen), mature leaves, green stems, young roots, woody stems, and woody roots. According to the amount of poison in the plant, however, virulency would be greatest during the period of full leaf. This factor gives way before the far greater balance of factors just mentioned.

This theoretical consideration of the liability to Rhus poisoning from a botanical point of view has its counterpart in clinical statistics. The latter lend analogous evidence to the conclusion that spring has the greatest number of cases, that a sudden decrease in cases occurs during the time of the autumn tints, and the least number of cases takes place during the dormancy of the plant from November until February. It should be noted, also, that in 1915 the greatest number of cases among Berkeley students (Table V) was in March, previous to the opening of flowers about April 4, and that in 1916 the maximum number of cases occurred during February previous to the maximum flowering period (March 22–May 1) of that year. This evidence contradicts the belief prevalent among many people that the plant is most malignant during its flowering period. Some of the opinions expressed in medical literature in regard to malignancy are as follows: most cases usually in spring (Busey, 1873); most noxious at the period of efflorescence (Yandell, 1876); most cases in summer and autumn (Park, 1879); greatest activity during the flowering season, from May to October (Philadelphia; Blackwood, 1880); most virulent from July 1 to September 1 (Hubbard, 1885); worst in December when buds are coming out and in May when leaves fall (California; Baldwin, 1887); poisonous at all seasons of the year (Philadelphia; Beringer, 1896); most poisonous when in bloom (Davis, 1897); cases most prevalent at the season of the year when the foliage is beginning to show itself (Cantrell, 1898); most poisonous when in bloom (Harriman, 1898); especially virulent just as the buds come in the spring (Thudichum, 1903); more active (in New York) during the summer months, the last two months of spring, and the two first months of autumn (Hadden, 1906).

The number of cases of dermatitis from *R. diversiloba* is influenced, not only by the condition of the plant, but also by those conditions which tend to make individuals come in contact with it or with substances coated with its poisonous sap. The clinical statistics, therefore, do not constitute a true index of the virulency of the plant, since the total number of persons exposed is not known. The number of exposed persons in all probability varies at different times of the year, according to the weather conditions, state of other vegetation, individual freedom, etc.

Many attractive wild flowers are found in the same locality with *R. diversiloba* shrubs, such as Clarkias, Godetias, Collinsias, Brodiaeas, and larkspurs (Parsons, 1907). John Muir (1911) "oftentimes found a curious twining lily (*Stropholieion Californicum*) climbing its branches." Robert Louis Stevenson (1883) describes a tramp in California woods as follows:

> We struggled toughly upward, canted to and fro by the roughness of the trail, and continually switched across the face by sprays of leaf or blossom. The last is no inconvenience at home; but here in California it is a matter of some moment. For in all woods and by every wayside there prospers an abominable shrub or weed, called poison-oak (*Rhus diversiloba*).

The desire to gather spring wild flowers is often greater than the fear of *R. diversiloba*. Circumstances thus combine to bring a person in contact with the plant at the time when it is capable of doing the most harm.

# CHAPTER VII

## THE NON-BACTERIAL NATURE OF THE DERMATITANT[1]

In a previous publication (McNair, 1916*a*) I have stated that the principal poisonous constituent of poison oak (*Rhus diversiloba* T. and G.) (i.e., that portion of the plant that produces Rhus dermatitis) was chemical. Since that time a contrary opinion has been published by another writer (Frost, 1916). For this reason I take the present opportunity to attempt to set forth more clearly my reasons for believing that the etiology of poison oak dermatitis is not bacterial.

To my present knowledge Rhus poison was first thought to be bacterial in 1882 when Burrill attributed the poisonous action of poison ivy (*R. Toxicodendron* L.) to a micro-organism. The description of this micro-organism as it appeared in the *American Naturalist* (Burrill, 1883) is as follows:

> *M. toxicatus.*—Cells globular, single and in pairs, rarely in chains of several articles 0.00002 inches in diameter, movement oscillatory only. In species of *Rhus*, and believed to be the peculiar "poison" for which these plants are noted. They may be found in the interior tissues of the stem as well as upon the leaves. Transferred to the human skin they multiply through the sweat ducts (?), set up the inflammation so well known. If again transferred to healthy skin the same phenomenon follows.

As Burrill changed his opinion in regard to the bacterial nature of the poison, his own words make reply to his early articles in his letter to the editor of the *Garden and Forest* (Burrill, 1895):

> Sir,—You ask for a statement from me as to the poisonous principle of *Rhus Toxicodendron.* I wish such statements could be made with confidence, but it must be acknowledged that I do not know as much about the matter as I once supposed I did. . . . . It is well known that in Rhus poisoning the effect shows only after 12 to 24 hours, suggesting incubation. This led me to undertake some studies upon the matter. I put some carefully secured juice of the growing plant upon a marked spot on my arm. Very serious results followed, though I had not considered myself very susceptible to the poison. After 12

[1] Reprinted from the *Medical Record* (June 16, 1917).

hours the spot was slightly reddened; at the end of 24 hours it was considerably inflamed and somewhat swollen, but was still nearly confined to the originally infected area. During the next 24 hours the inflammation greatly increased and spread widely until nearly the whole forearm became involved. Colorless serum began to exude, first from well-defined papules, then apparently from the entire surface. This serum was transferred to other parts of my body, and in one instance produced similar inflammation.

Minute spherical bodies had been found in the milk-sap of the plant, and similar ones were seen under high magnification in the exuding serum. These were taken to be micrococci. At this time no attempts were made to cultivate them in artificial media, and no other demonstration was had of the truthfulness of the assumption that the spherical bodies were living organisms. Infection experiments upon myself were discontinued for obvious reasons. But following up the idea of the parasitic nature of the disease (?), applications were made of various germicidal agents, with apparently favorable results. Since that time abundant evidence has been had of the value of carbolic acid—two to three per cent—in glycerine as a pallitative or curative lotion.

But some studies made a few years later tended to discredit the agency of bacteria in the case, at least as self-acting parasites. The particles in the milk-sap of the plant were found to be constituents of it, rather than independent organisms. As upon other leaves there are various kinds of bacteria common to those of *Rhus Toxicodendron*, but none could be found capable of such effects upon the skin. There are living organisms in great numbers, at least at times, in the exuding serum; but no cultivations from these were successful in securing such as cause inflammation. Here the matter was again dropped. There still seem to be some reasons for supposing bacteria have to do with the irritation, but proof of it must be considered wanting.

Frost in his paper in the *Medical Record* (1916) considers Rhus dermatitis "primarily a systemic infectious disease of the exanthematous type caused by the invasion by a definite bacterial organism." He describes a form of bacteria which he found constant on all the leaves examined. From culturing this bacillus he attempted to prove that it was pathological, and the cause of Rhus poisoning. He says: "The culturing of these bacilli lessened whatever virulence they possessed originally, for inoculation by inunction of the pure culture into the skin produced, after 48 hours, only a slight redness, without itching or burning, and followed by no further symptoms."

In support of his bacterial idea he cites (1) "the incubation period"; (2) "the complete natural immunity shown by certain individuals"; (3) "this immunity lost through a lowering of the physical resistance, or a hypersensitivity may be established";

(4) "exposure may be strictly limited to proximity of the plant"; (5) "the first appearance of the exanthema is often on an area untouched directly by the plant, and protected from subsequent indirect contagion or windblown virus"; (6) "febrile symptoms"; and (7) "anaphylaxis."

In answer to the foregoing points I give the following:

1. The incubation period although it may occur in bacterial diseases is in itself no absolute proof that the disease which it accompanies is bacterial. The incubation period is influenced by the dose, as can be easily proved by direct application of various alcoholic dilutions of the sap of *R. diversiloba* on areas of skin equal in area and on anatomically corresponding places of the body.

2. Although immunity toward this poison may exist, no case has yet been proved when the fresh plant sap or its extracts have been directly applied to the skin (Warren, 1909). Nor has any artificial immunity been experimentally established (von Adelung, 1912).

3. Sensitiveness to many chemical irritants is reduced or accentuated at times supposedly through a change in the physical resistance of the patient. Such a condition therefore constitutes no proof that bacteria alone may be thus affected.

4. Transmission of the disease from plant to person is not limited to the proximity of the plant. Actual contact with the resinous sap of the plant must occur. This can take place directly or indirectly, e.g., the hands can carry the poison to such parts of the body that exterior clothing, etc., do not reach. The poison is not wind-carried unless by smoke, or possibly by dust and insects. The pollen is non-toxic (McNair, 1916*b*).

5. The first appearance of the dermatitis may be on an area untouched directly by the plant but not protected from subsequent indirect contagion (McNair, 1916*c;* von Adelung, 1912).

6. Febrile symptoms accompany other diseases than those of bacterial origin. Febrile symptoms are the exception and not the rule in *R. diversiloba* dermatitis (McNair, 1916*c*).

7. Von Adelung (1912) in experiments with rabbits and guinea pigs was unable to secure either immunity or anaphylaxis. Ford (1907) considered at one time that he had established immunity

to *R. Toxicodendron.* Upon repeating his experiments, however, he was unable to secure successful results (von Adelung, 1912).

### CONCLUSION

1. In the consideration of the validity of the non-bacterial etiology of poison oak (*R. diversiloba* T. and G.) dermatitis, circumstantial evidence such as the incubation period, possible immunity, and possible anaphylaxis which do not positively prove either the bacterial or chemical nature of the poison, is of little value. (Immunity and anaphylaxis may be obtained by proteins of bacterial as well as non-bacterial origin.)

2. The principal poisonous constituent of *R. diversiloba* by direct evidence is non-bacterial for: (*a*) No bacteria have been isolated from the interior of the plant which will cause characteristic Rhus dermatitis. (*b*) No bacteria have been isolated from the surface of the plant which will cause characteristic Rhus dermatitis. An uninjured leaf, petiole, or green stem when rubbed on the skin of a sensitive person will not cause Rhus dermatitis. Cultures on artificial media of bacteria from poison ivy (*R. Toxicodendron* L.) by Burrill, and of bacteria from poison oak (*R. diversiloba* T. and G.) by Frost have failed to produce characteristic Rhus dermatitis. (*c*) No bacteria have been isolated from the serum of Rhus dermatitis vesicles and cultivated which are capable of producing Rhus dermatitis. (The presence of any bacteria in the serum may be due to secondary infection from scratching, etc.) (*d*) Serum from Rhus dermatitis vesicles when rubbed on the skin (which may even be lacerated) of a susceptible individual will not cause Rhus dermatitis. (*e*) Rhus dermatitis has only been successfully experimentally caused by direct contact with the resinous sap or sap products and the smoke from the burning plant. (*f*) Unlike bacteria when the sap is mixed in equal volume with 1/500 bichlorid of mercury and kept for forty-eight hours the mixture is still poisonous. (*g*) Unlike bacteria when the sap is heated to 210° F. moist heat in steam autoclave for two hours it will still produce Rhus dermatitis.

# CHAPTER VIII

## THE OXIDASE OF RHUS DIVERSILOBA[1]

### THE PRESENCE OF THE OXIDASE IN THE PLANT AND ITS RELATION TO THE PLANT POISON

It has often been noticed that when a plant of *Rhus diversiloba* T. and G., is injured, the exuding sap rapidly becomes brown and hardens into a black, shiny, varnish-like substance. This phenomenon becomes more interesting when it is realized that the violently irritating properties of the fresh sap are completely lost during the formation of this resin-like body. This change in toxic properties may be readily followed in connection with the darkening of the sap, as the poisonous property of the freshly exuded sap is soluble in 95 per cent alcohol, as well as its non-toxic black oxidation product. The poisonous and non-poisonous alcohol-soluble substances may readily be separated, however, for the oxidation product is insoluble in xylol, whereas the toxic substance is soluble in xylol.

No evidence is here set forth to prove that the substance darkened is the poison. The darkening of the sap through oxidation is considered here merely as an indicator of the extent of the loss of toxic properties.

This darkening and loss of toxic properties seems to be mainly due to oxidation in the presence of moisture, as the following experiments indicate:

Sap from a fresh incision in a *Rhus* plant was thinly coated for about 1 sq. cm. on the inside of test tubes, $\frac{3}{4}$ by 6 inches in size, which had been thoroughly cleaned in concentrated sulphuric acid saturated with potassium dichromate. The tubes were now filled with gases as follows: two with oxygen; two with hydrogen from the reaction of zinc and sulphuric acid, purified by bubbling successively through 10 per cent lead nitrate, 10 per cent silver nitrate, and alkaline pyrogallol; two with carbon dioxid; two with nitrogen

[1] Reprinted from the *Journal of Infectious Diseases*, XX (May, 1917), 485–98.

secured by shaking air with alkaline pyrogallol in a Hempel pipet, and two with air. These gases, before entrance to the test tubes, were dried by passing through calcium-chlorid tubes. One test tube of each gas had 1 c.c. of distilled water placed in it. The tubes were finally corked with rubber corks, sealed with paraffin,

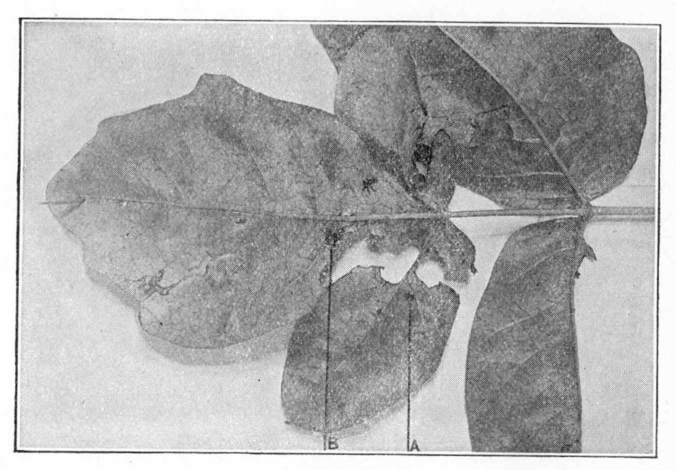


FIG. 5.—*Rhus diversiloba* leaf. *A* and *B* indicate the resinified poison on insect-injured leaf.

and kept at the temperature of the surrounding air, which at this time ranged between 13° and 19° C. The results are as follows:

In dry air, the sample did not appreciably darken.

In moist air, the sample darkened after five hours.

In dry oxygen, the sample did not appreciably darken.

In moist oxygen, the sample darkened after three hours.

In dry hydrogen, the sample did not appreciably darken.

In wet hydrogen, the sample darkened after two days.

In dry carbon dioxid, the sample did not appreciably darken.

In wet carbon dioxid, the sample darkened very slowly after two days.

In dry nitrogen, the sample did not appreciably darken.

In wet nitrogen, the sample darkened after two days.

In 20 mm. vacuo, the sample darkened after two days.

The absorption of oxygen during the drying of the sap can be readily followed by its increase in weight. Fresh sap spread in a thin layer within a beaker was dried in a desiccator in an atmosphere of hydrogen until constant weight had been attained (about twelve hours). The sap-coated beaker thus freed from moisture was placed in a damp place for several days. At the expiration of this time the beaker and contents were again placed in a desiccator until constant weight was secured. An increase in weight of approximately 1 per cent, together with the hardening and darkening of the sap, had occurred. The increase in weight, however, did not cease after several days, but continued for at least a month.

By the use of a combustion furnace it was found that fresh sap when dried contains a lower percentage of oxygen than a specimen which has been exposed to the air for a week. All the other elements remain constant. The increase in weight, therefore, is due to oxidation.

Experiments were next conducted to determine the effect of different temperatures upon the darkening of the expressed sap. Test tubes, the same size as those described and similarly cleaned, were thinly coated inside, over about 1 sq. cm., with fresh sap. One cubic centimeter of distilled water was now placed in each test tube, and rubber corks introduced. They were then individually subjected to the following temperatures:

At 5° C. a sample did not appreciably darken.
At 20° C. a sample darkened after four hours.
At 30° C. a sample darkened after four and one-half hours.
At 40° C. a sample darkened after five hours.
At 50° C. a sample darkened after seven hours.
At 60° C. a sample darkened after twenty-four hours.
At 80° C. a sample did not appreciably darken.
At 100° C. a sample did not appreciably darken.

These experiments indicate that the optimum temperature for the oxidation of the sap by the enzyme lies somewhere between 5° and 30° C. and nearer 20° than 30° C. The total range of its activity lies between 5° and 80° C.

Atkins (1913) has observed that a browning of expressed sap is invariably associated with the presence of an oxidase. (The brown saps which Atkins investigated were those from *Hedera helix*, *Syringa vulgaris*, *Magnolia acuminata*, *Catalpa bignonioides*, *Fraxinus oxyphylla*, *Fraxinus excelsior*, and *Helianthus multiflorus*.) This phenomenon is analogous to the changing of the sap of the lactree, *R. vernicifera*, when exposed to the air for some time. It is transformed into a very beautiful black varnish, which the Chinese and Japanese use for varnishing their furniture (Yoshida, 1883). It is not surprising then that an oxidase should be found in *R. diversiloba*.

Similar oxidizing enzymes have been found by Bertrand (1893, etc.) in plants destitute of chlorophyl, for example, two mushrooms, *Boletus euridus* and *Agaricus sanguineus*. The enzyme, then, is

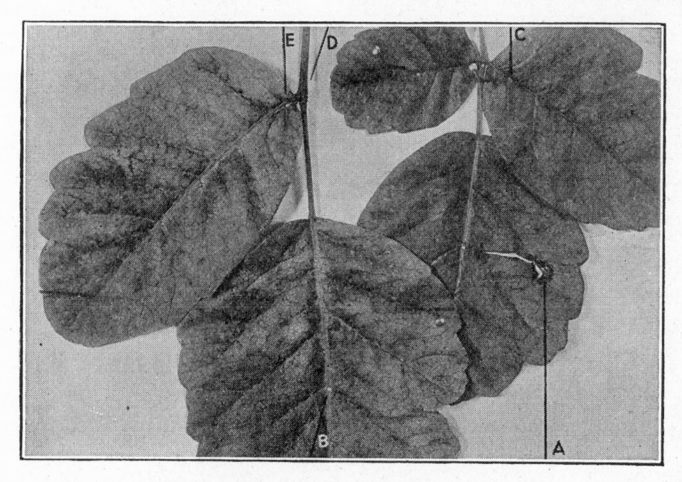


FIG. 6.—*Rhus diversiloba* leaves. *A* indicates resinified poison on injured part; *D*, resinified poison at base of leaflet; *B*, *C*, *E*, scale insects (*Aspidiotis*). A case of natural immunity. The scale insects were identified by Mr. G. A. Coleman.

not necessarily a dependent of chlorophyl, and when present in green plants it might be expected to continue its work of oxidation in the leaves after they have become destitute of chlorophyl. The death of the protoplasm, as well as the presence of conditions unfavorable to the normal metabolism of the cell, might not improbably be followed by increased oxidase activity. This has been found true in the case of insect injury to *R. diversiloba*, abscission of the midrib in the leaf, severe twisting of the stem, and a number of other instances. It has been noticed when mulberry trees were cut back too frequently that an abnormal yellow color and crinkled appearance resulted in the leaves; Suzuki (1900) investigated this to find that an excessive production of oxidases had taken place in such yellow areas. This he attributed to the lack of proper nutrition of rapidly growing tissues. Woods (1902) observed a similar phenomenon in the "mosaic disease" of tobacco plants which had been cut back.

Bunzel (1913) investigated the oxidase content of the normal and "curly top" diseased leaves of a sugar beet. He found that the diseased leaves had an oxidase content two or three times greater than that of healthy and normally developed ones. The roots of the two kinds of plants showed no marked differences, however.

When the mature leaves of *R. diversiloba* are green, they give no oxidase reaction with gum guaiac. For this experiment a finely chopped leaf was placed in a test tube with 10 c.c. of water heated to 25° C. Enough alcoholic solution of guaiac (strength about 1:60) to cause a turbidity was added. No blue color appeared in this mixture before it did in an aqueous check solution of the same temperature and concentration of guaiac. The failure of the green leaves to give this oxidase reaction may have been due to the presence of tannin or gallic acid in them, as these substances have been shown by Hunger (1901) to interfere with the guaiac test. The presence of tannin, gallic acid, or gallotannin was indicated by the reagent of Fletcher and Allen (0.05 gm. of pure potassium ferricyanid dissolved in 50 c.c. of water, and an equal volume of concentrated ammonia water added). This indicator produces a red coloration with tannin, gallic acid, or gallotannic acid in solution, being so sensitive that a drop of the indicator will detect one part of tannin in 10,000 parts of water.

A positive test for oxidase may be secured with guaiac after the inhibitor has been removed. A rapid method for separating the inhibiting substance and enzyme is that employed by Aso (1890) for tannin. The precipitation of the enzyme may be effected by pouring the expressed sap into six volumes of 95 per cent alcohol. The precipitate when redissolved in water gives the guaiac reaction. This color is destroyed by addition of the filtrate.

In autumn when the leaves become red and yellow, positive results are obtained for oxidase with gum guaiac and the leaves contain no tannin. (If sufficient tannin was added to the solution before testing, the guaiac test became negative.)

The alcoholic solution made from the autumnal leaves is less toxic than a similar solution of equal concentration from the normal leaves when applied to histologically corresponding areas of skin of a very sensitive person. Of the autumnal leaves the red are less toxic than the yellow, and when the leaves have finally withered and fallen they are non-toxic. I am indebted to Dr. Edward von Adelung, who is very sensitive to the poison, for the determination of these differences in toxicity.

This gradual loss of toxicity of the leaves through oxidation has led several observers to consider the poison volatile. For instance, Mackie (1903), writing on the value of oak leaves for forage, says:

> It would seem that the irritating and poisonous oil of poison oak is volatile at a comparatively low temperature. In gathering the specimens the writer was badly poisoned even though gloves were worn; yet after drying at ordinary room temperature, and the leaves pressed into the mill with bare hands, no poisoning effects followed.

That there is no volatile poison in the plant was known to Dr. von Adelung (1913), and this has been verified by further experiments as shown in chapter ix. This loss of toxicity is therefore due to the oxidation of the poison and the loss of fluidity of the sap.

### THE PREPARATION OF THE ENZYME EXTRACT

The plant leaves were used as sources of the ferment and the following method was pursued in its preparation: Fresh green leaves were washed in many changes of water, finally in distilled water. After draining, the leaves were finely cut with a meat chopper. The finely chopped material was mixed with distilled water, glycerine, and a small amount of chloroform, and allowed to soak for forty-eight hours. The mixture was now filtered through cotton and the filtrate reserved. (As this solution was made from green leaves it contained tannin but not sufficient to inhibit the guaiac reaction. In fact for some reason not investigated the addition of tannin to this solution did not interfere with the guaiac test.)

The constants of the filtered enzyme solution were as follows: density, 23° Baumé (sp. gr. 1.190) at 18.5° C.; glycerol content, 73 per cent, or 270.37 parts by weight of glycerine for each 100 parts of water; ash, 1.666 gm. per liter, or 0.0016 per cent.[1] This enzyme solution was used in the experiments which follow.

### RELATION OF THE MANNER OF ACTION OF THE ENZYME TO THE CHEMICAL COMPOSITION OF THE POISON

Emil Fischer (1894) has evolved the hypothesis that in the majority of ferment actions there exists a stereochemic relation between the acting substance and the body acted upon. According to him, it is necessary that the ferments and the substances they act upon have like geometric structures.

Any clue as to the nature of the substances acted upon by the oxidase of *R. diversiloba* may therefore be expected to throw some light upon the nature of the poison itself. So far all that has been done in the direction of defining the nature of this enzyme has been the discovery of its action upon the poison and the circumstances of reaction, etc., favoring this action. The oxidation of the poison by its enzyme is favored by alkalies—for example, potassium hydroxid and sodium hydroxid—and may be greatly retarded, if not inhibited, by the presence of acids.

Enzymes are considered as catalyzers and merely accelerate an oxidation that would take place in their absence at a slower rate. Attention was therefore directed to readily oxidizable substances. Of bodies most readily oxidized those of the aromatic series seem to be more susceptible than those of the aliphatic series. As the oxidation of polyphenols is considerably increased by small quantities of alkali (Holleman and Walker), it was thought the enzyme might be a phenolase. Consequently its action was tested with the diphenols, hydroquinon, pyrocatechin, resorcin, and the triphenols, phloroglucin and pyrogallol.

[1] Tannin, 0.0012 per cent, estimated by a comparison of the amount of ash with the amount of ash and tannin obtained by Mackie from water-free *R. diversiloba* leaves. His analysis yielded 9.15 per cent ash, 7.24 per cent protein, 26.56 per cent fiber, 6.79 per cent tannin (Günther), 43.39 per cent nitrogen-free extract, and 6.87 per cent ether extract.

When tested according to the *Qualitative Analysis* of Morgan (1907, p. 239) the ash gave positive indications for iron, aluminum, calcium, magnesium, silica, sodium, potassium, and phosphorus. This ash analysis shows the oxidase to be unlike that of Bertrand obtained from *R. vernicifera*, which contained manganese. On the other hand, Sarthou (1900 and 1901) found the oxidase of *Schinus molle* (a tree of the same family as *R. diversiloba*, namely, the Anacardiaceae) to contain iron, calcium, sodium, but no manganese.

THE PREPARATION OF HYDROCHINON SOLUTION AND THE COLORIMETRIC METHOD OF TESTING

One gram of hydrochinon was weighed rapidly so as to prevent oxidation as much as possible. The weighed phenol was placed in a 250-c.c. Erlenmyer flask with 99 c.c. of distilled water. Three such solutions were made with hydrochinon. From 5 to 15 c.c. of the enzyme solution were added to individual phenol solutions.

Some of the enzyme solution was boiled for five minutes (distilled water being added to keep the volume constant). After boiling and consequent cooling to room temperature this destroyed enzyme solution was added in varying amounts to 1 per cent hydrochinon solutions. The three phenol solutions, one normal, another with the added enzyme, and the third with the destroyed enzyme, were subjected to a temperature varying from 14° to 15° C. for three and one-half hours.

As hydrochinon has a strong tendency to oxidize in the air without any accelerating enzyme, check solutions were used in which equal amounts of the substance tested were placed without the enzyme. In order to decide whether the reactions were due to enzymatic or to an ordinary chemical change caused by the glycerine plant extract, checks were used in which an equivalent amount of enzyme solution was boiled before being added to the phenol solution. As the reaction was not equally accelerated by the boiled enzyme, it was concluded that its diminution in activity was caused by the destruction of a thermolabile oxidizing agent. The results are recorded in Table VI.

TABLE VI

FINAL COLORS AS ESTIMATED BY A DUBOSCQ COLORIMETER

| | No Enzyme (Depth, mm.) | 5 c.c. Enzyme Solution (Depth, mm.) | 10 c.c. Enzyme Solution (Depth, mm.) | 15 c.c. Enzyme Solution (Depth, mm.) |
|---|---|---|---|---|
| Normal enzyme | 20 | 23.5 | 26.5 | 31.0 |
| Boiled enzyme | 20 | 21.0 | 22.5 | 25.0 |
| Difference in depth of color | 0 | 2.5 | 4.0 | 6.0 |

The results obtained in a series of experiments were not very satisfactory and therefore the Van Slyke apparatus was tried.[1]

[1] The use of the Van Slyke apparatus for the experiments in this chapter was suggested by Professor T. Brailsford Robertson.

THE METHOD OF TESTING THE OXIDASE WITH THE VAN SLYKE APPARATUS

The apparatus used was that described by Van Slyke (1912). The structure of the apparatus and the manner in which it was set up are apparent in Figures 7 and 8.

As the Van Slyke apparatus does not appear to have been hitherto employed for the study of oxidases, directions for its manipulation follow.

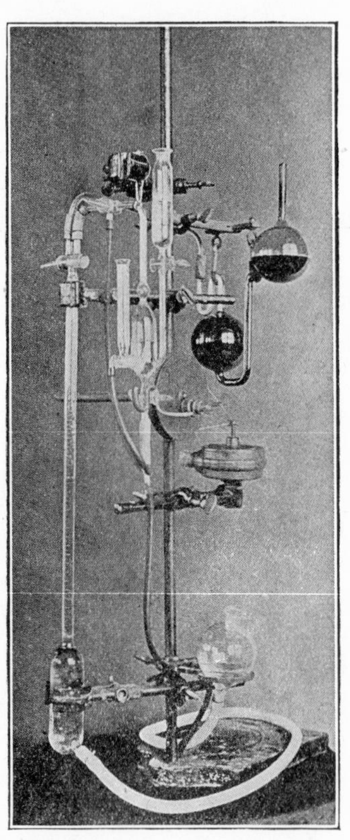

FIG. 7.—The complete Van Slyke apparatus

1. *The admission of the aromatic compound.*—Water from *F* fills the capillary leading to the Hempel pipet and also the other capillary as far as *C*. Into *A* one pours a volume of the phenolic solution to be oxidized sufficient to fill *D* up to the 20-c.c. mark (the excess may be drawn off by the cock *d*). One then closes *a* and turns *c* and *f* so that *D* and *F* are connected.

2. *The admission of the enzyme solution and the oxidization of the aromatic compound.*—One places the enzyme solution in *B*. The admission of the desired amount of enzyme solution into the oxidizing bulb *D* is accomplished by opening the cock between *B* and *D*. The oxidizing bulb is now connected with the motor, as shown in Figure 7, and shaken for the determined time.

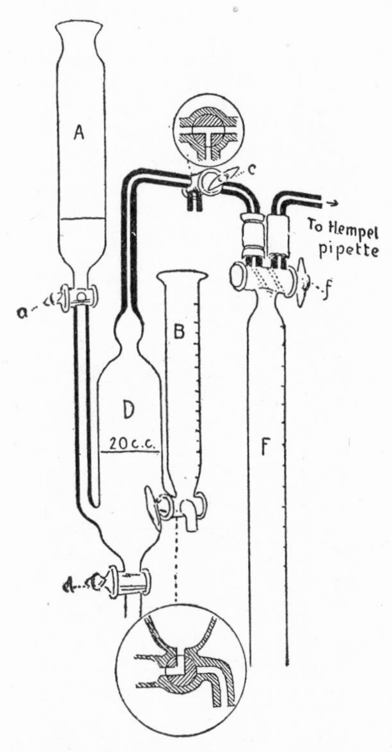


FIG. 8.—Oxidizing bulb and connections in detail. The Van Slyke apparatus

3. *The determination of the amount of oxygen absorbed by the aromatic compound.*—The reaction being completed, all the gas in *D* is displaced into *F* by distilled water from *A* and a buret reading taken by closing the cock *f* and lifting the bulb attached to the buret, until the meniscus in the buret and that in the bulb are on the same horizontal plane. After the reading is taken, the gas is forced over from *F* into the absorption pipet by merely opening *f* and lifting the buret bulb. The driving rod is then connected with the pipet

by lifting the hook from the shoulder of *d* and placing the other hook, on the opposite side of the driving rod, over the horizontal lower tube of the pipet. The latter is then shaken by the motor for five minutes, which, with any but almost completely exhausted alkaline pyrogallol solutions, completes the absorption of the residual oxygen. The residual, gas mostly, nitrogen is then measured in *F*.

The alkaline solution of pyrogallol used in the Hempel pipet is prepared by mixing together directly in the absorption pipet 5 gm. of pyrogallol dissolved in 15 c.c. of water, and 120 gm. of potassium hydroxid dissolved in 80 c.c. of water.

When tried with three isomeric diphenols, namely,

OH, OH (para) — hydroquinon, OH, OH (ortho) — pyrocatechin, and OH, OH (meta) — resorcin,

in the Van Slyke apparatus, it was seen that the quantity of gas absorbed was almost nil for the *meta*diphenol (resorcin), while the *para*diphenol (hydroquinon) oxidized very strongly. The *ortho*-diphenol (pyrocatechin) maintained an intermediate position.

TABLE VII

RESULTS OF THE TEST OF THE ENZYME WITH THE VAN SLYKE APPARATUS*

| | 2 Per Cent Hydroxyphenol (c.c.) | Enzyme Solution (c.c.) | Oxidizer Shaken (min.) | Gas (c.c.) | Pipet Shaken (min.) | Gas (c.c.) | Difference in Amount of Gas (c.c.) | Acceleration |
|---|---|---|---|---|---|---|---|---|
| Hydrochinon | 20 | 2 | 10 | 34.7 | 5 | 29.6 | 5.1 | 0.8 |
| | 20 | 0 | 10 | 34.5 | 5 | 28.6 | 5.9 | |
| Pyrocatechin | 20 | 2 | 10 | 35.4 | 5 | 29.9 | 5.5 | 0.6 |
| | 20 | 0 | 10 | 34.1 | 5 | 28.0 | 6.1 | |
| Resorcin | 20 | 2 | 10 | 34.8 | 5 | 28.7 | 6.1 | 0.1 |
| | 20 | 0 | 10 | 34.4 | 5 | 28.2 | 6.2 | |

* Room temperature throughout the experiment 23.5°–24° C.; barometric pressure throughout the experiment 752 mm.

The action of the enzyme was tested on two isomeric triphenols, namely, phloroglucin, in which all the hydroxyls are in the *meta* position (symmetrically placed), and pyrogallol, with its consecutive hydroxyls. It was found that phloroglucin did not oxidize, while pyrogallol absorbed oxygen rapidly.

OH
OH OH
phloroglucin

OH
OH
OH
pyrogallol.

TABLE VIII

RESULTS OF TEST OF THE ENZYME WITH PHLOROGLUCIN AND PYROGALLOL*

| | 2 Per Cent Hydroxyphenol (c.c.) | Enzyme Solution (c.c.) | Oxidizer Shaken (min.) | Gas (c.c.) | Pipet Shaken (min.) | Gas (c.c.) | Difference in Amount of Gas (c.c.) | Acceleration |
|---|---|---|---|---|---|---|---|---|
| Pyrogallol............ | 20 | 2 | 10 | 34.1 | 5 | 28.8 | 5.3 | 0.3 |
| | 20 | 0 | 10 | 34.1 | 5 | 28.5 | 5.6 | |
| Phloroglucin........... | 20 | 2 | 10 | 34.5 | 5 | 28.3 | 6.2 | 0.0 |
| | 20 | 0 | 10 | 34.8 | 5 | 28.6 | 6.2 | |

* Room temperature throughout the experiment 23.5°–24° C.; barometric pressure throughout the experiment 752 mm.

From the foregoing it would seem that the enzyme is a soluble ferment accelerating the oxidation of bodies of the phenol series which possess at least two hydroxyl groups, when these groups occupy the *para* or *ortho* position.

TABLE IX

RESULTS OF THE TEST OF THE ENZYME WITH THE VAN SLYKE APPARATUS*

| 2 Per Cent Hydrochinon (c.c.) | Enzyme Solution (c.c.) | Oxidizer Shaken (min.) | Gas (c.c.) | Pipet Shaken (min.) | Gas (c.c.) | Difference between Amounts of Gas (c.c.) (Observed Equivalent Constant) | Constant Calculated $Ft=k$ $k=30$ |
|---|---|---|---|---|---|---|---|
| 20 | 1 | 30.0 | 34.4 | 5 | 28.4 | 6.0 | 30 |
| 20 | 2 | 15.0 | 34.3 | 5 | 28.8 | 5.5 | 30 |
| 20 | 3 | 10.0 | 34.9 | 5 | 28.6 | 6.3 | 30 |
| 20 | 4 | 7.5 | 35.1 | 5 | 28.6 | 6.5 | 30 |
| 20 | 5 | 6.0 | 35.6 | 5 | 29.1 | 6.5 | 30 |
| | *F* | *t* | | | | *k* | *k* |

* Room temperature throughout experiment 18° C.; barometric pressure throughout experiment 759 mm.

The experiments recorded in Table IX, in which the amount of substrate is constant, show that this enzyme obeys the rule expressed by the formula $Ft$=constant ($k$). In other words, the acceleration of oxidation is directly proportional to the concentration of the ferment ($F$), and the time ($t$) required to achieve a given amount

TABLE X

DEPENDENCE OF RAPIDITY OF OXIDATION UPON THE CONCENTRATION OF ENZYME*

| 2 Per Cent Hydro-chinon (c.c.) | Enzyme Solution (c.c.) | Oxidizer Shaken (min.) | Gas (c.c.) | Pipet Shaken (min.) | Gas (c.c.) | Difference between Amounts of Gas (c.c.) (4–6) | Compara-tive Amount of Absorption (7–n) | Calcu-lated† |
|---|---|---|---|---|---|---|---|---|
| 20 | 0 | 10 | 34.6 | 5 | 27.9 | 6.7 | 0 | 0 |
| 20 | 1 | 10 | 33.7 | 5 | 28.5 | 5.2 | 1.5 | 1.34 |
| 20 | 2 | 10 | 34.5 | 5 | 29.5 | 5.0 | 1.7 | 1.90 |
| 20 | 3 | 10 | 34.5 | 5 | 29.9 | 4.6 | 2.1 | 2.32 |
| 20 | 4 | 10 | 33.0 | 5 | 28.9 | 4.1 | 2.6 | 2.68 |
| 20 | 5 | 10 | 33.9 | 5 | 30.5 | 3.4 | 3.3 | 3.00 |

* Room temperature throughout experiment 19° C.; barometric pressure throughout experiment 752 mm.

† Calculated $1.34\sqrt{\text{amount of enzyme}}$.

TABLE XI

DEPENDENCE OF THE AMOUNT OF OXIDATION UPON THE TIME OF EXPOSURE TO THE OXIDASE*

| 2 PER CENT HYDRO-CHINON (C.C.) | ENZYME SOLUTION (C.C.) | OXIDIZER SHAKEN (MIN.) | GAS (C.C.) | PIPET SHAKEN (MIN.) | GAS (C.C.) | DIFFERENCE IN AMOUNTS OF GAS | |
|---|---|---|---|---|---|---|---|
| | | | | | | Observed (c.c.) | Calculated† (c.c.) |
| 20 | 1 | 5 | 33.9 | 5 | 27.5 | 6.4 | 6.44 |
| 20 | 1 | 10 | 33.9 | 5 | 27.8 | 6.1 | 6.06 |
| 20 | 1 | 15 | 34.1 | 5 | 27.7 | 5.4 | 5.42 |
| 20 | 1 | 20 | 33.8 | 5 | 29.3 | 4.5 | 4.52 |

* Room temperature throughout experiment 25.5° C.; barometric pressure throughout experiment 754 mm.

† $5.57-0.128\left(\frac{t}{5}\right)^2$

of oxidation is inversely proportional to the amount of ferment present (Hedin, 1905, 1906, and 1908).

The enzyme solution was found to accelerate the oxidation of other bodies of the aromatic series, for example those containing amin groups, as paramidophenol $C_6H_4 \cdot OH \cdot NH_2$(1, 4) and paraphenylenediamin $C_6H_4 \cdot NH_2NH_2$(1, 4).

## DISCUSSION OF RESULTS

From the tabulated experiments the relations required by chemical dynamics for the simplest cases of catalytic reactions are found to be fulfilled by the action of the *Rhus* enzyme on 2 per cent hydrochinon: (1) approximate proportionality between the concentration of the enzyme and the velocity of the reaction (Duboscq colorimeter experiment); and (2) the validity of the rule $Ft=k$, indicating that the time required to achieve a given amount of oxidation is inversely proportional to the amount of ferment present.

It is interesting to note that the normal oxidation when combined with the accelerated oxidation is proportional to the square root of the amount of enzyme when the temperature is 25.5° C. This result is the same as that which Slowtzoff (1900) obtained with potato laccase. There is a remarkable difference between this result and that obtained at 19° C. At 19° C. the result of the combined oxidations is more nearly proportional to the square of the amount of time. This difference seems unexplainable when compared with the rate of most chemical reactions, which is doubled or trebled for a rise of 10 degrees. This general rate may be applicable to the normal oxidation of hydrochinon separately, but the acceleration of this particular reaction due to the enzyme is greater at 19° than at 25° C., as shown in the beginning of this chapter. At moderate temperatures the temperature coefficients of enzyme reactions are approximately the same as those of chemical reactions in general, but at temperatures in the neighborhood of 0° C.; the rate of change of the velocity constant with the temperature is often abnormally high, while at temperatures in excess of the optimum, that is, involving destruction of the enzyme, the velocity constant rapidly approaches zero. In the present instance the optimum temperature would appear to lie below 20° C.

## THERAPEUTIC ACTION OF THE ENZYME SOLUTION

As the enzyme has the power to change the poison to a non-toxic substance while on the plant, it was thought that it might change the poison to a non-toxic substance when on the skin and thus be a remedy for Rhus dermatitis. Experiments were conducted for me by Dr. Edward von Adelung to ascertain the value of the enzyme solution as: (1) poisonous or not; (2) a preventative of Rhus dermatitis; (3) remedy. The following results were attained: (1) The enzyme solution did not produce dermatitis though rubbed briskly into the skin. (2) When mixed with Rhus poison in alcoholic solution it did not destroy the poison. (The enzyme is active in 50 per cent alcohol.) (3) It has no remedial value.

These results are as might be expected, for the enzyme is present in the expressed sap of the plant, and yet, when the expressed sap is rubbed on sensitive skin, dermatitis results. (Positive results for the presence of the enzyme in the sap may be obtained by mixing the sap with six times its volume of 95 per cent alcohol, filtering, dissolving the precipitate in distilled water, and testing with guaiac solution as on page 60.) The enzyme is colloidal and will not pass through a semipermeable membrane, for example, parchment paper. The poison, on the other hand, is not colloidal, as when in ethylacetate solution the poison will pass through semipermeable membrane. Another evidence of the poison's ability to penetrate a semipermeable membrane is seen in its ability to penetrate the skin in the production of Rhus dermatitis (see chap. xi, p. 103). It is quite probable that the enzyme cannot penetrate the semipermeable skin and thus is unable to follow up and destroy the poison. Failure to show remedial properties in this enzyme solution, apart from its inability to penetrate normal skin, may be due to a matter of dilution. There are, however, oxidizers in the skin which seem to be incapable of the rapid destruction of the poison, for example, the leucocytes and nucleoprotein.[1]

SUMMARY

The browning of the sap of *R. diversiloba* is due to oxidation.

This oxidation results in the total loss of the irritating poisonous properties of the sap.

This oxidation is greatly accelerated naturally by an enzyme.

[1] There is another phenomenon that tends to explain the therapeutic failure of the enzyme solution namely, that the body may form an anti-enzyme specific in its inhibitive action against *R. diversiloba* oxidase. Gessard (1903) obtained a serum capable of retarding the action of the oxidase of *R. vernicifera* by the subcutaneous injection into a rabbit of preparations containing this enzyme.

1. The oxidase accelerates the transfer of molecular oxygen to phenols, and aromatic amins.

2. The oxidase accelerates the oxidation of *ortho*- and *para*-isomeric phenols more greatly than *meta*phenols.

3. The oxidizing power of the enzyme is accelerated by dilute alkalies.

4. The oxidizing power of the enzyme is retarded by dilute acids.

5. The oxidizing power of the enzyme is destroyed when boiled for a short time in aqueous solution.

6. *R. diversiloba* oxidase is probably similar to that isolated from *R. vernicifera* by Yoshida and Bertrand. Stevens and Warren (1907) observed a thermolabile enzyme in *R. Vernix*, probably an oxidase, which gave characteristic reactions with guaiac, alpha naphthol, and guaiacol. It is a soluble ferment accelerating the oxidation of readily oxidizable bodies, particularly those of the benzene series, which possess at least two groups hydroxyl or amin when these groups occupy the *para* or *ortho* position.

7. The oxidase apparently has no therapeutic value either as a preventative or as a cure for Rhus dermatitis.

## CHAPTER IX

## THE TRANSMISSION OF RHUS DIVERSILOBA POISON FROM PLANT TO PERSON[1]

My investigation of the transmission of the poison has been carried on from three standpoints: botanical, chemical, and pathological. The following chemical experiments were carried out:

1. One-half pound of fresh, finely chopped poison oak leaves was distilled normally at different temperatures up to the point of decomposition of the leaves. As a result, both the distillate and the residue were non-toxic.

2. Another lot of leaves similarly prepared was subjected to steam distillation. The distillate was non-toxic, but the residue in the retort remained toxic.

3. Distillation, either destructive or with ether, when done under reduced pressure, gave non-toxic distillates.

From the results of these distillation experiments it can be safely argued that the poison is non-volatile and that if non-volatile it cannot be carried by entrainment with a volatile substance. It has been considered by some as a non-volatile poison carried by a volatile oil.

In the investigation of the smoke of the burning plant (von Adelung, 1912), leaves were placed in a glass combustion tube. The glass tube was then heated until the leaves began to smoke. The smoke was blown against the skin of a susceptible individual. Dermatitis resulted. The experiment was repeated with the addition of cotton plugs in each end of the tube. Dermatitis did not result.

It was thought that perhaps condensation of the irritant might have occurred on the cotton. The experiment was therefore repeated (McNair, 1916*c*), glass wool plugs being used instead of

[1] Reprinted from the *American Journal of Botany*, VIII (May, 1921), 242–49. The substance of this chapter was presented by the author before the Graduate Botanical Club of the University of Pennsylvania, May 6, 1918.

For the early history of the poison of this plant as well as that of *R. Toxicodendron* see chapter x.

cotton. The glass wool was kept at the same temperature as the burning leaves. No dermatitis resulted. It is concluded, therefore, that the non-volatile poison is carried by particles of soot in smoke.

It is also possible to determine the non-volatility of the poison physiologically. A fresh leaf of poison oak was lightly glued to the concave side of a watch glass about 6 inches in diameter. The watch glass was then taped on the breast of a susceptible person (the concave side inward) and left there for half an hour. No dermatitis resulted. The foregoing experiment was repeated, substituting for the leaf a drop of sap. No ill effects resulted.

A drop of sap was now placed on the skin of a susceptible individual, and the area was covered by a watch glass. Dermatitis occurred after a few hours, but only in the area to which the sap was applied. It did not spread. If the poison were volatilized with moderate ease, at ordinary temperatures, it would have caused a general irritation at, as well as around, the area to which it had been applied. Volatile poisons rapidly penetrate into the tissues, and diffuse there with great ease. Such is the case with the various oils of turpentine, many ethereal oils from the vegetable kingdom, and numerous substances belonging to the aliphatic series, e.g., chloroform and ethyl chlorid. Petroleum, benzol, and other compounds of the aromatic series cause local irritation in essentially the same way (Schmiedeberg, 1895).

In another experiment, sap was placed on the skin of a susceptible person. After dermatitis had occurred, the affected section of skin was cut out and thin sections were mounted on microscopic slides. These sections showed that the poison had penetrated but slowly in the skin (McNair, 1916*c;* see also chap. xi). If the poison were volatile, penetration would occur more rapidly and diffusion would be greater.

In ordinary cases of Rhus poisoning, dermatitis is not noticed until about twelve hours or more after exposure. This long period of latency is much against the supposition that the poison is volatile. It would be much easier for a volatile poison to evaporate and diffuse through the atmosphere in twelve hours if it required a dozen hours to penetrate the skin.

From the preceding experiments, it is clear that the poison is non-volatile. But we still have the question to answer as to how poisoning occurs without contact with the plant. This question has been studied by von Adelung (1912), Schwalbe (1902), Hubbard (1904), Hadden (1906), and Frost (1916).

Von Adelung considered the pollen to be toxic and disseminated by the wind. As a matter of fact, the pollen may be rubbed on the skin of a susceptible person without ill effects. The skin may even be lacerated. The pollen grains, although small enough to be carried by the wind, have no winglike projections or tissues which would aid their flight, but on the contrary are covered with a sticky substance which tends to hold them in masses to the flower. Pollination is effected by insects. Similar non-toxic results have been obtained with the pollen of other poisonous species of *Rhus;* with that of *R. vernicifera* by Inui (1900), that of *R. Vernix* by Warren (1913), and that of *R. Toxicodendron* by Rost and Gilg (1912).

Schwalbe (1902) attributed poison transmission to the trichomes of the plant. The trichomes are very minute and are found in abundance on the young stems and on the under surfaces of the leaves. The trichomes were considered to be poisonous and carried by the wind.

In an investigation of this theory, fresh leaves were placed in an alembic, and a current of air was blown through. The outcoming air current was caused to impinge on the skin of a susceptible individual. No dermatitis resulted. The experiment was repeated, except that the outcoming air was caused to bubble for several hours through alcohol in which the poison is soluble. This alcoholic solution was concentrated and found to be non-toxic. In another experiment, the hairy side of an uninjured leaf (previously examined carefully with a hand lens for the absence of droplets of sap) was drawn across the skin with no ill effects. In another test an uninjured leaf was placed in 95 per cent alcohol at room temperature for ten minutes. The alcoholic solution was concentrated and found to be non-toxic.

Rost and Gilg (1912) carried on experiments with *R. Toxicodendron* to determine if the plant hairs drop off spontaneously, if they can be blown off from cut twigs, and if the poison, as in *Primula obconica*, can be obtained by contact from the undersides of the leaves. Two shells containing glycerine were placed under *Rhus* plants for two windy days in May. When this liquid was examined microscopically after the experiment, needle-shaped and club-shaped hairs were found. On October 17, 1911, three wide glass dishes containing glycerine water were placed under thickly leaved branches of *R. Toxicodendron*. These were left for four days. A microscopical examination on October 21 showed no hairs in the dishes. The preparations contained considerable dust. From the results of these experiments, it is evident that the hairs do not drop off to any great extent spontaneously at either the beginning or the end of the vegetative period.

To determine whether or not the trichomes could be forcibly blown off, five experiments were conducted in 1911: (*a*) at the end of July (Exp. Series 1 and 2); (*b*) at the end of August (Exp. Series 3); (*c*) at the end of September (Exp. Series 4); (*d*) after the middle of October (Exp. Series 5).

A branch was firmly fastened within a rectangular glass case (100×75×180 cm.) and was exposed to an air current of about 0.3 atmosphere pressure from a distance of approximately 15 cm. so that the leaves moved as if in a storm. The air current, after passing the leaves, struck an inclined glass plate on which were placed glycerine-covered slides. The current then left the case through a funnel closed with cotton. On the bottom of the glass case two more glycerine-covered slides were placed. During experiments the air current was often interrupted, especially at the beginning and toward the end. This was done to secure the strongest possible disturbances of the leaves. Each experiment lasted at least two hours. Freshly cut branches were used. These branches were afterward pressed and stored, for microscopical examination as to the presence of trichomes, which were found to have been left on the leaves in abundance.

The glycerine-moistened slides were examined under high and low magnifications. At the end of each experiment, preparations of the dried leaves were made in a chloral-hydrate solution to find if hairs still remained.

The branches used were:

| SERIES 1 | | SERIES 2 | |
|---|---|---|---|
| 1st day | Fresh | 1st day | Fresh |
| 2d day | One day old | 2d day | One day old |
| 3d day | Two days old | 3d day | Three days old |

*a*) *Experimental Series 1* (*July 26–28, 1911*).—Herbarium specimens and two microscopical cross-sections gave evidence of many hairs.

1. Wednesday, July 26: The experiment lasted eleven hours. During the first hour the position of the branch was changed twice. A microscopical examination of the glycerine-moistened slides on July 27 showed the absence of club-shaped hairs, but the presence of needle-shaped hairs, much dust, and other impurities.

2. Thursday, July 27: The branch used in the foregoing experiment was exposed to the blast again for two hours (from 11:15 A.M. to 1:15 P.M.). When examined microscopically on July 28, the preparations showed that the dried-up branch as well as the fresh one had not given off club-shaped hairs, but only needle-shaped hairs.

3. Friday, July 28: The almost entirely dried branch was subjected for the third time to the air blast (from 10:00 A.M. to 12:00 M.). A microscopical examination on the same day (July 28) showed the presence of needle hairs in all preparations, but of only one club-shaped hair.

At the end of Experimental Series 1, a chloral-hydrate preparation was made of the entirely dried branch. The underside of the leaves, as is the case in the fresh leaf, was covered with many club-shaped and bristle-like hairs.

*a*) *Experimental Series 2* (*July 28–31, 1911*).—In this series of experiments a branch of densely haired *R. Toxicodendron* was used. A part was pressed and a chloral-hydrate preparation made of it. This showed a dense covering of both kinds of hairs.

1. Friday, July 28: The experiment lasted from 12:30 to 2:30 P.M. On July 29, a microscopical examination disclosed a club-shaped hair in each of four preparations; the remainder showed many needle-shaped hairs.

2. Saturday, July 29: The dried branch was blown on for two hours (from 11:00 A.M. to 1:00 P.M.). A microscopical examination followed on Monday, July 30. This disclosed:

Preparation 1: Three club-shaped hairs, very many needle-shaped hairs, many dirt particles, and pollen grains of other plants.
Preparation 2: No club-shaped hairs.
Preparation 3: Four club-shaped hairs, one with a piece of epidermis.
Preparation 4: Two club-shaped hairs.
Preparation 5: Two club-shaped hairs, one containing yellow protoplasm.
Preparation 6: One club-shaped hair.
Preparation 7: Three club-shaped hairs.
Preparation 8: No club-shaped hairs.

3. Monday, July 31: The three-day-old branch was blown on from 11:30 A.M. to 1:30 P.M. A microscopical examination on August 1 showed one club-shaped hair in each of four out of eight preparations. Both the glycerine-covered slides on the bottom of the case were free from club-shaped hairs. The cotton in the funnel contained no club-shaped hairs (the cotton having been soaked in glycerine and the excess pressed out).

At the end of the experiment, a chloral-hydrate preparation was made from the three-day-old, entirely dried branch. Club-shaped hairs were present in abundance on the leaves. The club-shaped hairs could never wound the cuticle.

Three further experiments were made similarly to the first two, toward the end of August, in the second half of September, and soon after the middle of October, 1911. The results were similar. In the first days none, or at most one or two, club-shaped hairs could be found in eight to ten preparations. In the experiments with the twigs dried two or three days, only a few club-shaped hairs were blown loose. In many experiments in which preparations of hairs were spread on the skin, not the slightest irritation appeared.

The glycerine layer of one or more experiments was applied and dried on the uninjured skin of the underside of Rost's forearm. The results were negative. Rost was susceptible to the resinous sap of the same shrub. It seems evident, therefore, that the trichomes are non-toxic and are not a means of conveyance of the poison from plant to person.

Hubbard (1904) and Hadden (1906) thought insects might carry Rhus poison from the plant in ways similar to those by which flies carry bacteria from place to place. This method of transmission seems hardly practicable in many cases. It should be borne in mind that the insect could not transmit the poison by coming in contact with the uninjured plant.

Recently, Frost (1916) believed the poison to be bacterial. This has been refuted (McNair, 1917*b;* see also chap. vii).

The methods already discussed constitute all that have been suggested for the transmission of Rhus poison to a distance. As none of them prove very serviceable, we still have to consider the question as to how poisoning occurs without contact with the plant.

It has been found in an examination of the sap that: (1) the unelaborated sap of the xylem is non-toxic; (2) the elaborated sap of the phloem is non-toxic; and (3) the resinous sap of the resin canals is poisonous.

A further examination of the plant tissues shows that the xylem, epidermis, and trichomes which do not contain the resin canals are non-toxic.

When the flowers are examined, it is evident that resin canals do not extend more than halfway up the fully matured stamens, and so it would be expected that the pollen would be non-toxic. The flower of the female plant, on the other hand, contains resin canals in the pistil, and an abundance of resin canals surround the ovule. The ovule remains highly toxic until the seed has fully ripened. The poison, therefore, acts as a protection to the immature seed. This plant thus exemplifies the natural law developed by Kipling (1911) that the female is more deadly than the male. It has also been shown (see chap. vi, Table V, p. 45, and Fig. 4, p. 48) that the maximum number of cases of Rhus dermatitis recorded in the University of California Infirmary occurs previous to the opening of the flowers.

It has long been known that fresh leaves are more likely to produce poisoning than are dry or fallen leaves. This difference in malignancy has been attributed to a poisonous gas given off by the plant. Van Mons (1797) was convinced by the large number of cases among persons of his acquaintance, that the evil effects of *Rhus* were produced by a gaseous substance which escaped from the living plant, because the dry leaves or fallen leaves never cause trouble.

Professor Asa Gray also held this same opinion in 1872, as the following letter to Dr. J. C. White discloses:

My personal knowledge that Rhus dried specimens are harmless amounts merely to this: I handle over and over dried specimens with impunity, but am very sensitive to the fresh plant. Then the poison is volatile, as shown by its affecting persons who do not touch it actually; that of the leaves, I should say, must escape and dry out in the drying process, or in the course of time. In a stem it would not volatilize so soon; but I should not expect to be poisoned from any *old* herbarium specimen, either from twigs or leaves.

Likewise, Mackie (1903), writing on the value of oak leaves for forage, says:

It would seem that the irritating and poisonous oil of poison oak is volatile at a comparatively low temperature. In gathering the specimens the writer was badly poisoned even though gloves were worn; yet after drying at ordinary room temperature, and the leaves pressed into the mill with bare hands, no poisoning effects followed.

Opposed to these opinions is the experience of Bogue (1894) while investigating a herbarium specimen of *R. venenata* which had been deposited in the Ohio State University not less than three years. He was poisoned by the "sawdust" from the stems of the plant which was the result of borings from a beetle.

It has previously been conclusively shown that the poison is non-volatile, and the decrease in malignancy of the leaves in drying can be attributed only to a loss of fluidity of the sap and to the loss of toxicity of the poison from oxidation (McNair, 1917*c;* and chap. viii).

In concluding the botanical investigation, it seems evident that the plant is capable of poisoning only when injured in such a manner that the poisonous resinous sap exudes. This sap rapidly exudes from all parts of the injured plant. When on woolen cloth, it preserves its toxic properties for a length of time varying with the atmospheric and temperature conditions to which it is subjected. The sap gradually oxidizes and the poison loses its noxious properties, a black, indelible stain being left on the cloth. These stains are often prominently apparent on khaki, linen, etc., after the articles have been laundered. The oxidation is most rapid when the temperature is blood heat and the atmosphere humid. A cold atmosphere delays the oxidation.

The presence of the poisonous sap on clothing accounts for many of the recurrent cases of Rhus dermatitis. For example: A lady spent the night with her sister, whose husband was obliged to be absent on business. The husband had been poisoned about the head and neck with ivy a few days before leaving home. The pillow case on which he slept was not changed, and his sister-in-law, using it, became poisoned about the face and neck in consequence.

Poisoning without contact with the plant may occur by means of smoke from the burning plant or by contact with substances that have the poisonous sap on them, such as gloves (Hunt, 1897; Ward, 1908; Frost, 1826; Kunze, 1883); pocket-knife handles, croquet balls, and botanists' collecting cases (Hunt, 1897); hands of another (Hunt, 1897; White, 1873; Planchon, 1887; Cantrell, 1891; Maisch, 1866); clothing (Balch, 1906; White, 1873; Bibb, 1915; Lindley, 1908; Cundell-Juler, 1883); shoes one year after contact (Balch, 1906; Ward, 1908); instruments (Planchon, 1887); leather hat bands (Leonard, 1884); and firewood (Barnes, 1886).

Dermatitis caused by other plants is also sometimes attributed to *Rhus*, e.g., *Cypripedium* (Hurlburt, 1869); eczema and other eruptions may also be confused with that caused by *Rhus*.

## CONCLUSIONS

1. The principal dermatitant of *R. diversiloba* is not volatile, for:

*a*) It is not distillable normally by steam or under reduced pressure. It cannot be carried by entrainment with a volatile substance.

*b*) The smoke of the burning plant is not poisonous when filtered through glass wool at a high temperature.

*c*) Possible emanations from leaves are non-toxic when (1) the leaves are fastened on the concave side of a watch glass and then to the skin of a susceptible person; and (2) when a current of air is blown over the leaves and caused to bubble through alcohol, the alcohol is non-toxic.

*d*) Dermatitis occurs only on the area of skin to which the poisonous sap has been applied; a general irritation as by volatile irritants is not produced.

*e*) It does not diffuse rapidly in the skin, as is shown microscopically in sections of diseased skin.

*f*) The period of latency is too long.

2. Portions of the plant which do not cause dermatitis are: the pollen, the trichomes, the epidermis, the cork cells, and the xylem.

3. The poison is confined exclusively to the resinous sap.

4. Leaves decrease in malignancy in drying from the loss of fluidity of the sap and from the oxidation of the poison.

5. Poisoning without contact with the plant may occur from the smoke of the burning plant or by contact with substances that have the poisonous sap on them, such as clothing, shoes, cordwood, tools, the hair of animals, etc.

6. Dermatitis caused by other plants is sometimes attributed to *Rhus*. There is difficulty in distinguishing eczema from Rhus dermatitis.

# CHAPTER X

## THE CHEMISTRY OF THE POISONOUS PRINCIPLE[1]

### HISTORY OF THE CHEMICAL INVESTIGATIONS

The progress of our knowledge of the transmission of Rhus poison from plant to person reflects, in a general way, the development of our understanding of plants and plant products. This is shown prominently in tracing the history of experiments in regard to the volatility and chemical nature of the poison. In this connection it may be well to consider, besides the dermatitant from *Rhus diversiloba* T. and G., the similar irritant substances from *R. Toxicodendron* L. and from its other subspecies *R. radicans* L.

The earliest explanation of Rhus poisoning attempted was that the plant gives off an invisible colorless vapor, or emanation, which, when breathed or permitted to touch the skin, causes dermatitis. The North American Indian and negro shared in this belief (Thompson, 1892).

Some early writers associated Rhus poisoning with the fabulous stories told of the effects of the deadly upas tree (*Ipo toxicaria* Pers., *Antiaris toxicaris* Lesch.) of Java (Bennett, 1838).[2]

The theory that the poison is non-volatile has also had its adherents.

[1] Reprinted from the *American Journal of Botany*, VIII (May, 1921), 238–42; and from the *Journal of the American Chemical Society*, XLIII (January, 1921), 159–64.

[2] More light on the early physical and chemical nature of the principal irritant poison of this plant may be obtained through a study of the writings of Monti (1755), Hunold, Gleditsch (1777), Achard (1786), Willemet (1800), Pornai (1783), and Krüger. All of these investigators considered the poison volatile. That this conclusion should be drawn at that time is not so remarkable if we consider that the gaseous exchange in plants was not understood at that time. Although Priestly (1774) found in 1772 that plants give off oxygen, subsequent repetition of his experiment did not always give the same result. Ingenhousz (1779) showed that the air was purified by plants in sunlight. He concluded, however, that the atmosphere is made injurious to animals by emanations from all plants in the shade and at night. Not only were all plants supposed to give off volatile poisons in the shade or at night, but Conradi, Ackerman (1787), and Krauss (1819) believed the chief cause of various infectious diseases to be gaseous. As a result we have to this day the word malaria.

In 1788 Du Fresnoy, experimenting with *R. radicans*, steam-distilled its flowers and leaves. The distillate was not poisonous, but the residue in the still remained toxic.

Fontana (1787) experimented with *R. Toxicodendron*. Because of his marked susceptibility to the poison he was forced to stop before he had determined whether or not the poison is volatile.

Two years later, Van Mons (1797) collected about 15 cubic inches of gas given off by a plant of *R. radicans*. Chemical experiments were carried on with this. He then engaged his brother, who was very sensitive to the poison, to hold his hand for more than one hour under a glass bell jar containing gas from the plant obtained in the middle of the day. A month later, not having noticed any eczematous symptoms, he repeated the same experiment with gas collected under a cylinder covered with black cardboard. He felt, even during the immersion, a burning sensation, and developed a typical case of Rhus dermatitis. Van Mons concluded that the poisonous principle of *R. radicans* is a gaseous hydrocarbon which emanates from the plant only at night, on cloudy days, or in the shade.

In 1798, Horsfield, a medical student at the University of Pennsylvania, stated that some people were affected by the exhalations of *R. Vernix* and *R. radicans* to a distance of 20 feet from the plant. He also noticed that dermatitis was produced by the immediate application of the juice of the plant to the external surface of the skin. In analyzing *R. radicans* he placed 2 pounds of the flowers and leaves with several quarts of water in a small copper still. The distillate was not poisonous, but the residue in the still retained its toxicity.

Lavini (1825) considered the poison of *R. Toxicodendron* a gum resin, mixed with a "subtil" acid principle, qualified to combine with the hydrocarbon gas which emanates from the plant after sunset. According to him, the effect of the sap squeezed from the leaves is analogous, but less intense. The effect of "water" distilled from this plant was still less intense.

Khittel (1858) attempted a more thorough chemical analysis of *R. Toxicodendron*. Because of his inability to find the poison by the processes outlined, he considered it a volatile alkaloid.

Millon (1860–61), evidently unaware of the work of Khittel, also investigated *R. Toxicodendron*. He believed the poison a non-volatile gum resin requiring direct contact to cause dermatitis. He found its alcoholic solution to be toxic.

Discussing the experiments of Khittel, Maisch (1865) held the poison to be volatile and said:

> It is natural to suppose that, during the process of drying, the greatest portion of the poisonous principle should be lost. This must be still greater, if the dried leaves are powdered, a hot infusion prepared from them, and this infusion evaporated down to the original weight of the dried leaves. It is obvious that Khittel could not have selected a better method for obtaining the least possible quantity of the poisonous principle, if, indeed, it could be obtained by this process at all.

Later Maisch (1866) disagreed with Khittel and denied the presence of a volatile alkaloid. He thought that he had found a new volatile acid, which he held to be the active principle and which he called "toxicodendric acid." Maisch inclosed in a tin box a lot of freshly collected leaves of poison ivy, and introduced into this box a number of moistened test papers. The next morning he found that the blue litmus paper had been colored strongly red, whereas curcuma and red litmus paper were unaffected. He writes regarding this experiment: "This single experiment was at once a conclusive proof that the exhalations of these leaves contained a volatile acid, and that the poisonous properties were most likely due to it."

Maisch describes further how he obtained an impure watery solution of his toxicodendric acid by maceration of the leaves, expression and distillation of the expressed liquid. In preparing his acid, he suffered from a copious eruption and the formation of numerous vesicles on the back of his hands, fingers, wrists, and bare arms. He says further:

> Several persons coming into the room while I was engaged with it were more or less poisoned by the vapours diffused in the room, and I even transferred the poisonous effects to some other persons merely by shaking hands with them. The dilute acid, as obtained by me, and stronger solutions of its salts, were applied to several persons, and eruptions were produced in several instances, probably by the former, though not always, which was not likely owing to the dilute state of the acid.

Maisch did not isolate his acid nor any one of its salts; he never had the substance in question chemically pure. He proved only the presence of a volatile acid. He noticed the characteristic eruption on his own skin while working with the poison ivy. Persons coming to the laboratory at this time were often poisoned. He observed also that an eruption sometimes followed the application of the impure solution of this acid to the skin. From these very rudimentary experiments he drew the wholly unwarranted conclusion that his acid must be the active principle.

By far the most valuable work on *R. Toxicodendron* is that of Pfaff (1897). From a clinical study of Rhus poisoning, Pfaff came to the conclusion that the poison must be a non-volatile skin irritant. The more volatile the irritant, the quicker is its action on the skin. Formic acid acts very quickly; acetic acid, less volatile than formic, acts more slowly, but still much more quickly than poison ivy, the latent period of which is usually from two to five days. Pfaff thought that the volatile acid obtained by Maisch might have contained some of the poisonous principle as an impurity, but that it could not produce the dermatitis if prepared in a pure state. He therefore prepared a quantity of the acid by distilling the finely divided fresh plant with steam. The yield was increased by acidulating the mixture with sulphuric acid before the distillation. The acid distillate so obtained was freed from a non-poisonous oily substance by shaking the solution with ether. Barium and sodium salts were made by neutralizing the acid and were purified by crystallization. Analysis showed them to be salts of acetic acid, and they gave the characteristic tests for this acid. The "toxicodendric acid" of Maisch was thus shown to be acetic acid, and not therefore the poisonous principle of the plant.

Pfaff obtained the active principle by the process which he outlines. The lead compounds made in different preparations were analyzed and assigned the formula $C_{21}H_{30}O_4Pb$. The oil itself was not analyzed. Pfaff proposed the name toxicodendrol for the oil. He found that it is not volatile, is decomposed by heat, is soluble in alcohol, ether, chloroform, benzene, etc., but insoluble in water. Its effects upon the human skin were studied in many experiments upon himself and others. It was shown that an exceedingly minute quantity of the poison will produce the dermatitis, even 1/1000 milligram applied in olive oil being active. The oil was given internally to rabbits, its effects being most marked on the kidneys.

Acree and Syme (1906–7) found gallic acid, fisetin, rhamnose, and a "poisonous tar, gum, or wax" in the extract prepared by maceration of the leaves and flowers of poison ivy with ether, and subsequent distillation of the solvent. The lead compound of this poisonous substance was found to be soluble in ether. The authors utilized this property to free the poisonous material from admixed non-poisonous substances. Lead compounds were first prepared by precipitating an alcoholic solution (of the ether extract of the drug) with lead acetate. The precipitate was washed with water, partially dried over sulphuric acid, placed in a Soxhlet apparatus, and extracted with ether until the solvent came over colorless. A green solution was obtained which was washed with water and decomposed with hydrogen sulphid. On evaporating the solvent, a black, poisonous "tar or gum" remained. Upon hydrolysis with 2 per cent sulphuric acid, this poisonous substance gave fisetin, rhamnose, and gallic acid. The residue in the thimble was decomposed by hydrogen sulphid, shaken with ether, and evaporated. A hard, brittle, yellow, non-poisonous resin was obtained. The authors believe the poisonous principle of poison ivy to be a complex substance of glucosidal nature.

The work of Acree and Syme is probably erroneous for: (1) all three of the so-called constituents of the poison are found in two non-poisonous species of *Rhus;* (2) the natural glucoside yielding fisetin, rhamnose, and gallic acid is non-toxic; and (3) there is not sufficient evidence that the poisonous substance which Syme attempted to decompose was not a complex containing a poisonous body and one or more non-toxic glucosides in addition. McNair (1916*a;* see also Sando and Bartlett, 1918), working with *R. diversiloba,* concluded that the poison of this plant is not a glucoside of rhamnose, fisetin, and gallic acid. A different method was used for extracting the poison, and none of these substances could be obtained on hydrolysis.[1]

[1] Similar findings resulted from a similar chemical analysis by the author in 1921 of *R. Toxicodendron* leaves and flowers gathered in Washington, D.C.

Chyser in 1910 considered the poison of *Rhus* a toxalbumin formed by the combination of a liquid acid with albumin. He puts forth the following evidence in support of this conclusion: (1) the small amount of poison (0.000005 gm.) necessary to produce itching and burning on the skin; (2) similarly to a toxalbumin, it loses its toxicity by heating to 50° C. on a water bath; likewise at 75° C. and 100° C. The toxicity was tested by rubbing with a probe on the skin of the upper arm. In no case was irritation evident. This evidence is inconclusive of the poison's being a toxalbumin, for: (1) other substances besides toxalbumins are poisonous when in such small amounts; (2) the poison remains toxic if heated on glass in a steam autoclave for one hour under 20 pounds' pressure per square inch (temperature 126.2° C.); and (3) the poison contains no nitrogen.

The specific cause of skin poisoning from *R. Toxicodendron* L. and its two subspecies, *R. diversiloba* T. and G. and *R. radicans* L., has thus far been ascribed successively to: an emanation of vapor; a hydrocarbon gas; a gum resin, mixed with a "subtil" acid principle, qualified to combine with hydrocarbon gas which emanates from the plant after sunset; a volatile alkaloid; a non-volatile gum resin; a volatile organic acid (toxicodendric acid); an infection by bacteria (*M. toxicatus*, Burrill, 1882); a non-volatile oil (toxicodendrol); a glucoside of fisetin, rhamnose, and gallic acid (toxicodendrin); a toxalbumin; and finally to something other than a glucoside of fisetin, rhamnose, and gallic acid.

# METHODS OF ANALYSIS OF RHUS POISON[1]

## ACHARD (1787)

16 ozs., 6 quent. fresh leaves pressed of *Rhus Toxicodendron*

EXPERIMENT 1.—Extract 8½ ozs. formed a green sediment on standing. Sap transparent, light green, somewhat milky, with strong disagreeable odor.

EXPERIMENT 2.—2 ozs. of sap evaporated with gentle heat to thick brown syrup. No odor remained. Therefore odoriferous principle volatile.

EXPERIMENT 3.—Sap treated with different reagents as follows:

Tinc. of litmus or "violen syrup" not changed in color. Therefore sap neither acid nor alkaline.

$AgNO_3$ forms white ppt. which turns black whether exposed to light or not.

$Hg(NO_3)_2$ forms yellow ppt.

Pb in $HNO_3$ forms no ppt.

"Calcareous earth" in $HNO_3$ produces no change.

"Liver of Sulphur" results in S ppt. and S odor.

EXPERIMENT 4.—Leaves dried and extracted with:

(A) Water gives a gummy extract.

(B) Strong alcohol gives a resinous extract which took up no water.

EXPERIMENT 5.—Wood of plant dried at moderate heat. Powdered. A portion gave a gummy extract with water. A portion gave a resinous extract with strong alcohol.

EXPERIMENT 6.—Dried powdered root. Two portions extracted as above gave similar results.

EXPERIMENT 7.—5 ozs. dried root distilled in glass retort on sand bath with gradually increased heat: no volatile salt either on sides or on neck of retort. At beginning a "pflegma" passed over, little odor and no color; then followed a yellow liquid, very acid odor; next a syrupy empyremic oil with odor and consistency similar to that obtained by distillation of all vegetable substances. Watery portion had odor and characteristics of a strong acid, colored litmus and "violen syrup" red, gave strong effervescence with dissolved salt of tartar ($K_2CO_3$) and a considerable quantity necessary for saturation. Residual coal was ashed—extract lye had little taste, colored "violen syrup" green. Insoluble residue dissolved in acids with effervescence; $H_2SO_4$ added to soln. in $HNO_3$ gave ppt. in form of a "selenits."

"The above experiments teach us the composition of *Toxicodendron* in so far as they can be determined by the variety of decompositions which for vegetables are very limited and incomplete."

## VAN MONS (1797)

*Rhus radicans*

I. Gas collected from one branch of *R. radicans* in hot sunlight was nearly pure oxygen.

II. 15 cu. in. of gas from the plant. Manner of collection not stated.

(A) 5 cu. in. passed through concentrated caustic alkali in tube on mercury. Mixed this with equal volume of oxygen. Electricity discharge through mixture. Inflammation doubtful. Volume reduced one-third. Sides of tube covered with moisture. Gas now passed through lime water. Lime water whitened. Gas reduced to one-quarter of its original volume.

(B) 5 cu. in. burned on water by means of "muriatic oxygen gas." Condensation immediately occurred. One-half inch of gas remained. Sides of glass bell jar were covered as well as the surface of the water with a light layer of fat. Apparently no carbonic acid gas formed.

(C) 5 cu. in. shaken with 2 drams of perfectly clear animal oil. At end of fourth day oil a perceptible brown color with slight empyremic odor. Interposed gas separated by plunging the phial in boiling water. Gas washed with alkali water and burned with oxygen with aid of electric spark. It condensed in large part, without forming very much carbonic acid gas, as was shown by mixing the remaining gas with lime water. The oil, therefore, had absorbed most of the carbon from the gas. Volume of gas increased nearly one-tenth.

The deleterious gas, therefore, is a hydro-carbon.

[1] The following abbreviations have been used: tinc., tincture; ppt., precipitate; soln., solution; gms., grams; decomp., decomposed; sol., soluble; evap., evaporate; q. s., quantity sufficient; alc., ethyl alcohol; dil., dilute; wt., weight; xls, crystals; R., radical; temp., temperature; sep., separates; conc., concentrate.

## JOSEPH KHITTEL. I (1858)

*Rhus Toxicodendron*

1,000 gms. powdered air-dried leaves extracted with ether. Ether distilled.

- (A) Distillate
  - No poison detected.
- (B) Residue
  $H_2O$ added and evap. until all ether driven off. Filtered.
  - (C) Residue
    Extracted with alcohol.
    Alcohol distilled. $H_2O$ added. Filtered.
    - (I) Residue
      Waxy matter and traces of chlorophyll. Extracted with cold $H_2O$. Filtered.
      - (K) Residue
        Extracted with dil. HCl. Filtered.
        - ($K_1$) Residue
        - ($K_2$) Filtrate
          $NH_4OH$ added to excess caused gelatinization (pectin) and separated a white powder (calcium oxalate).
      - (L) Filtrate
        Albumin acid reaction. $NH_4OH$ gave golden-yellow color. $FeCl_3$ gave greenish color. I gave blue color. Therefore starch.
    - (J) Filtrate
      $Pb(C_2H_3O_2)_2$ added. Filtered.
      - ($J_1$) Precipitate contained tannin.
      - ($J_2$) Filtrate contained sugar by Trommer's test.
  - (D) Filtrate
    On standing 2 days green powder separated.
    - (E) Precipitate
      Green. Melted on heating to yellow liquid and on further heating decomp. giving aromatic odor, acid fumes and finally burned with residue.

      Easily sol. in ether, or alcohol. Slightly sol. in cold $H_2O$.

      Solns. neutral. Gave white ppt. on addition of $Pb(C_2H_3O_2)_2$. **No sugar or nitrogen.**
    - (F) Filtrate
      Evap. redissolved in $H_2O$. Filtered. $Pb(C_2H_3O_2)_2$ added. Filter.
      - (G) Precipitate
        Suspended in $H_2O$ and decomposed with $H_2S$. Contained coloring matter, $H_2SO_4$, phosphoric acid.
      - (H) Filtrate
        Contained organic matter.

## JOSEPH KHITTEL. II (1858)

*Rhus Toxicodendron*

3 ozs. powdered leaves extracted with hot $H_2O$. Strained and expressed after three days.

(A) Residue

(B) Filtrate
Evap. to 3 ozs. KOH added and distilled to one-half.

- (C) Residue
- (D) Distillate
  Clear, colorless, alkaline reaction. Odor resembling henbane or hemlock. $H_2SO_4$ added, and evaporated. Residue treated with one-half alcohol, one-half ether. Filtered.
  - (E) Residue of $(NH_4)_2SO_4$
  - (F) Filtrate
    Evap. spontaneously. Distilled with KOH.
    - (G) Residue
    - (H) Distillate
      Alkaline. Neutralized with HCl. Ppt. with PtCl

Therefore the poison of *R. Toxicodendron* is a volatile alkaloid!

## JOHN M. MAISCH. I (1866)

*Rhus Toxicodendron*

8¾ ozs. leaves immersed in alcohol q.s. to cover, made acid with $H_2SO_4$. Allowed to stand 9 mos. Then evap. alc. spontaneously, residue expressed, mixed with $H_2O$, again expressed. Soln. distilled with excess lime.

(A) Residue

(B) Distillate
Alkaline, odor of henbane and hemlock. HCl added to excess, odor still the same, evap. to dryness in current of dry air 120° F.

- (C) Evaporate
- (D) Residue
  Partly crystalline
  - (E) Residue
  - ($F_1$) Solution
    Portion of residue D was dissolved in water. Neutral. Light yellow ppt. with phospho-molybdic acid which yields with KOH odor of $NH_3$. No ppt. with Mayer's KHgI in acid soln. which yielded ppt. with KOH. No ppt. with tannin. No ppt. with I.
  - ($F_2$) Solution
    Portion of residue D was dissolved with dil. $H_2SO_4$. Evap. to near dryness, made almost neutral with KOH, 3 vols. 95 per cent alc. added, same amount ether added, allowed to stand over night. Filtered.
    - (G) Residue
    - (H) Filtrate
      Evap. spontaneously. Not alkaline. Ppt. with phospho-molybdic acid.

## JOHN M. MAISCH. II (1866)

*Rhus Toxicodendron*

12 ozs. fresh leaves infused in cold $H_2O$, expressed, repeated. Distilled with CaO.

(A) Residue
$H_2SO_4$ added until strongly acid. Distilled.

(C) Residue

(D) Distillate
In $Ba(OH)_2$ suspension had similar odor to distillate experiment I, part B.
With $AgNO_3$ white ppt. Soln. in $HNO_3$. Black ppt. on standing.
With $HgCl_2$ white ppt.
With $PtCl_2$ ppt.
With AuCl reduced.
With $Pb(C_2H_3O_2)_2$ white ppt. sol. in $HNO_3$.
With $Fe_2(SO_4)_3$ ppt. of $BaSO_4$ and red color.
Reactions indicate formic acid.

(B) Distillate
Acified with dil. $H_2SO_4$.
Spontaneously evap. in warm air 120° F.

(E) Evaporate

(F) Residue
Neutral with $KHCO_3$. Treated with one-half alc., one-half ether with same results as experiment I.
Therefore *R. Toxicodendron* contains no volatile alkaloid as Khittel assumed.

## JOHN M. MAISCH. III (1866)

*Rhus Toxicodendron*

(A) Fresh leaves placed in tin box with moistened test papers. Next morning curcuma and red litmus papers unaffected but blue litmus paper turned red. Therefore leaves contained a volatile acid to which the "poisonous properties were most likely due."

(B) These leaves bruised with 6 per cent of their wt. of slacked lime, macerated with $H_2O$, expressed.

(C) Residue

(D) Filtrate
Acidified with $H_2SO_4$ distilled.

(E) Residue

(F) Distillate
Collected in $Ba(OH)_2$ suspension. Another portion of distillate collected separately. This was colorless, acid (white ppt. with $Pb(C_2H_3O_2)_2$ insol. in boiling $H_2O$, sol. in $HNO_3$). No ppt. with $HgCl_2$ or $PtCl_2$.
AuCl reduced.
$AgNO_3$ reduced.
$HgNO_3$ not affected.
HgO (red) dissolved on boiling.
PbO dissolved on boiling.
$CuCO_3$ dissolved on boiling.
$FeCl_3$ (neutral) not affected.
$KMnO_4$ reduced.
$KCrO_4$ not reduced.
Acid has more reactions in common with acetic acid than formic. Differs from both in behavior to AgO, $AgNO_3$, HgO, and $HgCl_2$. It is, therefore, "a new organic acid," toxicodendric acid.

## PFAFF (1897)

*Rhus Toxicodendron*

Steam distillation of finely divided fresh plant, acidified with $H_2SO_4$.

(A) Residue

(B) Distillate
Not altered when $H_2SO_4$ not previously added.
Acid.
Oil of peculiar odor sol. in ether.
Salts formed with Ba and Na.
Separate BaR, dissolve in NaCl soln., heating soln. nearly to boiling, add alc. until faintly cloudy. On cooling crystals formed.
Heat xls with $H_2SO_4$ and alc. Gave odor of acetic ether.
$H_2O$ soln. of xls plus $FeCl_3$ gave blood red color.

Barium Salt

Water found

| I | II | III | IV | VI | Calculated for $Ba(C_2H_3O_2)_2$ plus $H_2O$ |
|---|---|---|---|---|---|
| 6.36 | 6.49 | 6.56 | 6.55 | 6.39 | 6.59 per cent $H_2O$ |

Found

| | I | II | III | IV | V | VI | Calculated for $Ba(C_2H_3O_2)_2$ |
|---|---|---|---|---|---|---|---|
| Ba | 53.95 | 53.96 | 54.08 | 54.07 | 54.18 | 53.84 | 53.71 |
| C | | | 18.69 | 18.58 | 18.45 | | 18.83 |
| H | | | | 2.66 | 2.66 | | 2.35 |

"Maisch's toxicodendric acid proved to be nothing but acetic acid, and was, therefore, not the real cause of the peculiar dermatitis caused by poison ivy."

## PFAFF (1897)

*Rhus Toxicodendron*

Extract from plant with alcohol and distil.

(A) Distillate

(B) Residue
Wash the black oily residue with $H_2O$

(C) Extract

(D) Residue
Dissolve in ether, wash with $H_2O$ and dilute $Na_2CO_3$ and $H_2O$. Evap. ether.

(E) Distillate

(F) Residue
Dark, oily, poisonous, add 10–15 vols. 95 per cent alc. Let stand 2 days at room temp. Filter.

(G) Residue

(H) Extract
Add alc. sol. $Pb(C_2H_3O_2)_2$

(I) Filtrate
Add $(NH_4)_2S$. Add $H_2O$, shake with ether, separate, evap. Residue oil of agreeable odor not irritant.

(J) Residue
Add $H_2O$, add $(NH_4)_2S$, shake with ether, evap. Poison, Toxicodendrol.

## ACREE AND SYME (1906)

*Rhus Toxicodendron*

Fresh leaves and flowers extracted with ether. Ether soln. separated and dried with anhyd. $Na_2SO_4$. Ether distilled.

(A) Residue
5 gms. freed from gallic acid and sugar Dissolved in alc. Dil. 2 per cent $H_2SO_4$ added. Heated on $H_2O$ bath approx. 32 hours. Evap. alc. Filter.

(B) Residue
Tar

(C) Filtrate
Shaken with ether. Two layers.

(D) Ether soln. green.
Evap. gave green material pleasant ester odor.

(E) Purple soln.
Divided into 3 parts (*a*) (*b*) (*c*)
(*a*) neutr. exactly with $Na_2CO_3$. Blue-black color with $FeCl_3$ and red on addn. $Na_2CO_3$. Indicating *gallic acid*. Also reduced Fehling's soln. (*b*) made alk. with $Na_2CO_3$. Formed red-brown ppt. Filter. Filtrate no color with $FeCl_3$ but reduced Fehling's soln. gave test with α-naphthol for *rhamnose*. (*c*) made alk. with $Na_2CO_3$. Formed ppt. Ppt. dissolved in $H_2(C_2H_3O_2)$. Soln. yellow. $FeCl_3$ gave gallic acid test. Probably contained *fisetin*.
Filtrate. Evap. until $Na_2CO_3$ sep. Alc. added to completely ppt. $Na_2CO_3$. Heated and filtered. Filtrate. Conc. to syrup. Reduced Fehling's and gave α-naphthol test for *rhamnose*.

The poison, "toxicodendrin," a glucoside of gallic acid, fisetin, and rhamnose.

## McNAIR (1916)

*Rhus diversiloba*

Chips of limb or leaves extract in 86° Baumé gasoline.

(A) Residue

(B) Extract
Evaporate. Pulverize 25 gms. black residue in glass mortar, add 2 liters distilled water, shake once a day for a week. Decant.

(C) Extract
Evap. to dryness residue 3 mg. per liter. Non-poisonous

(D) Residue
Repeatedly extract with 95 per cent alcohol until 800 cc. Add 2 gms. conc. $H_2SO_4$ and 100 c.c. $H_2O$, heat on water bath 24 hours. Evaporate alcohol.

(E) Extract
Contained no rhamnose, gallic acid, fisetin. Non-poisonous. Not optically rotatory.

(F) Residue
Black, tarlike. (Gasoline extract not optically rotatory.) Extract with ethyl acetate.

(G) Residue

(H) Extract
Evaporate spontaneously. Yellowish-brown viscous residue. Poisonous.

Residue F purified also by dissolving in acetone and fractional precipitate by gradual addition of distilled water. Therefore, poison is not a glucoside of rhamnose, gallic acid, and fisetin.

## LOBINOL—A DERMATITANT FROM R. DIVERSILOBA (POISON OAK)

The following attempt at the separation of the principal irritant poison (lobinol) of *R. diversiloba* represents the culmination of a number of attempts at the separation of a pure substance. It is presented herewith in the hope that someone will continue the work further and determine the structural formula of the poison. The analysis of the crystalline compounds obtained may be of assistance in this direction.

### EXTRACTION AND PURIFICATION OF LOBINOL

Bark from old branches of *R. diversiloba* T. and G. was shaved off with a two-handled draw knife. The pieces of bark thus obtained were immediately placed in 95 per cent alcohol, this mixture was heated on a sandbath under a reflux condenser for several days. The alcoholic solution was drawn off, concentrated to one-tenth its original volume by distillation from a Kjeldahl flask and placed in a separatory funnel which had previously been filled to one-fourth its capacity with petroleum ether. Water was now added until it represented three times the amount of alcoholic solution. The mixture was shaken in the separatory funnel, and the watery layer drawn off and discarded. The petroleum ether layer was then shaken with several portions of 95 per cent alcohol. The alcoholic layer was saved and the petroleum ether discarded.

Saturated sodium chlorid solution was added. The substance thus obtained as a supernatant layer is a clear, amber-red, oily, non-volatile, viscous, poisonous liquid.

It was further purified from alcohol and sodium chlorid by washing with distilled water.

It cannot be positively stated that the foregoing method of isolation yields a definite chemical individual, but it is apparently at least a mixture of appreciably uniform composition, appreciably free from contamination.

The principal constituent gives positive tests for carbon, hydrogen, and oxygen.

*The probable position of oxygen in lobinol.*—The substance reduces ammoniacal silver nitrate solution in the cold. As this action is common to aldehydes, polyhydric phenols, and a few carbohydrates, it was thought lobinol might give a positive test for the carbonyl group. When it was tested with the fuchsin aldehyde reagent as well as with sodium hydrogen sulphite the results were negative. A portion of the substance was also tested by heating with a mixture of phenylhydrazine and Fehling's with negative results. These results indicate that the principal constituent is not an aldehyde or a ketone.

*Probable absence of the carboxyl group.*—Approximately 0.5 gm. of the viscous liquid was shaken with 50 c.c. of distilled water. When the aqueous solution was titrated with 0.1 *N* potassium hydroxid solution only two drops of alkali were required to make the solution alkaline.

When a solution of the substance was made in neutral alcohol it reacted similarly toward alkali.

In a further test for the presence of the carboxyl group some of the material was shaken with 10 per cent aqueous sodium carbonate solution and filtered. When the filtrate was acidified with hydrochloric acid and shaken with ether no organic acid could be detected in the ethereal layer.

It is evident, therefore, that the presence of the carboxyl group cannot be positively proved.

The foregoing tests do not exclude the possibility of the presence of a lactone structure.

*Presence of the hydroxyl groups.*—Lobinol forms an acetyl derivative when dissolved in benzene together with acetyl chlorid and the solution boiled until the evolution of hydrochloric acid ceases.

Lobinol forms an acetyl derivative when mixed with an equal weight of dry sodium acetate and three or four parts of acetic anhydride, and boiled for two or three minutes in a reflux apparatus, according to the method of C. Liebermann and O. Hormann (1878).

A benzoyl derivative of lobinol also was formed by means of benzoyl chlorid. The Schotten-Baumann method was used as follows. Ten c.c. of lobinol was placed in a 3-liter glass separatory funnel. On account of the instability of lobinol in the presence of caustic alkali the flask was filled with oil gas. In order that benzoylation should be as complete as possible, 500 c.c. of 10 per cent aqueous potassium hydroxide and 60 c.c. of benzoyl chlorid were alternately added in small portions (Pechmann, 1892). Shaking and gentle cooling were continued for about twenty minutes. In place of caustic alkali, sodium carbonate, sodium hydrogen carbonate, or sodium acetate may be used, as these make it unnecessary to fill the flask with illuminating gas (Pictet, 1891; Meyer and Jacobson, 1893). The precipitated benzoyl derivative is white and semi-solid. It gradually hardens and crystallizes on prolonged contact with water. To make sure of the removal of all traces of benzoyl chlorid or benzoic acid the derivative was dissolved in ether, the ether distilled off, and the residue treated with alcohol which decomposed the last portions of benzoyl chlorid that had not been removed by prolonged shaking of the ethereal solution with the concentrated alkali. The alcoholic liquid was treated with soda in excess, precipitated with water, and the alcohol and ethylic benzoate removed by means of a current of steam. The residue was then repeatedly crystallized from alcohol.

A benzoyl derivative of lobinol may also be prepared from its ether or benzene solution, with the aid of dry alkali carbonate (Claisen, 1894).

From the preceding experiments it is evident that the oxygen contained in lobinol may be contained in a hydroxyl group or groups.

### PROBABLE PHENOLIC NATURE OF THE DERMATITANT

*Nitration.*—Like many aromatic compounds, lobinol is easily nitrated. The nature of the substance varies with the conditions of the reaction. On continued boiling with strong nitric acid the derivative is first a solid of orange color, then a yellow liquid from which crystals of oxalic acid separate on standing.

*Probable phenolic character.*—When sodium or potassium hydroxid is added to an alcoholic solution of lobinol the liquid assumes a color varying from green to brown. A highly dilute alcoholic solution of lobinol gives a green color with ferric chlorid, which turns red on the addition of sodium carbonate. This result might lead one to consider the dermatitant an *ortho*dihydric phenol. Also, as in the case of polyhydric phenols, lobinol reduces metallic salts, e.g., a solution of ammoniacal silver nitrate in the cold to form a silver mirror.

*Phenolic ether formed.*—In common with other benzyl ethers of phenols, lobinol benzyl ether is produced by heating with benzyl chlorid and sodium ethylate for three or four hours. The ether is a neutral yellow liquid soluble in hot alcohol and ether, and gives no apparent reaction with ferric chlorid or sodium hydroxid.

According to the results of the foregoing experiments the principal dermatitant of *R. diversiloba* may contain a phenol group.

### UNSATURATION

To about 0.1 gm. of substance in 2 c.c. of carbon tetrachlorid two or three drops of bromine solution were added. The bromine solution was prepared by dissolving 2 c.c. of bromine in 50 c.c. of carbon tetrachlorid. Decolorization took place without evolution of hydrogen bromid, either immediately or within three minutes, or even when warmed gently for two minutes. The substance therefore may be unsaturated (Biddle, 1911).

Lobinol is easily brominated when bromine is added to its ethereal solution.

### CONCLUSION

The principal dermatitant of *R. diversiloba*, if pure and not a mixture, has an unsaturated compound of the aromatic series containing carbon, hydrogen, and oxygen. The oxygen may exist combined as hydroxyl.

Its behavior is phenolic and it may contain two hydroxyl groups in the *ortho* position. This chemical finding is in agreement with the action of *Rhus* oxidase (McNair, 1917*c*; also chap. viii). This oxidase accelerates the oxidation of readily oxidizable bodies, particularly those of the benzene series, which possess at least two hydroxyl or amine groups when these groups occupy the *para* or *ortho* positions.

In accordance with reactions to halogens lobinol is unsaturated.

From the evidence at hand the principal dermatitant appears to be a poly-hydricphenol and I propose for it the name of lobinol. The terminal syllable *ol* of this word refers to its phenolic nature in accordance with the rules of the Chemical Society of London. The first two syllables of the word, *lobi*, are derived from the species name of the plant *diversiloba*.

PROVISIONAL REACTIONS OF LOBINOL

1. It absorbs bromine readily.

2. Its alcoholic solution upon the addition of ferric chlorid turns temporarily green, then black, and forms a black precipitate.

3. When its alcoholic solution is highly dilute the addition of ferric chlorid produces a green color which turns red when sodium carbonate is added.

4. It forms a gummy mass with hydriodic acid, whose alcoholic solution turns green when ferric chlorid is added.

5. Metallic carbonates are not decomposed by it.

6. Acetyl chlorid or acetic anhydride produces an acetyl derivative. Benzoyl chlorid yields a benzoyl derivative.

7. It forms an α-naphthyl-urethane with α-naphthyl-isocyanate. Phenyl-isocyanate forms a phenyl carbonate.

8. A phenolic benzyl ether is formed with benzyl chlorid and sodium alcoholate.

9. Millon's reagent gives a red color with it, a property of the hydroxyphenyl group.

10. A salt is formed when picric acid is added to its alcoholic solution.

11. It is easily darkened, dried, and hardened by means of manganese peroxid, barium peroxid, magnesium peroxid, litharge, manganese hydroxid, and potassium dichromate.

12. It hardens at a temperature above 96° in the absence of its enzyme or any oxidizing agent.

13. It is slightly soluble in aqueous potassium hydroxid, but entirely soluble in alcoholic potassium hydroxid.

14. It reduced metallic salts, especially silver nitrate, on heating and ammoniacal silver nitrate in the cold.

15. It is precipitated by lead acetate, and forms a green precipitate with barium hydroxid.

16. On gradually adding alkali to its alcoholic solution a temporary green color is first produced which, on successive additions of alkali, turns red and brownish-red.

17. It forms a nitro compound with a violent reaction when concentrated nitric acid is added to it.

18. It is soluble in ether, chloroform, alcohol, methyl alcohol, benzin (b. p. below 60°), benzene, toluene, xylol, acetone, toluidine, pyridine, quinoline, carbon tetrachlorid, amyl acetate, acetic ether, nitrobenzol, turpentine oil, glacial acetic acid, 80 per cent solution of chloral hydrate, and concentrated sodium and potassium hydroxid solutions.

19. It is precipitated from alcoholic solution by lead acetate, silver nitrate, mercurous nitrate, cupric acetate, ferric chlorid, barium hydroxid, bromine, iodine, platinum chlorid, gold chlorid, uranium acetate, and copper nitrate.

# CHAPTER XI

## PATHOLOGY OF RHUS DERMATITIS[1]

### DEFINITION

Rhus dermatitis caused by *Rhus diversiloba* and *R. Toxicodendron* is an irritation of the skin caused in the case of *R. Toxicodendron* by Pfaff's toxicodendrol and in the case of *R. diversiloba* by lobinol, a non-volatile substance which may contain a polyhydrophenol with unsaturated side chains. These toxic substances may or may not have the same chemical composition.

### ETIOLOGY

I have shown in preceding chapters that the active principle lobinol is neither bacterial nor volatile, and that poisoning occurs from actual contact with the resinous sap of the plant. This contact, however, may result through an intermediary agent, which carries the sap, such as particles of soot in smoke, clothing, cordwood, croquet balls, and shoes.

### AVENUES OF INFECTION

A suitable channel must be present so that the pathogenic lobinol may enter the body and produce its specific disease. Such avenues of infection are the cutaneous surfaces, the respiratory, alimentary, and genito-urinary tracts, and the conjunctival surfaces. The entrance of lobinol into the respiratory system is rare, although instances have been known in which the inhalation of smoke from the burning plant has caused infection. Alimentary infection is more common, as many people, seeking to gain immunity to the poison, chew the leaves and swallow the juice. There is one case on record in which a person thoughtlessly chewed a portion of the stem of the plant and developed severe symptoms. The external genitals, especially in the male, represent a frequent seat

[1] Reprinted from the *Archives of Dermatology and Syphilology*, III (April, 1921), 383-40.

Through the kindness of Dr. R. T. Legge, I have been permitted to utilize statistics from the University of California.

of the disease. This is due, in many cases, to handling of the penis and scrotum by infected hands during micturition. The genitals of the female are seldom involved. Instances may also be cited in which conjunctivitis has been the result of touching the eyes with hands on which the resinous sap was present.

*The sebaceous glands.*—The sebaceous glands are sometimes the seat of Rhus dermatitis, as is demonstrated by the accumulation of leucocytes around them in the diseased tissue. These glands are chiefly associated with the hair follicles, but they also occur independently and in those parts of the skin in which the hairs are wanting, as on the lips, angles of the mouth, prepuce, and labia minora. Those portions of the body which have the largest sebaceous glands are frequently the seat of Rhus dermatitis, i.e., the nose, the cheeks, the eyelids (meibomian glands), the scrotum, and the anal region. The liability to poisoning in these places may not be due primarily to the presence of the glands, but may possibly be explained by the prevalent thinness of the skin in these parts and the liability of the glands to poisoning on account of their position. Large sebaceous glands are also found on the areola of the nipple, the mons veneris, and the labia majora. The areola of the nipple and the labia majora are susceptible and are sometimes the seat of the disease (Busey, 1873, and others), but because of the protected position of the nipple and the fact that the vulva is seldom touched by the hands, neither the nipple nor the vulva become affected often. The skin of the mons veneris is effectively protected by its dense covering of hair.

The amount and quality of the sebaceous secretion varies considerably at different times in the same person, in different persons, and on different parts of the body. Usually the secretion is more abundant where the glands are largest and most numerous. Abnormal or excessive secretion is most commonly noted between the ages of fifteen and twenty-five, when the sebaceous glands are especially active. Variation in this secretion may possibly constitute a partial index of variation in susceptibility.

Many persons assert that they are more susceptible to the poison when they are perspiring; this is stated by Kalm (1748), Horsfield (1798), Schwalbe (1903), Thudichum (1903), Hadden (1906), Ward

(1908), and Lindley (1908). At such times the skin temperature is raised, the peripheral blood vessels are dilated and the sebaceous secretion is increased. Increased oiliness of the skin is also caused by a warm external temperature. Under these conditions the increased amount of oil on the surface of the skin would constitute an increase in the lipoid solvents for lobinol, and consequently susceptibility might be increased.

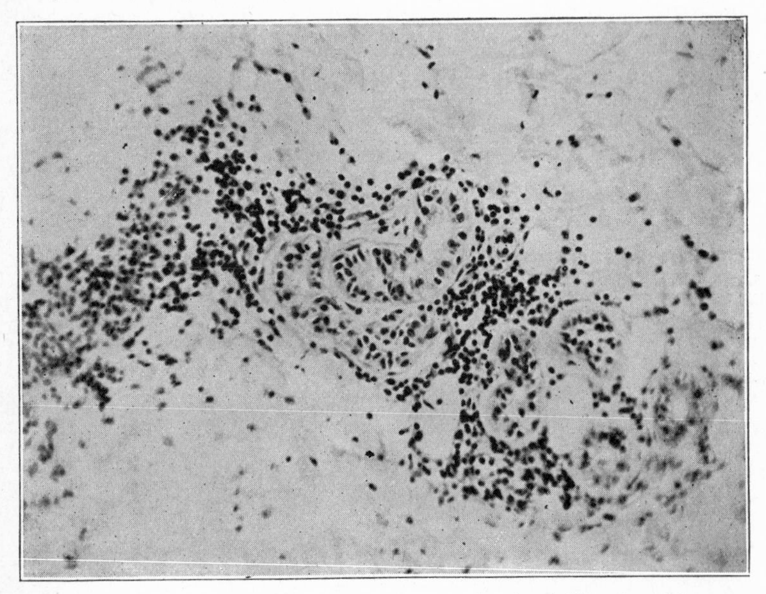

FIG. 9.—Section of skin affected by poison oak, showing infiltration of leucocytes around a sudoriparous gland; ×190.

This diminution in immunity would be the result if increased perspiration did not take place. The conditions which tend to cause a large sebaceous secretion also tend to increase the amount of perspiration. As lobinol is insoluble in the perspiration, any increase in this secretion would tend to lessen susceptibility.

Perhaps the apparent increase in susceptibility during perspiration is explained by the removal of protective clothing, such as the removal of coats and the rolling up of sleeves. Thus the skin area directly liable to contact with the plant and its poison is increased.

*The sweat glands.*—The sweat glands may also become infected by Rhus poison, as is evidenced by the large number of leucocytes surrounding them in the diseased skin. These glands occur within the integument of all parts of the body, with the exception of that covering the red margins of the lips, the inner surface of the prepuce, and the glans penis. They are especially numerous in the palms and soles and fewest on the back and buttocks. While the sweat glands are most numerous on the palms and soles, Rhus dermatitis, as a rule, occurs only on palms whose stratum corneum is thin, as, for instance, those of a woman. The prepuce, on the other hand, in which these glands are absent, is sometimes the seat of Rhus dermatitis; in one case it became the seat of fibrinous infiltration.

Misled by Maisch's statement that the poison was an acid, von Adelung (1912) made a series of observations on sweat reactions as determined by litmus paper in order to find out whether the acidity or the alkalinity of the sweat bears any relation to susceptibility to the poison. A number of sweat reactions were taken and recorded, each person being asked whether he was susceptible to the poison. In each class—acid, alkaline, and neutral—there were some susceptible and some immune persons. Among them was one person with strongly acid sweat, who was extremely susceptible, but there was another equally susceptible whose reaction was strongly alkaline; so that no relation to sweat reaction could be determined, even though account was taken of the physiologic change of reaction during exercise.

As alkalies accelerate the oxidation of lobinol (McNair, 1917*c;* see also chap. viii), and thus diminish its toxicity, it might be expected that persons with alkaline perspiration would be less susceptible. However, even in cases of markedly alkaline perspiration, the alkalinity is of comparatively low degree, and therefore would affect the poison little.

*Hair follicles.*—The hair follicles are frequently channels for Rhus infection, as is shown by the multitude of leucocytes located near them in skin affected by Rhus poison. The hairs are present over almost the entire body, and Rhus dermatitis seldom affects those regions in which the growth is sufficiently long to constitute a complete covering.

*Skin surface.*—Not only does the poison enter the skin by way of the cutaneous glands and hair follicles, but it may gain entrance through the surface of the skin itself, as is evidenced by the abnormal accumulation of leucocytes in parts of the corium foreign to glands and hair follicles. The variety and distribution of the glands

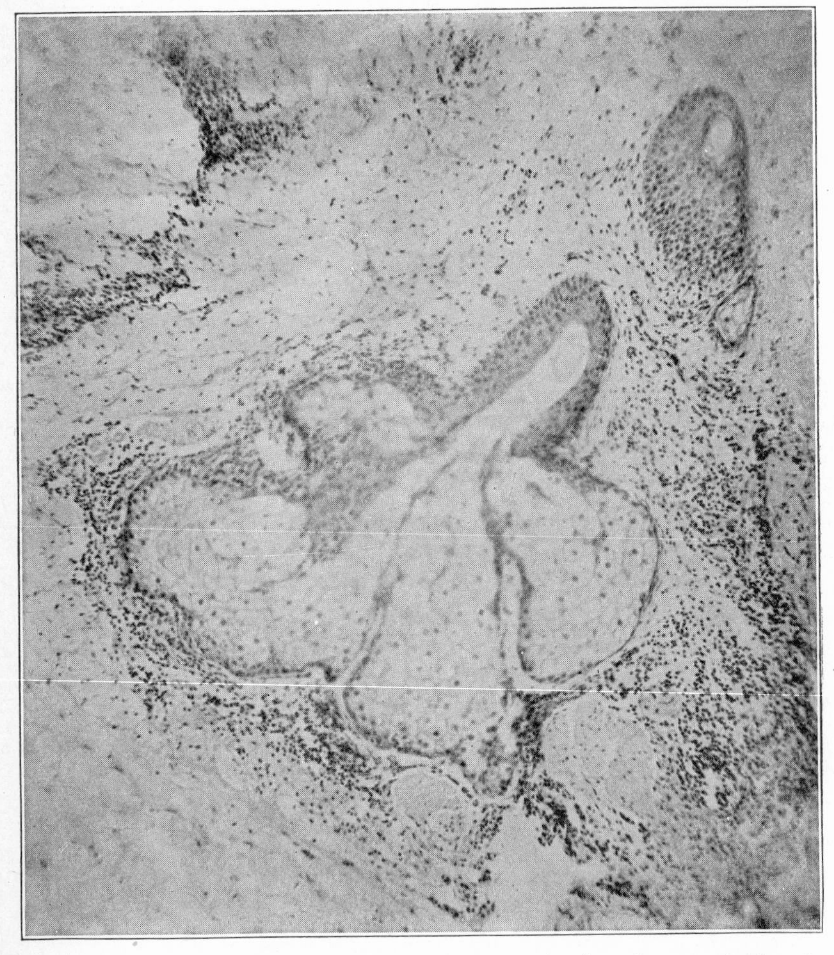

FIG. 10.—Section of skin affected by poison oak, showing sebaceous gland and infiltration of leucocytes; ×100.

and hair follicles play a smaller part in the transmission of lobinol than the thickness and condition of the various layers of the skin.

Before the poison can enter the epithelium it is liable to undergo a certain amount of oxidation and loss of toxic properties. This loss of toxicity, however, is relatively slight, as such oxidation ordinarily proceeds slowly. A certain amount of localized destruction of epithelium somewhat similar to that due to carbolic acid and other phenols probably takes place before the poison is transmitted inward. In its inward transmission the poison must first pass through the stratum corneum. In so doing some of it is left behind

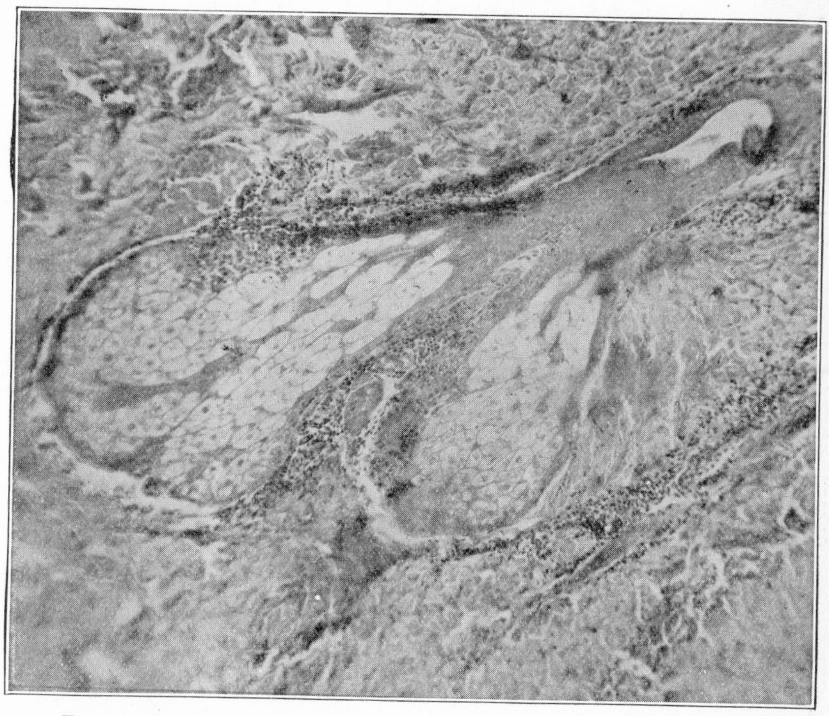

FIG. 11.—Section of skin affected by poison oak, showing sebaceous gland and infiltration of leucocytes; $\times 100$.

by adsorption and absorption. The thickness of the stratum corneum is, therefore, one important factor in the susceptibility of various persons and the various parts of the body to attack by lobinol. The epidermis varies in thickness from 0.08 to 0.10 mm. It is thus easy to explain how the primary lesion may not be at the point on the skin which first came in contact with the resinous sap. For instance, the palms may have the poison on them and yet not be affected with dermatitis. They may transfer the poison to parts of the body with thinner and more sensitive skin, such as the scrotum and penis or ears and eyelids, and the latter parts may

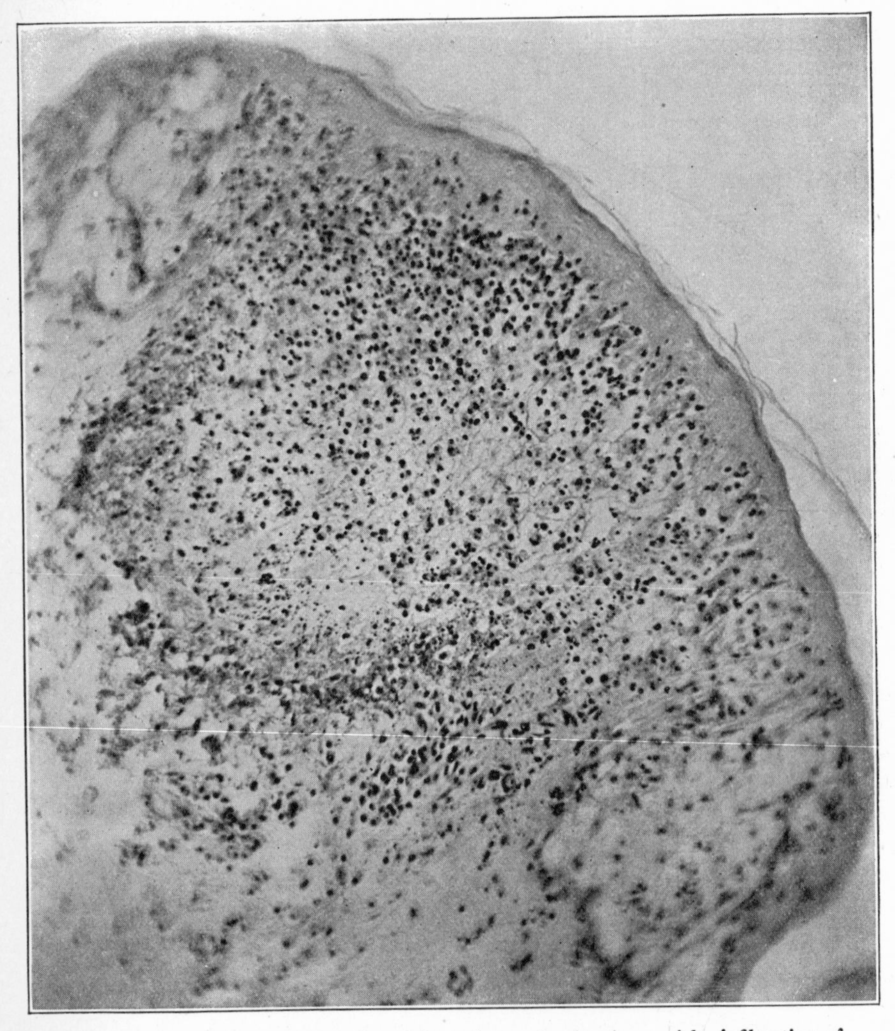

FIG. 12.—Section of skin affected by poison oak, showing vesicle, infiltration of leucocytes, and slowly diffusible character of the poison.

be the first to give evidence of inflammation. Rhus dermatitis, too, is much more often found on the flexor surfaces where the skin is thin than on the extensor surfaces, where it is thick.

Before the poison reaches the stratum germinativum it must pass either through the walls of living cells or between them. As, however, the intercellular substance is reduced to a minimum in the epithelial tissues, the cells generally lie in almost immediate apposition. It is evident, therefore, that the poison can probably pass as easily through the cell membrane as between the cells. Microscopic evidence appears to support this view. The cell

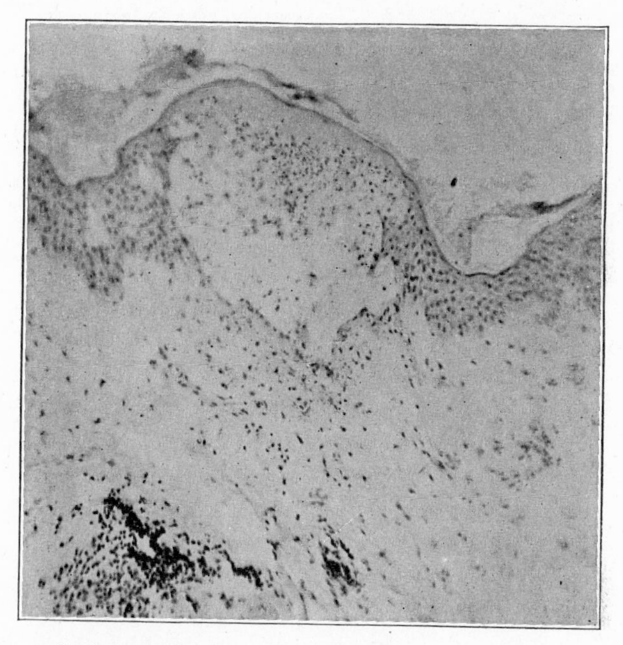

FIG. 13.—Section of skin affected by poison oak, showing vesicle, infiltration of leucocytes, and slowly diffusible character of the poison; ×190.

membrane in these cells is an inconspicuous structure. There is no direct chemical or microscopic evidence to show the composition of the animal cell membrane, but by observations on its behavior when the cells are in various solutions, facts have been collected indicating that lecithin and cholesterol, and probably the allied fatlike bodies, "protagon" and cerebrin, are prominent constituents. The substances that diffuse through most cell walls are just the substances that are soluble in or dissolve these lipoids, that is, alcohol, chloroform, ether, etc., and it is probable that the anaesthetic effects of many of these substances depend in some way on their fat-dissolving power and the large proportion of lipoids in nerve cells (Overton and Meyer, 1899, 1900). As lobinol is more

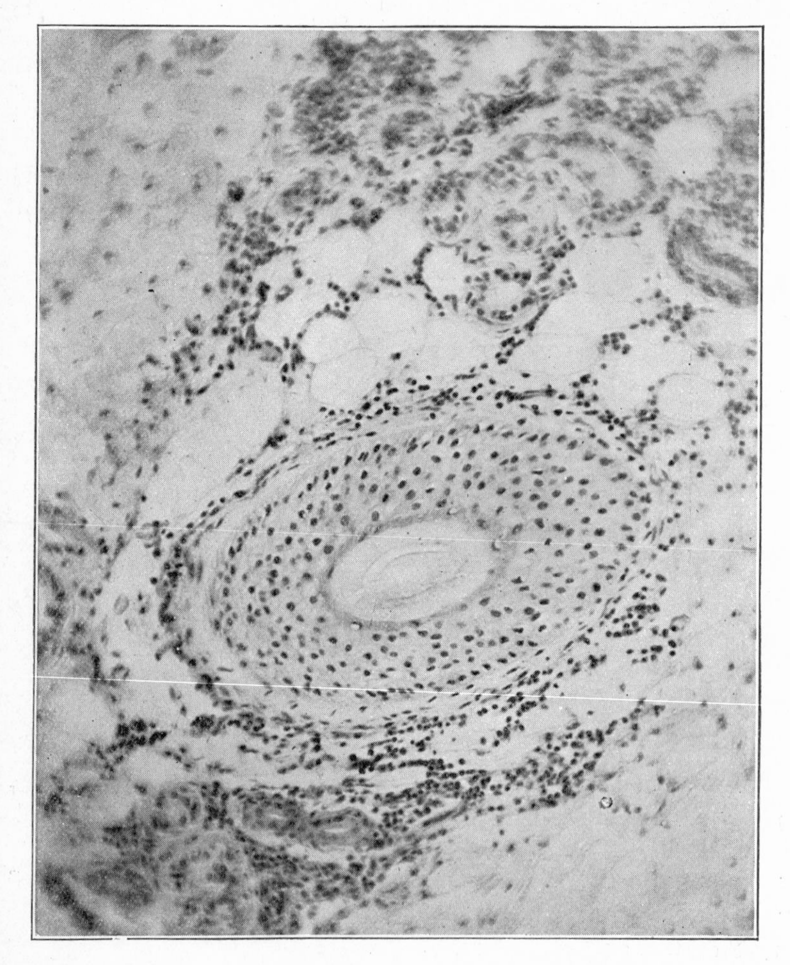

FIG. 14.—Section of skin affected by poison oak, showing infiltration of leucocytes around hair follicle; ×190.

soluble in lipoids and lipoid solvents, it might be expected to penetrate the cell wall easily and it is probable that the intense irritating effect of this poison similarly depends on its solubility and consequent penetrability of the nerve cells.

The fact must not be overlooked, however, that lobinol is diffused through the skin slowly; to this phenomenon is due the period of latency. Besides lipoids, the cell membrane is considered to be partially made of protein. The cell wall, therefore, is probably a "mosaic" structure, some of the blocks being lipoids or lipoid compounds, and others protein without lipoids. Robertson (1908) suggests that there is a superficial film of concentrated protein about the cells underlaid by a discontinuous lipoid layer. Some such structure is evidently necessary to permit the entrance of the common foodstuffs into the cell, such as water, sugar, amino acids, and salts which are not lipoid soluble. Lobinol may have a coagulating effect on the protein lining of the cell in such a way as to retard its permeability. This same coagulating function, however, might, by its corrosive action, tend to make entrance to the cell easier for the poison.

The contents of the cell may play an equally important part in retarding or accelerating permeability. In this connection, osmosis, surface tension, and diffusion must be considered.

Of the constituents of the cytoplasm of the cell, the lipoids would tend to dissolve lobinol, the proteins to absorb it, and probably the glycogen and sulphates to change chemically and combine with it and render it less toxic, as is true of other phenols in the body. The amount of glycogen as a source of glucuronic acid, and the amount of sulphates normally in the epidermal cells of a person, may possibly have a great deal to do in physiologically neutralizing and retarding the penetration of the poison and thus serve as a partial index of immunity.

### REACTIONS AND DEFENSIVE SUBSTANCES IN THE BODY

The variety of reactions and the variety of defensive substances in the body are, according to present knowledge, remarkably small in number. The reactions are: oxidation and reduction, hydration and dehydration, and perhaps simple addition (that is, methylation). The chief known protective substances are the alkalies of the blood proteins, hydrogen sulphid, sulphuric acid, glycocoll, urea, cystein, bile acids, glucuronic acid, and acetic acid. Of these substances we would expect lobinol, if it is a polyhydrophenol with unsaturrated side chains, to react and become less organotropic with glucuronic acid and sulphuric acid by forming a phenol glucuronate and a phenol sulphate. Whether or not other substances would form defensive chemical compounds with lobinol would depend on the nature of its unsaturated side chains which are at present uninvestigated.

The susceptibility of lobinol to oxidation must not be overlooked. There may be oxidases, as there are in the nuclei, which may tend to render the poison harmless.

Not only is this disease caused by the direct action of lobinol, but perhaps also by the indirect chemical change in the body cells induced by altered cell metabolism. The substances formed may be called body toxins and may be similar to those produced in superficial burns (Bardeen, 1898; Wells). The evidence for such intoxication is not altogether similar to that of burns as no delirium, haemoglobinuria, vomiting, or bloody diarrhea has been demonstrated in superficial Rhus dermatitis. On the other hand, in severe cases of Rhus dermatitis there is albuminuria, which may be caused by the partial elimination of these hypothetical poisons by the kidneys. Rhus albuminuria, on the other hand, may be due to the direct action of lobinol, as it has been found that when *Rhus* sap has been introduced per os in a rabbit, albuminuria results. Five c.c. of the poisonous sap mixed with 15 c.c. of cottonseed oil were introduced per os into a rabbit weighing 3,171 gm. A test for albumin in the urine was found positive four hours after the poison was introduced (McNair, 1916*c*). Similarly, Pfaff (1897), by the introduction of toxicodendrol per os in a rabbit, caused albuminuria. Some cases of Rhus albuminuria, however, may be due to latent nephritis excited by the increased work thrown on the kidney following the loss of the excretory function of large areas of skin. An examination of forty-nine severe bed cases of Rhus dermatitis showed that thirty-two, or 65.3 per cent, were negative with respect to albumin; and seventeen, or 34.6 per cent, were positive. One of the patients having albuminuria developed and recovered from acute nephritis simultaneously with dermatitis.

TABLE XII

URINE ANALYSES WITHOUT ALBUMIN OF UNIVERSITY OF CALIFORNIA INFIRMARY PATIENTS

| Case Number or Name | Specific Gravity | Color | Appearance | Reaction (to Litmus) | Sugar | Albumin | Microscopic Appearance |
|---|---|---|---|---|---|---|---|
| A. | 1.021 | ... | ... | ... | 0 | 0 | |
| J. P. A. | 1.016 | Pale | Clear | ... | 0 | 0 | |
| M. B.* | 1.005 | Straw | Clear | Acid | 0 | 0 | |
| J. D. | 1.015 | Straw | ... | Acid | 0 | 0 | |
| L. R. D. | 1.020 | Straw | Cloudy | Faintly alkaline | 0 | 0 | |
| A. E. | 1.010 | Amber | ... | Acid | 0 | 0 | |
| E. F. | 1.025 | Amber | ... | Acid | 0 | 0 | |
| S. F. | 1.031 | ... | ... | Acid | 0 | 0 | |
| C. M. H.* | 1.011 | Yellow | ... | Faintly acid | 0 | 0 | |
| P. W. H. | 1.014 | Yellow | ... | Neutral | 0 | 0 | |
| G. J. H. | 1.008 | Light lemon | Clear | Neutral | 0 | 0 | |
| O. J. | 1.023 | ... | ... | ... | 0 | 0 | |
| E. M.* | 1.031 | Straw | ... | Acid | 0 | 0 | |
| E. S. R. | 1.026 | Amber | Clear | Alkaline | 0 | 0 | |
| C. H. S. | 1.033 | Amber | ... | Acid | 0 | 0 | |
| H. S. | 1.013 | Light yellow | ... | Alkaline | 0 | 0 | |
| M. T. | 1.030 | Amber | ... | Acid | 0 | 0 | |
| J. V. | 1.030 | Light yellow | Clear | Acid | 0 | 0 | |
| 5665* | 1.020 | Lemon | Slightly turbid | Acid | 0 | 0 | Negative |
| 5073 | 1.038 | Amber | Turbid | Acid | 0 | 0 | |
| 5072 | 1.032 | Amber | Clear | ... | 0 | 0 | |
| 4923 | 1.017 | Lemon | Turbid | Faintly alkaline | 0 | 0 | Heavy sediment |
| 4814* | ... | Amber | Very turbid | Acid | 0 | 0 | Normal. Amorphous urates |
| 4810 | 1.018 | Amber | Clear | Acid | 0 | 0 | |
| 4719 | 1.016 | Lemon | Clear | Neutral | 0 | 0 | Normal |
| 4714 | 1.030 | Amber | Clear | Acid | 0 | 0 | |
| 4713* | 1.020 | Lemon | Clear | Faintly alkaline | 0 | 0 | Sediment normal |
| 4710* | 1.017 | Lemon | Clear | Alkaline | 0 | 0 | Sediment normal. Amorphous phosphates |
| 4559 | 1.010 | Lemon | Clear | Neutral | 0 | 0 | |
| 4536* | 1.020 | Amber | Clear | Acid | 0 | 0 | Few scattered pus cells |
| 4473 | ... | Lemon | Clear | Neutral | 0 | 0 | Sediment |
| 4472 | 1.010 | Lemon | Slightly turbid | Acid | 0 | 0 | |

* Female patients; all other samples from males.

## TABLE XIII

### Urine Analyses with Albumin of University of California Infirmary Patients

| Case Number or Name | Specific Gravity | Color | Appearance | Reaction (to Litmus) | Sugar | Albumin | Microscopic Appearance |
|---|---|---|---|---|---|---|---|
| E. W. B. | 1.015 | Straw | Cloudy | Faintly acid | ..... | Trace | Epithelial cells, mobile organisms, occasional calcium oxalate crystals |
| L. R. C* | 1.012 | Straw | Cloudy | Faintly acid | 0 | Trace | |
| W. C. | ........ | ........ | ........ | Alkaline | 0 | Trace | |
| S. H. D. | 1.023 | Amber | Clear | Faintly acid | 0 | Trace | Round epithelial cells |
| E. | 1.018 | Amber | Slightly cloudy | Alkaline | 0 | Faintly trace | |
| I. G. | 1.032 | Amber | Cloudy | Acid | 0 | Trace | |
| J. B. H. | 1.009 | Straw | Clear | Very acid | 0 | Trace | |
| 5634* | ........ | Amber | Clear | Acid | 0 | Trace | Negative |
| 5078* | ........ | Deep amber | Clear | Faintly acid | 0 | Faintly trace | Many pus cells. No red cells. No casts |
| 5000* | ........ | Lemon | Clear | Acid | 0 | Trace | Slight sediment |
| 4944 | 1.012 | Lemon | Clear | ........ | 0 | Faintly trace | Normal |
| 4916 | 1.022 | Amber | Clear | Alkaline | 0 | Faintly trace | Amorphous phosphates. No casts |
| 4723* | 1.033 | Amber | Turbid | Acid | 0 | Faintly trace | Amorphous deposit |
| 4695 | 1.023 | Amber | Clear | Neutral | 0 | Faintly trace | |
| 4675 | 1.024 | Lemon | Clear | ........ | 0 | Faintly trace | |
| 4529 | 1.030 | Deep amber | Clear | Acid | 0 | Faintly trace | Negative |
| 4392 | 1.017 | Deep lemon | Clear | Neutral | 0 | Faintly trace | |

* Female patients; all other samples from males.

### SUMMARY OF TABLES XII AND XIII

| | | Per Cent |
|---|---|---|
| Samples with albumin | 17 | 34.6 |
| Samples without albumin | 32 | 65.3 |
| Total | 49 | 100 |

The poison in the samples of urine examined could not be detected in a free condition. Three liters of urine were shaken up with ether, and the ethereal layer separated and concentrated by evaporation. This ethereal extract did not give any chemical reaction for the poison, and when concentrated by evaporation and applied to the skin of a sensitive person, it did not cause dermatitis.

The urine was not abnormal in color, as is sometimes the case when phenol (Koster-Syke, 1886; Browne, 1885; Dreyfous, 1885; Penasse, 1886; Rose, 1884; Brun, 1886) or pyrogallol is externally applied (Jarisch, 1878; Allen, 1886). The urine had no abnormal odor, such as is noticeable upon the inunction of turpentine or drugs of that series (Brochin, 1879; Berenguier, 1874; Garland, 1886). These results may be due to the fact that the poison is either entirely absent from the urine or only present in a very small amount.

Table XIV describes the case involving a simultaneous acute nephritis.

Leucocytosis is an accompaniment of the severer cases of poison oak dermatitis. The severity of the leucocytosis seems to vary directly with the size of the area involved and the severity of the infection. For instance, in a case in which the face, hands, arms, and chest were severely affected, a blood count showed 31,600 leucocytes; in a milder case, in which only one forearm was affected, 14,000 leucocytes were found. Blood counts frequently indicated the presence of more than 12,000 leucocytes to the cubic millimeter. In the marked increase in leucocytes in twelve cases examined, there seemed to be no disproportionate change in the polymorphonuclear leucocytes with no eosinophilia. A microscopic examination of sections of the diseased human skin, however, disclosed a predominance of mononuclear leucocytes. It is suggested, therefore, that either in the parts of the skin affected a mononuclear leucocytosis results while the systemic leucocytosis is disproportionate, or else the character of the leucocytosis varies in different stages of the disease. The leucocytosis thus produced tends, among other things, to oxidize the poison by the contained oxidases of these cells.

The blood stream, as well as the lymphatics, contributes its leucocytes and consequent oxidative power. The erythrocytes

TABLE XIV

DERMATITIS VENENATA AND ACUTE NEPHRITIS

| Time | Temperature C. | Pulse | Respiration | Analysis of Urine | | | | |
|---|---|---|---|---|---|---|---|---|
| | | | | Sp. Gr. | Color | Appearance | Reaction | Albumin |
| First day A.M. | 36.6 | 70 | 16 | 1.015 | Amber | Cloudy | Acid | 0.0025 Esbach |
| Second day A.M. | 36.6 | 64 | 18 | 1.013 | Straw | Clear | Neutral | 0.006 |
| Second day P.M. | 36.9 | 74 | 16 | ... | ... | ... | ... | ... |
| Third day A.M. | 36.4 | 64 | 18 | ... | ... | ... | ... | ... |
| Third day P.M. | 36.6 | 80 | 16 | ... | ... | ... | ... | ... |
| Fourth day A.M. | 36.6 | 68 | 18 | 1.015 | Amber | Clear | Acid | Fairly large amount |
| Fourth day P.M. | 36.4 | 68 | 18 | ... | ... | ... | ... | ... |
| Fifth day A.M. | 36.6 | 84 | 18 | 1.013 | Amber | Clear | Acid | Fairly large amount |
| Fifth day P.M. | 36.4 | 68 | 18 | 1.031 | Amber | Cloudy | Acid | 0.0025 |
| Sixth day A.M. | 36.4 | 72 | 18 | ... | ... | Cloudy | Acid | Trace |
| Sixth day M. | 36.5 | 80 | 16 | ... | ... | ... | ... | ... |
| Sixth day P.M. | 36.4 | 68 | 18 | ... | ... | ... | ... | ... |
| Seventh day A.M. | 36.4 | 68 | 18 | 1.036 | ... | ... | Acid | Trace |
| Seventh day P.M. | 37.0 | 68 | 16 | ... | ... | ... | ... | ... |
| Eighth day A.M. | 36.6 | 68 | 18 | ... | ... | ... | ... | ... |
| Eighth day P.M. | 37.0 | 72 | 18 | ... | ... | ... | ... | ... |
| Ninth day A.M. | 36.6 | 68 | 18 | 1.023 | Amber | Cloudy | Alkaline | Trace |

White blood counts: First day, polymorphonuclear 64 per cent; small mononuclear 20 per cent; large mononuclear 6 per cent; eosinophils 10 per cent; seventh day, polymorphonuclear 57 per cent; small mononuclear 35 per cent; large mononuclear 6 per cent; eosinophils 2 per cent. Total count, 13,600.

Heart: Slightly enlarged, action accentuated, premature contraction, otherwise regular, sounds strong; soft systolic at left sternal edge. No oedema in ankles. Slight oedema in upper and lower eyelids, due at least partly to poison oak. Blood pressure 110. Assythema (asystoles) continues.

Urine: Epithelial casts and cells; no pus.

contribute haemoglobin, the iron of which has the power to combine with lobinol. Likewise the blood brings glucose, which, on its conversion into glucuronic acid, probably has power to combine with and lessen the noxious properties of lobinol.

$$\underset{\text{glucose}}{CH_2OH-(CHOH)_4\overset{\overset{O}{\|}}{C}-H}+O_2\rightarrow \underset{\text{glucuronic acid}}{HOOC-(CHOH)_4\overset{\overset{O}{\|}}{C}-H}+H_2O$$

There is reason to believe that Rhus poison is not transmitted by the body fluids because, first, lobinol is insoluble in water (McNair, 1916*a*), in horse blood serum, in physiologically normal salt solution, and in Ringer's solution; and, secondly, the vesicular exudate of Rhus dermatitis is non-toxic even when well rubbed into the scratched skin of a sensitive person. Brown (1922) made twenty similar experiments. White, in 1873, opened the vesicles on his wrist, one of twenty-four, another of eight hours' duration, and their clear and colorless contents were applied and scratched into the epidermis on the wrist of a man who was especially sensitive to the poison of *R. Toxicodendron*, as he had suffered two attacks of the poison that summer (1873) and had had many severe attacks during past seasons as a result of contact with *R. Toxicodendron*. The results were wholly negative. Bigelow (1817, 1820) reports that Pierson inoculated with the serum from vesicles on the second day, and with the discharge from the later stage, but without effect. The freest handling of parts affected in all stages of the efflorescence fails to transfer the disease to the hands of another. Third, if the skin is inoculated with the poisonous sap of *R. diversiloba* and the spot covered with a watch glass or zinc oxid plaster, the resulting dermatitis will not spread, but will remain confined to the locality on which the sap was placed. Von Adelung (1913) made similar confirmatory experiments. In 1912 Rost and Gilg made several experiments in which a drop of fresh sap from *R. Toxicodendron* was placed on the arm and covered with a watch glass. Brown (1922) and Spain (1922), in using alcoholic extracts of *R. Toxicodendron* covered by adhesive plaster, got spreading in two instances. Perhaps these last results were caused by imperfect technique.

The apparent spreading, that is, the successive appearance of Rhus dermatitis on different areas of the body, generally reaches its maximum during the period of invasion. This spreading may be due to (1) the direct transference of the poison itself by the finger nails or hands from one part of the body to another, or to new areas from the clothes or hair; (2) reflex irritation; (3) contiguity of tissue; and (4) varying durations of latency for the different skin surfaces on the body (varying with the respective thicknesses of their stratum corneum, chemical and physical differences in the skin, etc.).

### LATENCY OF RHUS DERMATITIS

The prevalence of *R. diversiloba* on the campus of the University of California and the possibility of indirect contact with the poison make the exact period of latency questionable.

In experimenting with *R. Toxicodendron* in 1795, Fontana found the period of latency to be three, four, and six days. Van Mons, in 1797, found it to be from eight to ten days. Horsfield, in 1798, stated that the period of latency varied from a few hours to several days. Other writers have also given varying limits, for instance: Dakin, (1829) one to three days; Busey (1873), seven days; White (1873), generally less than forty-eight hours, but sometimes five days; Park (1879) from a few hours to a few days, generally from thirty-six to forty-eight hours; Cundell-Juler (1883), about twenty-four hours; Morrow (1887), from several hours to four or more days; Pfaff (1897), in experiments found the latent period to be as long as four days; Schamberg (1906), twenty-four to forty-eight hours usually; Conner (1907), often within twenty-four hours; Brown (1922) (alcoholic extract), seventeen, twenty-seven, forty-eight, seventy-six, and one hundred forty-four hours; of other cases, six cases after one day, five after two days, six after three days, and one after eight days; Spain (1922) (alcoholic extract), eighty individuals, forty-eight or 60 per cent after three days, and forty or 50 per cent after seven days. It is thus evident that the dermatitis caused by *R. Toxicodendron* has a latent period similar in length to that caused by *R. diversiloba*.

## TABLE XV

LATENCY OF RHUS DERMATITIS IN DISPENSARY PATIENTS

| Name | Date and Hour of Exposure | Irritation First Noticed | Parts Affected | Approximate Period of Latency in Days |
|---|---|---|---|---|
| Dorothy C. | Unknown | January 25, 1919 | Lower half of left cheek | ............ |
| T. Jean J. | January 25, 1919 P.M. | January 26, 1919 | Face, chest, neck, arm | 1 |
| Eva S. P. | January 26, 1919 P.M. | January 27, 1919 | Neck, face, left arm | 1 |
| Dorothy H. | January 26, 1919 P.M. | January 28, 1919 | Chin and neck | 2 |
| George E. W. | January 26, 1919 A.M. | January 29, 1919 | Face and scrotum | 3 |
| John F. D. | January 26, 1919 | January 28, 1919 | Face | 2 |
| William W. B. | January 26, 1919 | January 29, 1919 | Face and scrotum, thighs | 3 |
| Helen G. H. | January 26, 1919 | February 1, 1919 | Arms, legs | 6 |
| Alice L. | ? | February 4, 1919 | Face and neck | ? |
| Karl J. M. | January 26, 1919 | February 1, 1919 | Forearms | 6 |
| Sherman R. B. | January 26, 1919 | February 3, 1919 | Body | 8 |
| Perry K. | February 1, 1919 | February 3, 1919 | Wrists and hands | 2 |
| Franck H. R. | February 1, 1919 | February 3, 1919 | Wrists and legs | 2 |
| George A. P. | January 31, 1919 M. | February 6, 1919 | Face, arms | 6 |
| Howard M. B. | February 2, 1919 | February 5, 1919 | Forearms | 3 |
| Anne H. | February 2, 1919 | February 8, 1919 | Face and legs | 6 |
| Amy J. A. | February 2, 1919 | About 1 week later; spread gradually; February 14 extensive | Legs, wrist, face, neck | 6 |
| Lyell H. P. | February 9, 1919 | February 9, 1919 | Right arm | 1 |
| Kathleen G. L. | February 16, 1919 | February 17, 1919 | Face | 1 |

## THE EVOLUTION OF THE DISEASE IN EXTERNAL POISONING

The features of Rhus dermatitis are the shortness of its course and, typically, its differentiation into stages. The following stages, in their proper sequence, are recognized generally in acute Rhus dermatitis:

*Stage of infection.*—This is the period of time occupied by Rhus poison in getting in firm contact with the outer surface of the skin.

*Stage of latency.*—This is the period of time in which the Rhus poison is diffusing through and reacting with the skin up to the point of producing symptoms. Generally this stage is an appreciably limited one and its duration lasts from about twelve hours to five days. The amount of poison entering the skin influences more or less the length of this stage, within certain limits. The length of this stage must be influenced by various other factors: stratum corneum, the thickness and composition of the cell walls, the variety and amounts of the cell contents, such as glycogen or glucose, as a source of glucuronic acid; sulphuric acid or forms of sulphur that might be available to form lobinol sulphate; lipoids, which might aid by their solvent power in diffusion or absorption of lobinol; water, which might hinder the diffusion of lobinol; protein, which might adsorb or absorb lobinol, oxidases, etc.

*Stage of prodromes.*—Vague symptoms of skin irritation now appear about the points of entrance of the poison. It is evident at this time that the poison is sufficiently active to produce moderate symptoms, but none as yet characteristic of the disease. They may appear in connection with some weak part of the system, such as the eyes, face, and scrotum, thus establishing a local erythema. This stage is usually of fairly definite length, but this depends on the same general factors as the preceding stage.

*Stage of outbreak.*—In this stage the symptoms characteristic of the disease make themselves manifest. Two types are recognized, namely: (1) a frank or sudden outbreak and (2) insidious or gradual outbreak. The former is doubtless due to a sudden and marked intoxication, while the latter is the result of a more gradual action. When the frank outbreak takes place, naturally this stage is well separated from the prodromal, but the two stages gradually merge one into the other in the insidious attacks.

One of several factors may cause a frank outbreak: (1) The poison may suddenly penetrate the tissues, owing to a greater presence of lobinol solvents, weak resistance of the tissues, or very thin skin. (2) The poison may have gradually accumulated in a given focus owing to defective drainage into the interior, and then, by the extension of the infectious focus into looser tissue, a large quantity of lobinol is suddenly absorbed. (3) Some sudden cause may be operable in reducing the vitality of the person so that a given volume of poison has an extreme and sudden effect.

The primary effect of the poison is to stimulate one or more functions of the system, while the secondary or final result is to depress or pervert such functions subsequent to the production of degenerative and necrotic changes. The nervous and circulatory activities receive especial stimuli. The effect on the circulatory system consists of increased cardiac force and vasoconstriction, that is, a rise of blood pressure. In the frank outbreak there is not only a suddenness of onset of the symptoms, but also a marked severity of the same.

Certain effects are noted in the several parts of the body in the most severe cases:

The pulmonary area is congested. Dyspnea may be induced by nervous influences and by a reduction in the air space of the lungs due to congestion. A sense of discomfort may be noted in the thorax. Bronchial congestion may cause some transudation and a cough may appear with watery sputum.

The cerebral area is so closely associated with the large vascular trunks that it shares in the congestion. A feeling of fulness, together with more or less headache and throbbing of the temporal arteries, is likely to develop. Congestion of the conjunctivae, tinnitus aurium, and disturbances of vision are likewise referable to congestion. The face, being so closely related, is usually flushed, even though dermatitis may not involve it. With this there is often epistaxis and sore throat. Delirium sometimes occurs (Horsfield, 1798).

In the peripheral area the temperature of the skin is raised. In the inflammatory process the capillaries immediately surrounding the point or points of contact of the irritant become enlarged and produce a visible hyperemia, thus establishing a local erythema. This, if it has not proceeded farther than the prodromal stage, would perhaps affect only a minute area and form a small red point, a macule, or extend over a considerable area, and present a uniform and extensive field of redness. It might be fugitive, lasting but a few minutes, or continue for hours or days and finally disappear without the production of any other apparent tissue change. But an erythema cannot exist for any considerable time without a slowing of the current of circulation in the enlarged capillaries, followed by oedema. This serious transudation is in some degree inseparable from an erythema of more than evanescent duration.

Sometimes these changes are limited to circumscribed areas. Under peculiar forms of irritation an erythema is rapidly excited, which is followed by a sudden oedema, so violent as to distend the involved portions of the skin in the form of abrupt elevations with sharply defined borders, and to compress in turn the capillaries of such areas so as to occlude them and thus produce lesions characterized by flat, strikingly white prominences, which are generally surrounded by a halo of erythema (wheals). They may exist for only a few minutes, or for one or more hours, but they are always of brief duration. The capillaries in the stage of involution begin to absorb the effused serum, the swelling sinks down, the redness returns to the area, and finally the hyperemia disappears. The whole process is one of the most sudden and striking exhibitions of morbid action to which the skin is liable, and is a frequent phenomenon in dermatitis venenata.

As has been previously pointed out, the disease is not contagious and cannot be transferred from one area of the skin to another by the blood, nor by the serum escaping from broken vesicles on the surface of the body. Nevertheless, the inflammation may spread in two ways, by contiguity of tissue, and, according to Blackwood, by reflex irritation. Blackwood (1880), by inciting friction at a part as yet apparently unaffected by Rhus dermatitis, transferred the disorder to that locality when the experiment was made during the height of the disease. That the transfer was not merely inoculated by the finger nails in cases which he had carefully watched was proved by allowing the scratching to be done by a person not affected.

*Stage of maximum symptoms.*—This is in reality but a continuation of the preceding stage, and is not clearly defined therefrom. If the hyperemic state of the skin be prolonged beyond a brief duration, other changes ensue besides the escape of serum; the leucocytes of the blood escape through the vessels and add to the previous swelling or oedema.

The leucocytes are deposited in the upper layers of the corium about the superior capillary plexus in vast numbers. Owing to their presence, the skin offers a firmer resistance to pressure than that caused by the simple oedema, and presents in time a decided thickening. This change may affect considerable areas uniformly, producing a general thickening and elevation of the part affected, or may concentrate itself within the papillae especially, the exudation from their vascular loops causing them to enlarge either singly or in groups, and forcing them with their epidermal coverings above the general surface of the integument in the form of sharply pointed or hemispherical elevations, red in color, and varying in size from that of a pinhead to that of a small pea. This condition may last a few days, or much longer, and slowly disappear as the effused elements, serum and blood cells, are reabsorbed by the vessels, and leave no later sign of its existence, or at most a slight scale. On the other hand, the epithelial covering of the tip of the softened tissues may be easily removed by violence, and thus the elongated papillae be exposed, allowing the contents of the papule to escape, or the enlarged capillaries may themselves be ruptured; in either case, an excoriation and crust are formed, thus complicating the process of involution.

If the tip of one of these inflammatory papules is carefully pricked with a needle so as not to open one of its blood vessels, a minute quantity of clear serum or lymph will exude, showing the abundant presence of fluid in it. Under the continuance or greater intensity of the inflammatory process this is poured out with such force, or in such quantity, as to tear apart the soft plastic cells in the lower layers of the rete, thus forming vesicles or blebs.

Vesicles, however, may not be the highest stage in this progressive formation of surface lesions in Rhus dermatitis. If it advances, they are transformed into pustules. These also may disappear by the absorption of their contents, or, if they are ruptured, the process of involution will complete itself beneath a crust or scab. Pustules, however, may form as such without a preceding vesicular stage. They are generally deeper seated than the superficial forms of inflammation thus far considered, and are often seated primarily about the glandular structures, or even in a subcutaneous tissue.

Such are the primary lesions of acute dermatitis. They may be only progressive steps of the inflammatory process, marked by certain well-defined stages—the hyperemic macule, papule, vesicle, and pustule; or any one of them may arise independently as such, and disappear without undergoing further evolutionary change. Several or all of them may be present at the same time, or any one of them may represent the whole process in any case.

At the beginning of this stage, stimulation of the functions occurs, together with congestion and febrile disturbances. The pyrexia is in all probability more nervous than toxic, as lobinol is apparently neutralized in the skin before it reaches the systemic circulation.

Increase of metabolic activity and an increase of body temperature are the most striking phenomena of the complex symptoms of fever. An increase in cardiac action is seen, and for each degree (Fahrenheit) in rise of temperature there is usually an increase of ten beats per minute. There is an increase in respiratory action so that for every four beats of the heart in excess there is added one respiration. There is an increase in blood pressure, nervous, muscular, and glandular activity of the intestinal tract. There is a slight afternoon and evening rise of temperature, as was observed by Burgess in 1880. As maximum temperatures, Prichard (1891) noticed a temperature of 103° F., accompanied by a pulse rate of 112. Lindley, in writing a résumé of the disease among California Indians, gave a temperature range in severe cases of from 102° to 105° F. The highest temperature registered in forty-five severe cases at the University of California was 99.5° F. Febrile symptoms present, which involve the alimentary system, are a coated tongue, loss of appetite, nausea, and vomiting. The latter symptoms have been noted by Dunmire (1881) and Ward.

Diarrhea, which is often present, may be an expression of excessive muscular and glandular activity of the intestinal tract. Constipation sometimes accompanies this disease, as was observed by Farquhar in 1888 and by Ward in 1908. Both constipation and

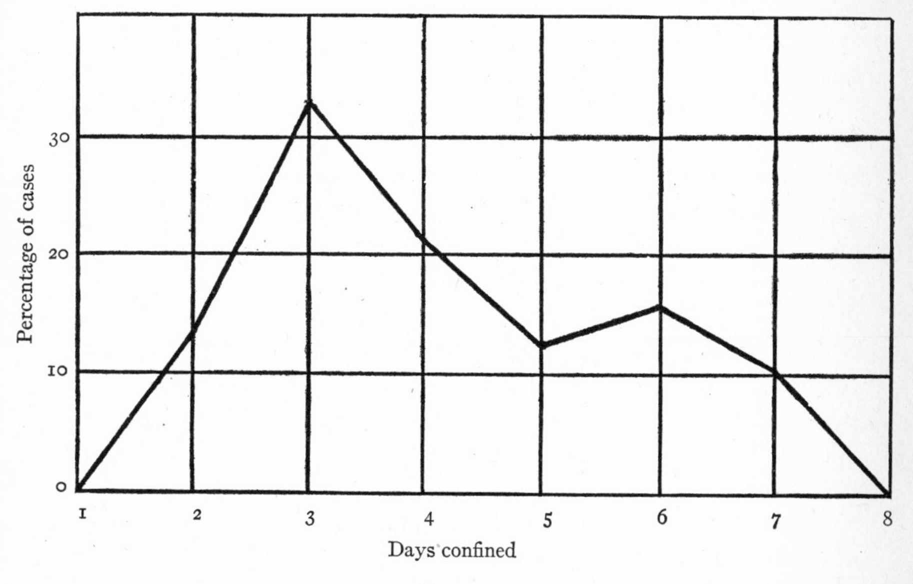


FIG. 15

| Days confined...... | 1 | 2 | 3 | 4 | 5 | 6 | 7 | 8 | Total |
|---|---|---|---|---|---|---|---|---|---|
| No. of cases........ | 0 | 10 | 25 | 16 | 9 | 12 | 4 | 0 | 76 |
| Percentage ......... | 0 | 13.15 | 32.89 | 21.05 | 11.84 | 15.79 | 5.26 | 0 | 99.98 |

Frequency polygon showing length of confinement of Rhus dermatitis bed patients at the Infirmary of the University of California. The stage of evolution of the disease upon entrance to the Infirmary is not known, but the chart can be depended upon to give at least minimum periods of time during which patients are confined to bed.

diarrhea have been recorded by Lindley. Constipation, which is more apt to occur in the later stages, may possibly be taken as an index of the weakness induced by degenerative changes. The volume of urine may vary during the course of the fever, as it is dependent on the filtrative capacity of the tissues, and this in turn is dependent on the amount of blood actively moving through the kidneys. A moderate increase of pressure accelerating the blood would tend to increase the urinary output, but a marked increase of pressure retards the flow of the blood, and suppression of urine results. Suppression may occur also in conditions of low blood pressure. During this stage of the disease albuminuria sometimes occurs.

Insomnia is a frequent symptom. Swelling of the neighboring lymph glands has been observed by Baldwin and by McNair (1916*c*).

*Amphibolic stage.*—This is the sequel of the preceding stage, and is not clearly differentiated therefrom. It is also known as the wavering stage, for at this time the symptoms are often changeable and there may be a sudden rise or fall of temperature. This stage probably represents the interaction of the body processes and the influences of the poison. If at this time the protective powers of the body are sufficient to combat successfully the action of the poison, a reduction of temperature will occur and the disease will decline. Conversely, if the poison and its effects prove stronger, the patient finally succumbs to the process.

I have found records of only three cases of external poisoning by *Rhus* which terminated fatally. In one, the victim was a boy six years old, who died within three weeks (White, 1873). In another case (anonymous, 1897) a woman, sixty-nine years old, exposed in July to *R. Toxicodendron*, died after two months of severe suffering. Payne, in 1894, reported the case of a man who had slept in a wood in which *Rhus* was growing, who was so severely poisoned that he died from the effects.

An intermediate condition may infrequently develop, in which a chronic disease is the sequel. This is brought about through infection of the skin lesions with pyogenic bacteria (Trielle, 1904) or through a continuance of the degenerative changes and the development of fibrosis, as is well exemplified in a case of fibrous infiltration of the prepuce reported by Seabrook in 1891.

*Stage of decline.*—This may be of *two types:* A rapid disappearance of symptoms, decline by "crisis"; or a slow disappearance, decline by "lysis." The symptoms which were directly due to the poison disappear early, while those incident to the inflammatory and metabolic disturbances are the last to disappear.

The secondary lesions which occur in Rhus dermatitis are the changes in the primary forms of eruption, either incidental to the decline of the inflammatory process, or the result of accidental interference with their natural course.

*Stage of convalescence.*—The disease itself has now disappeared, and this stage represents the attempt at restitution of the body structures. The length of this period and the ability of the system to recover completely from the effects of the disease are due to the vitality of the body tissues, which are dependent on age, nutrition, sanitary surroundings, etc. One must keep in mind the possibility of development of other diseases during this period on account of the depression of vitality.

There may be some reasons, however, for the belief that certain diseases of the skin sometimes follow Rhus poisoning. Many patients have ascribed development of various of these affections to such a cause. They say, "I always had a healthy skin until I was poisoned by ivy, and afterward it was affected in this way," after an interval of weeks, months, or, it may be, years. There are good grounds for the belief that in some cases the incidence of conditions of the skin is influenced by Rhus poisoning. This, however, does not authorize the conclusion that they are directly caused by its action, or are in any way specific in their character. There is no evidence of a continuance or renewal of the operation of the poison after its primary impression on the skin has exhausted itself. The characteristic features of the cutaneous manifestations of this period do not repeat themselves in the subsequent conditions, which may be fairly referred to the prior poisoning as an indirect cause. They are usually forms of ordinary eczema. White has seen the following conditions develop subsequent to such attacks of Rhus poisoning, which have occurred under his personal observation:

1. A young lady, whose face had been severely poisoned in October, after a rapid recovery, the following January had an attack of facial eczema.

2. Another young lady, after severe poisoning of the face and hands, in a few months had an outbreak of facial acne.

3. An old man, whose hands a short time before had been poisoned, had, immediately following his recovery, an eruption of eczema covering his arms.

4. A young man, after being severely poisoned on the face, was immediately attacked by acne which lasted a long time.

5. A man of middle age was poisoned on the hands and forearms. A few months afterward he had an obstinate subacute eczema of the legs. Bigelow (1820) stated that Pierson, who was severely poisoned while assisting him in the experiments with the juice of *R. venenata*, had eczema of the hands for a year afterward.

In all these cases, it is to be understood that the secondary condition mentioned occurred for the first time in the patient's history and after the specific primary manifestations of the poisoning had disappeared. It is impossible to say that the same conditions might not have occurred when they did if the patients had not been poisoned previously, because they are of such frequent occurrence; but, considering that eczema and acne are pathologic conditions of the skin such as might readily follow the disturbance in its tissues and glands necessarily consequent on severe poisoning by *Rhus*, it should not be considered illogical to refer the appearance of these conditions under such circumstances to the morbid impression the poison may have left on them. These, however, are the only possible sequelae in my experience that might be so interpreted (White, 1873).

In other medical literature the following sequelae are given: lingering ulcers (Horsfield, 1798), swelling of tongue and ulceration of the mouth (Horsfield, 1798), enlargement of the lymphatic glands (Horsfield, 1798), itching (Horsfield, 1798), boils (Horsfield, 1798; Beringer, 1896; Baldwin, 1887), scars (Lindley, 1908), eczema and furunculosis (Ward, 1908), hypersensitivity to skin irritants to which the patient was previously immune, that is, common ivy and sunlight (Stirling, 1913), pyogenic infection (Trielle, 1904).

During convalescence there may be a recurrence of Rhus dermatitis; this may be called a relapse. Relapses may be caused not only by direct contact with the plant but also by contact with its poisonous sap, which may be on gloves (Frost, 1826; Hunt,

1897), croquet balls (Hunt), the hands of another (Maisch, 1866; Busey; Planchon; Cantrell, 1891; Hunt), firewood (Barnes, 1886; McNair, 1916*b*), clothing (Cundell, 1883; Kunz, 1883; Walker, 1891; Balch, 1906; Lindley, 1908; McNair, 1917*c*), tools (Planchon; Hunt; von Ádelung, 1913), and on knife handles (Hunt). Walker, in 1916, noticed that pressed *Rhus* leaves from across the Atlantic when used as a table decoration caused dermatitis. Bogue, in 1894, noticed that a herbarium specimen of *R. Toxicodendron*, which had been in the herbarium three years, caused dermatitis. Lindley wrote of a white woman, serving in the capacity of boys' matron at the Indian school in northern California, who became so frequently infected through handling the clothing of the boys under her charge that she was forced to seek a transfer to another school.

There are many persons who believe in recurrent Rhus dermatitis without re-exposure (Horsfield, 1798; Parrish, 1851; Busey; Beringer; Nicholson, 1899). This recurrence is usually considered as being annual and as occurring in the summer.

It is difficult to prove that recurrent Rhus dermatitis occurs without re-exposure to the poisonous sap. Several of the so-called recurrences have been caused by *Rhus* (Nicholson); other so-called recurrences have been caused by other irritant plants such as, for instance, *Cypripedium* (Hurlburt, 1869). It is difficult to diagnose correctly a case of Rhus dermatitis, as eczema and other eruptions may be confused with this condition.

# CHAPTER XII

## DIFFERENTIAL DIAGNOSIS OF RHUS DERMATITIS

In the diagnosis of Rhus dermatitis it is necessary to clearly distinguish it from eruptions caused by other plants and irritants as well as to distinguish it from idiopathic eczema. To make such a distinction is difficult, for although the skin expresses its inflammatory disturbances in certain distinct types, these types are nearly the same whether the irritation is caused by external irritants or is a result of influences expressed from within.

Rhus dermatitis, similarly to the dermatoses produced by many other individual irritants, is eczematous in character, and can be distinguished from ordinary idiopathic acute eczema in many cases only by the most experienced observer.

In many cases the distinction of Rhus dermatitis from idiopathic eczema may be obtained through the following observances. In Rhus dermatitis the onset is more sudden, the evolution of primary lesions is rapid, the location on the skin is peculiar, the inflammation is more intense, and the areas affected are sharply defined, possess a marked asymmetry, and have an artificial-appearing configuration. The evidences of idiopathic eczema are best distinguished from those of an artificial eruption when a detailed history of the case is considered.

It is important before treating a case of probable Rhus dermatitis, therefore, to make sure of at least a possible contact with the poisonous resinous sap of the plant. This should be done also after the exclusion of all other plants with similar irritant properties. The irritant plants which grow in the locality suspected should be known.

The botanical description of *Rhus Toxicodendron* and *R. diversiloba* is found in chapter i.

Dr. James C. White has listed many of these plants to which such action has been attributed.

The common names for these plants can be found in most of the American botanies. Dr. White's list follows:

ALISMACEAE
*Alisma plantago*
ANACARDIACEAE
*Rhus venenata*
*Rhus Toxicodendron*
*Rhus diversiloba*
*Semecarpus anacardium*
APOCYNACEAE
*Nerium oleander*
ARACEAE
*Arisaema triphyllum*
*Symplocarpus foetidus*
ARALIACEAE
*Aralia spinosa*
ARTOCARPACEAE
*Antiaris toxicaria*
AURANTIACEAE
*Citrus vulgaris*
BERBERIDACEAE
*Podophyllum peltatum*
BIGNONIACEAE
*Catalpa bignonioides*
BORRAGINACEAE
*Borago officinalis*
CACTACEAE
*Cactus grandiflorus*
COMPOSITAE
*Anacyclus pyrethrum*
*Arnica montana*
*Bidens frondosa*
*Erigeron Canadense*
*Lappa officinalis*
*Leucanthemum vulgare*
*Maruta Cotula*
*Xanthium strumarium*
CONIFERAE
*Abies Canadensis*
*Abies excelsa*
*Juniperus Virginiana*
*Juniperus Sabina*
*Thuja occidentalis*
CRASSULACEAE
*Sedum acre*
CRUCIFERAE
*Lepidium sativum*
*Nasturtium Armoracia*
*Sinapis alba*
*Sinapis nigra*
*Sisymbrium officinale*
CUCURBITACEAE
*Bryonia alba*
DROSERACEAE
*Drosera rotundifolia*
ERICACEAE
*Chimaphila umbellata*
*Oxydendrum arboreum*
EUPHORBIACEAE
*Buxus sempervirens*
*Croton tiglium*
*Euphorbia corollata*
*E. ipecac., et al.*
*Hura crepitans*
*Hippomane mancinella*
*Jatropha urens*
*Stillingia sylvatica*
FUNGI
*Ustilago*
IRIDACEAE
*Iris florentina*
LEGUMINOSAE
*Andira Araroba*
*Mucuna pruriens*
LILIACEAE
*Allium sativum*
*Asparagus officinalis*
*Urginia scilla*
LINACEAE
*Linum usitatissimum*
LOASACEAE
*Mentzelia oligosperma*
*Mentzelia Lindleyi*
LOBELIACEAE
*Lobelia inflata*
LOGANIACEAE
*Gelsemium sempervirens*

MELANTHACEAE
*Colchicum autumnale*
*Veratrum sabadilla*
MYARTACEAE
*Eugenia pimenta*
*Myrcia acris*
ORCHIDACEAE
*Cypripedium pubescens*
*Vanilla planifolia*
PAPAVERACEAE
*Chelidonium majus*
*Sanguinaria Canadensis*
PHYTOLACCACEAE
*Phytolacca decandra*
PIPERACEAE
*Piper nigrum*
POLYGONACEAE
*Polygonum hydropiper*
*Polygonum acre*
RANUNCULACEAE
*Aconitum napellus*
*Actaea spicata*
*Anemone nemorosa*
*Anemone patens*
*Clematis Virginica*
*Delphinium consolida*
*Delphinium staphisagria*
*Helleborus niger*
*Ranunculus*
RUBIACEAE
*Cephaelis ipecacuanha*
*Cinchona*
RUTACEAE
*Ailanthus glandulosa*
*Ruta graveolens*
*Pilocarpus pennatifolius*
SALICACEAE
*Populus candicans*
SCROPHULARIACEAE
*Verbascum thapsus*
SOLANACEAE
*Capsicum fastigiatum*
*Datura stramonium*
THYMELEACEAE
*Daphne mezereum*
*Dirca palustris*
TROPEOLACEAE
*Tropeolum majus*
UMBELLIFERAE
*Ferula galbaniflua*
*Heracleum lanatum*
*Thapsia garganica*
URTICACEAE
*Laportea Canadensis*
*Urtica chamaedroyoides, dioica, gracilis, purpurascens, urens*

Of these plants the following are not found native in the United States:

*Semecarpus anacardium*
*Nerium oleander* (cultivated)
*Antiaris toxicaria*
*Borago officinalis* (cultivated)
*Cactus grandiflorus* (cultivated)
*Anacyclus pyrethrum*
*Sedum Acre* (cultivated)
*Buxus sempervirens* (cultivated)
*Croton tiglium*
*Hura crepitans*
*Andira araroba*
*Mucuna pruriens*
*Allium sativum* (cultivated)
*Asparagus officinalis* (cultivated)
*Urginia scilla*
*Linum usitalissimum*
*Corchorus olitorius*
*Colchicum autumnale*
*Eugenia pimenta*
*Myrcia acris* (cultivated)
*Vanilla planifolia*
*Piper nigrum*

*Aconitum napellus* (cultivated)
*Helleborus niger*
*Cephaelis ipecacuanha*
*Cinchona*
*Ailanthus glandulosa*
*Pilocarpus pennatifolius*
*Ruta graveoleus* (cultivated)
*Capsicum fastigiatum*
*Daphne niezerum*
*Tropaeolum majus* (cultivated)
*Ferula galbaniflura*
*Thapsia garganica*

The chief characteristics of Rhus dermatitis are as follows. First, the peculiarities with regard to the seat of the eruption: The hands are the parts most frequently affected. It appears most easily where the skin is thinnest and also where it is most likely to come in contact with the plant. Therefore, it is generally first found upon the lateral surfaces of the fingers, or along their edges, later upon the dorsal surfaces, and latest if at all, upon the thickened palms. If the patient has heavily calloused hands the poison may not have been able to penetrate the stratum corneum. Dermatitis, therefore, would not occur on those parts, but the poison may have been carried by the hands to other parts of the body. For this reason the genitals are almost always affected in the male when the hands are the original seat of the disease. Frequently one hand alone comes in contact with the plant and the areas of the body affected are those which can be reached by that hand only. The exposed parts of the body are those most frequently attacked. The eruption consequently appears on the face, especially the eyes, the neck, chest, arms, hands, and genitals. It is very seldom that those areas of the body not easily reached by the hands are the seat of the eruption, such as the dorsal surfaces. The author has never known of the eruption occurring on areas well protected by a dense covering of hair.

The eruption often occurs in sharply defined patches, elongated streaks, or irregular shapes, as marked out by the original contact with the plant. If cotton moistened with the following formula be applied to the skin the poison on the surface will appear as darkened spots and lines (Toyama, 1918):

| | Gm. or c.c. |
|---|---|
| Caustic potash (KOH) | 1.0 |
| Alcohol | 30.0 |
| Glycerine | 10.0 |
| Water | 60.0 |

These spots and lines can be removed by the application of an alcoholic solution containing 1 per cent of nitric acid.[1] The saps of other plants than *Rhus* are darkened by alkali, for instance, pine resin. The darkening, therefore, is no proof of the presence of *Rhus* sap.

When Rhus dermatitis occurs on the thin skin it is more irregular in distribution than eczema, annoyance from *Rhus* is greater, the *Rhus* eruption is more strikingly vesicular, and the intermediate stages are short or not evident.

There may be a slight difference in color of the vesicles of Rhus dermatitis from those of idiopathic eczema. White (1873) considers the vesicles caused by *Rhus* to be less transparent and of a peculiar lurid color. Cantrell (1898) states that the boiled sago grain appearance of the vesicles and the peculiar color of the discharge (a yellowish-gray sticky mass) are usually sufficient to differentiate Rhus poisoning from other cutaneous affections.

These are some of the differences by which a case of Rhus dermatitis may generally be recognized and distinguished from idiopathic eczema. In some mild cases, however, it may be impossible to determine positively whether we have a case of one or the other to deal with.

### CONCLUSION

It is necessary to distinguish Rhus dermatitis from dermatoses caused by other substances as well as from idiopathic eczema.

Rhus dermatitis is characterized by a sudden onset, rapid evolution of primary lesions, peculiar distribution and configuration, sharply defined areas, and intense inflammation.

The best criteria for Rhus dermatitis are the history of the case, and the appearance of small darkened spots or lines upon dampening affected areas with dilute caustic soda or potash, which can be decolorized with dilute nitric acid. Similar darkened areas are obtained when tincture of iodine or tincture of ferric chlorid are applied.

[1] This darkening of the poison by alkali has been shown by McNair (1916*b*, 1917*c*). Tincture of iodine as well as tincture of ferric chlorid will also cause the poison to darken.

## CHAPTER XIII

# INTERNAL POISONING FROM RHUS[1]

### ETIOLOGY

Most cases of internal poisoning by *Rhus* have been caused by chewing the leaves of the plants and swallowing the juice in order to attain immunity to the poison. One of these cases terminated fatally (Alumbaugh, 1903). Dakin (1829) aptly commented on this procedure nearly a century ago:

> Some good meaning, mystical, marvelous physicians, or favored ladies with knowledge inherent, say the bane will prove the best antidote, and hence advise the forbidden leaves to be eaten, both as a preventive and cure to the external disease. I have known the experiment tried, which resulted in an eruption, swelling, redness and intolerable itching, around the verge of the anus.

In 1907, Conner reported one case caused by thoughtless chewing of a tender shoot of *R. Toxicodendron*. Brown (1922) reports a case of mucous membrane immunity although the skin was susceptible. Two cases are recorded in which children were poisoned by eating the fruit of *R. Toxicodendron* (Moorman, 1866; see p. 196). Root infusions were cited as a cause by French in 1903.

In internal Rhus poisoning the amount of poison ingested is generally larger than in Rhus dermatitis. There is also a possibility of other poisons than that which is the principal cause of dermatitis being absorbed from the plant.

The unripe fruits of *R. Toxicodendron* and *R. diversiloba* produce dermatitis, but when fully ripe they do not cause dermatitis (McNair, 1917). The latter fact does not prove that the fruit is not poisonous when swallowed.

The fruit of *R. coriara*, a plant listed among the non-dermatitis-producing *Rhus*, will produce severe poisoning when swallowed (Escafet, 1847). The symptoms of children who had swallowed the seeds were similar to those cited in the cases of the two children who

[1] Reprinted from the *Archives of Dermatology and Syphilology*, IV (July, 1921), 62–66.

ate the fruit of *R. Toxicodendron* reported by Moorman. In cases of poisoning caused by both these fruits the patients became drowsy and stupid and in a short time vomited partially digested fruit and fluid the color of wine. Convulsions followed.

Orfila (see p. 197), in 1866, carried on a series of experiments on dogs with an aqueous extract of *R. radicans*. In some cases fatal results followed the ingestion of the extract, its injection into the jugular vein, or its application to a wound in the leg. The application of the extract to the cellular tissue on the back of a dog produced no "remarkable phenomena." The principal irritant of *R. radicans* is practically insoluble in water. The poison in the aqueous extract may have been tannin.

### COURSE OF INTERNAL RHUS POISONING

The features of internal Rhus poisoning which are similar to those of Rhus dermatitis are the shortness of its course and, typically, its differentiation into stages. The following stages in their proper sequence are generally recognized:

*Stage of infection.*—This stage covers the period of time required by the poison to enter the outer surface of the mucous membrane and lining tissues in the mouth, throat, and alimentary tract.

*The stage of latency.*—This stage covers the period of time in which the poison continues to enter the tissues up to the point of the production of symptoms. In a case in which poisoning occurred through the inhalation of smoke from burning Rhus an irritation of the throat was immediately noticed (Seabrook, 1891). In the cases of two children, one six and the other eight years of age, who had eaten fruit of *R. Toxicodendron*, symptoms and drowsiness appeared in a few hours (Moorman, 1866). In a case in which a young shoot of *R. Toxicodendron* had been thoughtlessly chewed, symptoms of burning and itching of the lips and mouth were evident in about twenty-four hours (Conner, 1907). This and other evidence at hand proves that the symptoms of internal Rhus poisoning become evident in a shorter length of time than in the average cases of external poisoning. The stage of latency, therefore, is an appreciably limited one, and its duration is a matter of a few hours at most when a considerable quantity of poison has been ingested.

During the time of ripening, the fruits of *R. diversiloba* and *R. Toxicodendron* contain an increasing amount of fat which has a maximum of about 20 per cent (McNair, 1917) in the mesocarp. As the irritant poison is soluble in this fat, the fat may aid in the absorption of the poison. Fat absorption, however, is mainly a function of the intestines, whereas the poison produces stomatitis and gastritis, as well as enteritis.

*Stage of prodromes.*—In this stage vague symptoms appear, such as headache, lassitude, and possibly some irritation about the point of entrance of the poison. These prodromal symptoms are usually of brief duration; the duration depends on the same general factors that are indicated in the preceding stage. In a case of poisoning by the inhalation of smoke from burning *Rhus*, irritation of the throat and general malaise occurred within a day after exposure. In a case of poisoning, probably caused by Rhus smoke coming through an open car window, a sensation similar to sunburn was noticed in about twenty-four hours. Symptoms developed in a case of stomatitis in about the same length of time.

*Stage of invasion.*—In this stage the symptoms characteristic of the disease make themselves manifest. As in Rhus dermatitis, two types are recognized, namely, a frank or sudden invasion and an insidious or gradual invasion. The former is, doubtless, due to a sudden and severe intoxication, while the latter is due to a more gradual action. When the frank invasion occurs, naturally this stage is well separated from the prodromal, but they gradually merge during the insidious invasion. One of several factors may account for a frank invasion: (1) Poison swallowed in a large amount comes in contact with a large surface. Although it may be slowly absorbed, much is absorbed at the same time. (2) Some very sudden cause may be operative in reducing the vitality of the person, so that a given volume of poison may have an extreme and sudden effect. (3) The poison may have accumulated in a given focus owing to defective drainage, and then, by a sudden discharge of the poison into the system, a large quantity may be absorbed.

*Primary effect.*—The primary effect of poisoning in this stage is to stimulate one or more functions of the system, while the secondary or final effect is to depress or pervert such functions subsequent to the production of degenerative and necrotic changes. Practically every function may be affected and metabolic and circulatory activity may receive an especial stimulus. Either with or without a direct effect on the thermogenic centers, the excessive metabolic activity is liable to increase the body heat as well as to increase the amount of waste products. The effect on the circulatory system is equally striking; this consists of increased cardiac force and vasoconstriction, as shown in a rise of blood pressure. In the frank invasion there is not only a suddenness of onset of symptoms, but also great severity of symptoms. Internal Rhus poisoning may be ushered in by some special phenomena, such as nausea and vomiting, followed by convulsions when the poison acts on the central nervous system. Children are more likely to show the latter effects than adults.

Effects are noted in several parts of the body:

*Abdominal area.*—This shows distinct congestion. In the gastro-intestinal tract increased peristalsis and diarrhea may be caused. Nausea is common. Intense congestion of the kidneys may cause a diminished output of urine, while slight congestion may somewhat increase the amount.

*Pulmonary area.*—This area likewise is congested. Dyspnea is induced by nervous influences and perhaps by a reduction of the air space of the lungs due to congestion. A burning in the throat and a dry hoarse cough may occur.

*Cerebral area.*—This area is so closely associated with the large vascular trunks that it shares in the congestion. A feeling of fulness and headache, of greater or less severity, is likely to develop.

The pupils are dilated. The face is usually flushed.

*Stage of acme.*—This is in reality but a continuation of the last stage, and is not clearly differentiated from it. The lesions of this period are dependent on congestion, increased metabolism, and degenerative changes. Naturally, extension of an inflammatory process may occur by continuity of structure. For instance, in a case of Rhus proctitis and vulvitis (Dunmire, 1881), peritonitis developed with "great pain and tenderness over the bowels, particularly on the left side, which afterward extended over the abdomen.

The slightest pressure would produce pain." At the beginning of the stage of acme, stimulation of the functions occurs, together with congestion and febrile disturbances.

*Amphibolic stage.*—This is the sequel of the preceding stage, and is not clearly differentiated from it. It is the wavering stage, for at this time the symptoms are often changeable, and there may be a sudden rise or fall of temperature. If, at this time, the protective powers of the body are sufficient to combat successfully the action of the poison, a reduction of temperature will occur and the disease will decline. Conversely, if the poison proves to be the stronger, the patient finally succumbs to the process. Only one death is recorded from internal Rhus poisoning. A patient suffering from Rhus dermatitis chewed some *R. Toxicodendron* leaves to produce immunity; he died two days later (Alumbaugh, 1903). If death does not take place in this stage, it is followed by the stage of decline.

*Stage of decline.*—In this stage the symptoms which are directly due to the poison disappear, while those incident to the degeneration, inflammatory, and metabolic disturbances may persist.

*Stage of convalescence.*—The disease itself has now disappeared, but this stage represents the attempt at restitution of the body structures. The length of this period and the ability of the system to recover completely from the effects of the disease are dependent on age, nutrition, sanitary surroundings, and other conditions. Other diseases may develop during this period due to depression of vitality, but I have found no record of sequelae or relapses that have occurred in persons poisoned internally by *Rhus*.

# CHAPTER XIV

## IMMUNITY TO DERMATITIS FROM RHUS DIVERSILOBA[1]

### DEFINITION

The word "immunity" is used in this article to designate the effective resistance of the organism against the principal, or most active, irritant in *Rhus diversiloba*. A high degree of immunity, therefore, designates a low degree of susceptibility and vice versa. Immunity is generally used to designate a low degree of susceptibility toward foreign protein. As the irritant poison of *R. diversiloba* is not a protein, the term is used in this chapter to denote a natural or acquired resistance toward non-protein substances, such as occurs with alcohol, chloroform, ether, atropin, cocain, and opium. In this terminology, immunity includes what is commonly known as tolerance.

Judging by the evidence at present at hand, there seem to be two forms of immunity—natural and acquired.

### NATURAL IMMUNITY

According to Kolmer, natural immunity is the resistance to infection normally possessed, usually as the result of inheritance, by certain persons or species under natural conditions.

This type of immunity to lobinol (the poisonous principle of *R. diversiloba*) is frequently relative and seldom, if ever, absolute. Persons are frequently found who are immune to lobinol when it is applied in the same concentration and condition as it exists in the sap of the plant, but when applied in a more concentrated form these persons are affected by it. Von Adelung, in 1912, found that the concentrated alcoholic extract of *R. diversiloba* affected every immune person to whom it had been applied. Similar

[1] Reprinted from the *Archives of Dermatology and Syphilology*, III (May, 1921), 625–33.

See discussion on immunity by Lain, Pusey, and Hazen at the Seventy-second Annual Session of the American Medical Association, Boston, June, 1921, in the *Journal of the American Medical Association*, LXXVII (1921), 910–13.

results were obtained by Warren, in 1909, with *R. Toxicodendron*. Brown (1922), in experimenting on nine individuals with an alcoholic poison ivy extract of unknown strength, found three immune. Spain (1922), in experimenting on eighty individuals, all but one over eight years old, with an ethyl alcoholic poison ivy extract of unknown strength, found fifty-two or 65 per cent susceptible. Bibb, in 1914 and 1915, however, in experimenting with the sap of *R. Toxicodendron*, found a person on whom it had no deleterious effect. Earlier immune results with the sap of *R. Toxicodendron* were noted by Kalm, in 1748, by Van Mons, in 1797, and Blackwood, in 1880. I have observed similar cases with *R. diversiloba*. The sap of both the poison ivy and the poison oak has frequently been observed to have been transmitted from the hands and clothing of immune gardeners and those who have been working with the plants to others who were susceptible to it (Planchon, 1887; Busey, 1873; White, 1873; Lindley, 1908). Similar examples of relative immunity are found in experiments with bacteria and toxins on animals; for instance, rats are highly immune to diphtheria toxin, and readily withstand the effects of an amount equaling 1,000 lethal doses for a guinea pig, but still larger doses may prove fatal; hedgehogs possess complete or almost complete immunity for the amount of snake venom deposited in an ordinary strike, but if venoms of several snakes are collected and injected at one time, death will result.

The commonly considered species immunity to Rhus dermatitis in cases of the lower animals is frequently due to the protection of the skin by hair. White, in 1873, noticed that hunting dogs which have traversed woods infested with poison ivy are sometimes affected about the eyes. Hunt (1897) states that "dogs exposed . . . . die with dilated pupils without coma or convulsions, but with general swelling of the body." Horsfield (1798) considered poison ivy as without harm to horses, cows, and sheep. Bommer (1907) states that "animals, presumably cattle, are as badly affected as humans, the lips becoming swollen, stiff and scabby, so that they cannot eat." Guernsey (1913) states that horses, pigs, sheep, and goats eat poison ivy without harm. Kobert, in 1906, stated that sheep and goats that eat the leaves and fruit of poison sumach

(*R. Vernix*) become sick and much harm results. Mackie, in 1903, said:

> On the ranges the leaves and berries of [poison oak] are readily eaten by sheep, goats, and horses, but not by cattle, as far as could be ascertained by observation and numerous inquiries. Many of the bushes are stripped entirely of leaves before they would naturally drop them.

Pfaff, in 1897, when administering toxicodendrol per os to rabbits, noticed that it caused nephritis and death of the animals. Ford, in 1907, made similar statements. McNair, in 1916*b*, cited one case in which a rabbit was given the sap of *R. diversiloba* per os, which caused albuminuria (see chap. xi, p. 110).

Many birds normally eat the fruits of the poisonous *Rhus* (see list of birds on p. 41).

It seems to be well liked by horses, according to interviews with United States government forest rangers. Jepson, in 1902, noted one observer, however, who asserted that "horses who fed on poison oak if driven until they become warm tremble and shake, and will die if not taken off the roads. Driven cattle are similarly affected."

Racial immunity is that type of natural immunity which exists among members of the same species. Dakin, in 1829, noted that mulattoes, negroes, and Americans were equally susceptible to *R. Toxicodendron*. French, in 1903, also stated negroes were not immune to *R. Toxicodendron*. Lindley, in 1908, noted that the full-blooded Indians in California were immune while the half-breeds were susceptible to *R. diversiloba*. Hrdlicka, in 1908, listed remedies for this dermatitis used by the Indians of the southwest. In writing of the plants used by Indians of the Missouri River region, Gilmore (1911–12) states that poison ivy (p. 100) was called *Hthi-wathe-hi*, "the plant that makes sore" (*hthi*, sore; *wathe*, to make; *hi*, plant, bush, tree, and plant body). The Indians knew and dreaded the poisonous effects of this plant.

The *American Encyclopedia* (XLV [1906]) and also McAtee (1920) says:

> *Rhus diversiloba*, although greatly dreaded by the Cherokees who endeavor to conciliate it by addressing it as "my friend," does not seem to injure certain California tribes so much. They even use it as medicine, though sometimes poisoning themselves internally by the practice.

Severe cases occur quite frequently in California among the Mexicans, Chinese, and Japanese, as well as among the native and foreign whites. There seems, therefore, to be no high degree of immunity existing among the principal types of races toward *R. diversiloba* or toward *R. Toxicodendron*, as far as present knowledge extends.

Examples of individual immunity toward infection by both poison ivy and poison oak are not infrequent. All of these so far tested are relative and none are absolute.

There are many conflicting statements as to whether blonds are more susceptible than brunettes. Blonds, however, as far as I have been able to ascertain, have never been said to be less immune than brunettes, but, on the contrary, always have been said to be more susceptible. The question, however, is of little value as both are affected in large proportions. Dakin stated that persons with light and dark skins were equally susceptible. Planchon regarded blonds as not more susceptible than brunettes. Lindley considered those with fair skins more liable to attacks than those with dark skins. Ward, in 1908, noted that brunettes were slightly less susceptible than blonds, although he said this observation was not to be relied on.

Horsfield, in 1798, made the statement that females are more susceptible than males to *R. radicans*. In compiling the statistics of the cases of *R. diversiloba* dermatitis treated at the infirmary of the University of California for five years, the percentage of cases among males was less than the percentage of cases among females (McNair, 1921*d;* see also chap. vi, Table V, and Fig. 4). This may be due to the fact that the skin of the female is generally more susceptible. The statistics, however, are not reliable for drawing these conclusions as (1) the total number of males and females exposed is not known, (2) the total number of males and females affected is not known, (3) the table shows only the number of students who came to the infirmary for treatment, which is not the total number affected, although it may be nearly the total number.

According to Baldwin (1887), fat people are more susceptible than thin people to the effects of *R. diversiloba*.

Some physicians believe also that children are less immune than adults (Horsfield, Dakin). Spain (1922) tested eighteen infants, between five weeks and eighteen months old, with alcoholic extract of poison ivy and obtained negative results. There are cases in which the reverse condition holds true, as stated by Blackwood and by Cundell-Juler (1833). It is quite probable that people after reaching the age of sixty years have a diminishing immunity in accordance with the general pharmacologic law.

Certain persons appear to possess a definite immunity to the poison or poisons, although they may be freely exposed for many years. In other persons immunity may increase or decrease. I have known of a forest ranger, in service in a California forest for many years, who escaped infection, though he frequently was brought in contact with the sap of poison oak in clearing trails; finally he contracted the disease on returning to the habitat of the plant after a number of years' absence. Similar cases are common occurrence in medical literature, especially in connection with poison ivy (Kalm, Dakin, Blackwood, and Cundell-Juler).

Such variations of the degree of susceptibility in the same person may be dependent on the condition of the general health (Blackwood, 1880). Yandell, in 1876, stated that enfeebled persons were most likely to be poisoned. The condition of the glands of the skin may have an influence, as has been previously considered (McNair, 1921*d;* see also chap. xi, p. 101). Horsfield considered persons more susceptible immediately after than before a full meal. Park (1879) enlarged on this idea when he said that a "patient with an irritable skin, which reacts promptly to irritation in the digestive tract or elsewhere, should be particularly liable to annoyance from contact with such a pronounced irritant as *Rhus*."

There may be a relation between the sensitivity of the skin to *Rhus* and toward other irritants. Attacks of Rhus dermatitis are known to have left a hypersensitivity toward sunlight and common English ivy (Stirling, 1913). Perhaps the reverse holds true as well. Several persons immune to *Rhus* are greatly annoyed by mosquitoes while they are not bothered by fleas. On the other hand, one person who is quite susceptible to both *Rhus* and fleas is not appreciably susceptible to mosquitoes. Perhaps tolerance to *Rhus* may establish, or be the result of, a tolerance to other irritants of the same class, as the prolonged use of alcohol creates a tolerance for chloroform. Chloroform and alcohol are considered to act on the same nerve cells and in the same direction.

*Causes of natural immunity.*—(1) Various non-specific factors may prevent infection. Among these may be mentioned the thickness and imperviousness of the skin, especially of the stratum corneum, and the physical action of the various secretions of the sebaceous and sudoriparous glands.

2. The particular structure of the sebaceous and sudoriparous glands and the chemical nature and abundance of their secretions. This phase of the subject has previously been exhaustively considered in a previous article (McNair, 1921*d;* see also chap. xi, p. 101).

3. Phagocytosis may be of importance in natural immunity. Leucocytes may act either by engulfing and carrying away small particles of the poison, or their oxidizing and other enzymes may have a protective action against the poison.

4. A natural antitoxin immunity may exist. Although attempts to demonstrate such an immunity have never been successful either with lobinol, according to von Adelung (1912), or with toxicodendrol, according to Strickler (1918), this failure may be due to the unsuitability of the present methods. Ford, in 1907, demonstrated the acquirement of tolerance in guinea pigs and rabbits to six or seven times their minimum lethal doses, as well as the immune properties of the resultant serum. These experiments von Adelung was unable to repeat.

The chemical defense against lobinol may include oxidation, reduction, hydration, dehydration, substitution, and addition. Such protective substances as may play a part may include carbonates, phosphates, protein, sulphur-containing substances, and glucuronic acid. The probable phenolic nature of lobinol (McNair, 1921*c;* see also chap. x, p. 96) would cause one to expect that it might form lobinol glucuronate and lobinol sulphate.

As iodine has the power to render lobinol non-toxic in vitro (von Adelung, 1913), perhaps the thyroid secretion may play a part in susceptibility. It would be interesting to determine whether there is any relation between susceptibility and goiter.

There may also be substances present that do not chemically combine with the poison to render it physiologically neutral, but which antagonize it by stimulating other defense mechanisms, causing an antagonism similar to that which exists between chloroform and strychnin.

5. It may be that even after the introduction of the poison no great harm results because of a lack of suitable solvents or receptors on the part of the body cells of the host for the transmission or union of the pathogenic agent. The effect of the poison, therefore, may remain strictly localized to the point of immediate contact.

6. Immunity may be due to the absence of synergists, the absence of substances in the tissue that increases the toxicity of the poison.

Acquired immunity may occur in two distinct forms: active and passive. A mixed type may exist.

*Active acquired immunity.*—Active acquired immunity is, according to Kolmer, that form of a resistance to infection brought about by the activity of the cells of a person or animal as a result of having had the actual disease in question, or as a result of artificial inoculation with a modified or attenuated form of the causative agent.

Such active acquired immunity may be found against Rhus dermatitis when the defense mechanism of the body is stimulated by an attack of Rhus dermatitis and antitoxic elaborations formed. Whether such a result is actually accomplished in Rhus poisoning has often been questioned. Many observers assert that by chewing the leaves of the plant and swallowing the juice immunity can be acquired (Duncan, 1916). I have not had an opportunity to experiment with such an immune person, but many cases are known in which susceptible persons who have followed these directions have been severely poisoned internally (Dakin; Conner, 1907; and Alumbaugh, 1903). I know of such cases in which the patient did not acquire immunity on recovery.

Another type of immunity may be caused similar to the common immunity toward nicotin. In acquiring such immunity by smoking tobacco the absorption of nicotin is not retarded nor its excretion accelerated, but the tissues become accustomed to small quantities of nicotin, and thus fail to react to it. Much of this tolerance is lost when the habit is discontinued, as in the case of opium.

Lindley states that "some persons doing manual labor are never free from the eruption entirely; it could be seen about the eyes, neck, and wrists almost constantly." The author contracted severe dermatitis several times from poison oak when about thirteen years of age, but has not been bothered with it since, although he not only frequently makes trips into the habitat of the plant but also rubs the sap on his hands. Over a period of six years during which he has been experimenting with poison oak, he has always been able to produce a mild degree of local dermatitis by applying the sap of the plant to the skin. The disease produced has never decreased in mildness with successive experiments. Strickler, in 1918, asserted that he had produced absolute immunity of short duration by the intramuscular administration of the poison.

There are many cases in which persons have been able to handle any variety of poisonous *Rhus* with immunity on whom later a small amount of the sap would cause severe dermatitis (Kalm, Blackwood, and Cundell-Juler). Persons who have frequently been subject to mild attacks may be liable to increased sensitivity, as shown in several University of California Infirmary cases (cases 4710, 4713, 4723, 5000, 5385).

The reverse has also been noticed. Horsfield, in 1798, stated that children are more readily poisoned than adults, and Dakin said that susceptibility recedes as age advances. I have known a number of people with a high degree of susceptibility which did not appreciably vary throughout a period of years. This opinion is supported by statements made by patients at the University of California Infirmary; for instance, the patient in Case 4536. Von Adelung (1913) has also maintained a low immunity for a number of years.

Fluctuating degrees of susceptibility may occur in the same person, as shown in some of the cases of the University of California Infirmary (cases 4814, 5665). Apparent changes in the degree of immunity may not always be actual, for the severity of the dermatitis is governed, to a certain extent, by the amount of poison acting, as well as on the degree of resistance of the person.

*Passive acquired immunity.*—As the name indicates, this is a form of immunity that depends on defensive factors not originating in the person or animal protected, but is passively acquired by the injection of serum from one that has acquired an active immunity to the disease in question, according to Kolmer (1917). Such immunity may perhaps result from drinking the milk of a cow fed on a mixture of grass and poison ivy plant, as cited by Dieffenbach (1917).

## SUMMARY

In this chapter immunity is used to include tolerance.

Natural immunity exists toward the principal irritant. It is usually relative and seldom absolute. Specie immunity exists among some animals and birds. As far as we know, racial immunity does not exist among Chinese, Japanese, Mexicans, negroes, the North American Indians, or any other race. There are examples of individual immunity in which immunity is relative rather than absolute. Blonds and brunettes are both affected in large proportions. Females are apparently more susceptible than males. According to one writer, fat people are more susceptible than thin people. Age may influence immunity. There is no proof, however, that children as a class are more susceptible than adults. In the same individual the degree of immunity may vary or may remain constant. The degree of immunity is probably influenced by the condition of the health and the condition of the skin. Natural immunity may be due to: the thickness of the skin and the condition of the dermal glands, phagocytosis, natural antitoxin, lack of a suitable solvent or receptors for the poison, and an absence of substances in the tissues that increase the toxicity of the poison.

# CHAPTER XV

## REMEDIES FOR RHUS DERMATITIS[1]

Practical therapeutics may be deductive or inductive; may, that is to say, be based on some general principles which in their turn depend on the conceptions held as to disease processes and the pharmacodynamics of certain substances; or they may be merely the result of more or less discrete observations as to the curative value of such substances in certain diseased conditions. The former method in therapeutics is often spoken of as *rational*, and the latter as *empirical*.

### EMPIRICAL REMEDIES

In the list of remedies for Rhus dermatitis of the empirical type, we may include all those remedies that do not take into account the chemical composition of the poison. Horsfield (1798), before anything regarding the chemical nature of the poison was known, listed these remedies: ashes of the leaves and wood of the poisonous *Rhus*, soot dissolved in milk, and aqueous solution of sodium chlorid, copper sulphate, or ammonium chlorid, leaves of *Datura stramonium*, juice of *Sanguinaria canadensis*, unguentum simplex, sweet oil, and emollient cataplasms, and an ointment of 1 dram of saccharum saturni with 1 ounce of unguentum simplex. Christy (1829) recommended topical applications of solutions of either lead acetate, ammonium chlorid, or an infusion of digitalis. He advocated producing blisters above inflamed parts. He recommended solidago canadensis, an Indian remedy, and said its roots were chewed and part of the resultant saliva swallowed and part rubbed on the inflamed area. Dakin, writing also in 1829, used locally in the treatment of this disease this prescription:

| | | Gm. or c.c. | |
|---|---|---|---|
| ℞ | Copper sulphate | 4 | ʒ i |
| | Precipitate of red mercury | 4 | ʒ i |
| | Venice turpentine | 12 | ʒ iii |
| | Lard | 30 | ℥ i |

Mix to form an ointment.

[1] Reprinted from the *Archives of Dermatology and Syphilology*, IV (August, 1921), 217–34.

In 1836, Pickett records the local application of an old Massachusetts Indian remedy of an infusion of the bruised leaves and twigs of *Diervilla canadensis* (bush honeysuckle).

In 1837, an anonymous article appeared, in which the treatment recommended for Rhus poisoning included a topical application of from 20 to 40 grains of silver nitrate to 1 ounce of water, the skin having previously been washed clean with warm water and soap. A topical application of from 10 to 20 grains of mercuric chlorid to 1 ounce of water is not considered so good as the silver nitrate. Remedies which are considered as of little or no value, whether in weak or strong solution, are: *Diervilla canadensis*, Prot. lead acetate, potassium nitrate, potassium carbonate, and sodium chlorid.

Smith, in 1851, was led to use tincture of iodine in Rhus poisoning, as it had been considered beneficial in the treatment of venomous reptile bites.

In 1858, Dr. Joseph Khittel announced that the poison of *R. Toxicodendron* is a volatile alkaloid. Seven years later, Maisch, in contrast to Khittel, considered the poison a volatile organic acid, which he named toxicodendric acid. These investigations had a noticeable effect on the rational treatment of the disease; but they are cited here merely to show that old remedies continued to be used and new ones were recommended, which did not take into consideration the volatile alkaloid of Khittel nor the volatile acid of Maisch.

In 1867, Canfield described the mode of using *Grindelia robusta* and *G. hirsutula* as antidotes for poison oak. Either the bruised fresh herb was rubbed on the affected parts or a strong decoction, made by boiling either the fresh or dried herb, was used to wash the poisoned surfaces.

Risk (1871) recommended the local application of a decoction of white oak. He also cites the alum solution of Hopkins, Dunn's decoction of cottonwood leaves for internal use, and the following formulas of Bailey:

| | Gm. or c.c. | |
|---|---|---|
| ℞ Mercuric chlorid | 2 | ʒ ss |
| Distilled water | 90 | ℥ iii |
| Add and dissolve | | |
| Ammonium chlorid | 4 | ʒ i |
| Potassium nitrate | 8 | ʒ ii |

Sig.: Apply thoroughly three times a day.

Dr. James C. White sums up the empirical treatment of the inflammation up to 1873 thus:

A great many remedies have been recommended, in both medical and botanical books, for the treatment of persons poisoned by rhus, while others of a "domestic" character are used in various parts of the country. Among the former, a solution of acetate of lead holds the most conspicuous place. Torrey, in his "Botany of New York," says one the best applications is a solution of sugar of lead, after the use of saline cathartics. Dr. Bigelow [1817–20] thinks the application of acetate of lead as useful as any external palliative, and that it should be used as cold as possible. Solutions of sulphate of copper and of other metallic salts have also been recommended by physicians. Among the domestic remedies, vinegar, and solutions of saleratus and carbonate of soda, are widely and highly esteemed. A decoction of Virginia snake root (serpentaria) is also supposed to possess special power over the poison. In an old copy of Bigelow's "Florula Bostoniensis," picked up in a second-hand book-store, I find, in connection with Rhus toxicodendron, a marginal note by its former owners, stating that, if soft-soap be rubbed thoroughly into the hands after handling specimens, its poisonous action will be prevented. The list comprises most of the other articles recommended by writers in medical journals as "cures" for rhus poisoning, many of which are stated to be "specific," and to act "like magic." It is needless to give the detailed directions for their application: Grindelia robusta, Comptonia asplenifolia, dulcamara berries (in cream), Cephalanthus occidentalis, Gelsemium sempervirens, rhamnus, Lactuca elongata, Collinsonia canadensis, Quercus alba (bark), Lindera benzoin, Sassafras officinale, Atropa belladonna, solutions of bromin, sulphate of zinc, chlorate of potash, chlorinated soda, sulphite of sodium, alum curd, and Turkish bath.

It is always a suspicious element in therapeutics when remedies are recommended as specifics, and when the list of cures for any one disease is exceptionally long. It is not strange, therefore, that we find even non-professional writers remarking that "the reputed remedies are more numerous than efficacious (Torrey and Gray)."

De Witt (1874) used the following prescription locally

| | | Gm. or c.c. | |
|---|---|---|---|
| ℞ | Glycerine | 60 | gr. x |
| | Tinct. iodine | 15 | ℥ ii |
| | Carbolic acid | 2 | ℥ ss |
| | Morphine sulphate | 0.66 | ʒ ss |

Humphrey (1874) in the same year recommended sponging the surface every hour with one part of zinc sulphate in twenty-four parts of water.

Morrison (1874) published the following formula to be applied constantly to the affected parts.

| | | Gm. or c.c. | |
|---|---|---|---|
| ℞ | Carbolic acid | 2 | fl℥ ss |
| | Sodium sulphite | 12 | ℥ iii |
| | Water | 120 | fl℥ vi |

He said that he did not know that the sodium sulphite was of any use in the formula; but he knew that it would not be of much use without the phenol (carbolic acid).

An anonymous contributor printed, in 1875, a prescription of mercuric chlorid, 10 grains, and lime water, 5 ounces, to be used locally. This he preferred to sodium chlorid and potassium bicarbonate, lead acetate, lead paint thinned with linseed oil, gunpowder and water, ammonia water and olive oil.

In 1876, Yandell recommended a dram of quinin in twelve pills, one-third to be taken each afternoon, with no local treatment. Of external applications, he considered mercuric chlorid the best.

In 1876, Bernard used the fluid extract of *Gelsemium sempervirens* externally, with good results.

Brown, in 1878, stated that bromine was a cure for Rhus poisoning when applied externally as a mixture of from 10 to 20 drops of bromine to an ounce of olive oil, petrolatum, or glycerine. This was to be rubbed gently on the affected parts, three or four times a day, and especially on going to bed at night. The oil was washed off twice daily with castile soap.

The year 1879 was a popular year for Rhus remedies; at least seven were published. Those authors that did not state the chemical nature of the poison were Kahler, Osborn, and Smythe. Kahler used for local application a mixture of ammonia water, 1 dram, and tincture of lobelia, 7 drams, every two or three hours. Osborn used locally a cloth saturated with lime water overnight, to be exchanged the next morning for a bandage saturated with oak bark decoction. Smythe applied to the affected parts soft cloths, kept wet with a saturated solution of sodium thiosulphate.

Within the decade between 1880 and 1890, published remedies and "specifics" became more numerous. Blackwood (1880) secured no real benefit by the use of alkalies (ammonia, sodium, and potassium), the sulphites and bisulphites, solutions of bromine, iodine, phenol, potassium permanganate, saturated infusions and tinctures of serpentaria and lobelia, stale beer, and milk. The use of lime water he considered the best local treatment. Burgess (1880) recommended the local application of a solution of lead acetate (2 drams to a pint of water) on lint covered with oiled silk. Hardaway, in 1881, specified a formula of ½ ounce of zinc sulphate in one pint of water for local use. In 1882, Edson, having used gelsemium for some years with much satisfaction in pruritic troubles, believed that it might at least alleviate the pain in Rhus dermatitis. He used the following formula which speedily stopped the pain:

| | | Gm. or c.c. | |
|---|---|---|---|
| ℞ | Phenol | 2 | ʒ ss |
| | Fluid extract of gelsemium | 8 | ʒ ii |
| | Glycerine | 16 | ℥ ss |
| | Water, sufficient to make | 120 | ℥ iv |

Kunze (1883) recommended local treatment with lactic acid, acetic acid, or salt water and lime juice. The lactic acid idea was the result of the buttermilk remedy, the acetic acid came from Central and South America, and salt water and lime juice are popular remedies for manchineel poisoning. Hinton (1883) stated recovery follows within twenty-four hours if a strong infusion of red sassafras root is applied frequently. Leonard (1884) gave the following list of four topical remedies:

| | | Gm. or c.c. | |
|---|---|---|---|
| ℞ | Tinct. lobelia | 60 | ℥ ii |
| | Sodium bicarbonate | 4 | ʒ i |
| | Water | 60 | ℥ ii |
| ℞ | Sodium thiosulphate | 30 | ℥ i |
| | Water | 500 | O i |
| ℞ | Spirit of nitrous ether applied without dilution several times a day. | | |
| ℞ | Bromine | 2–4 | ʒ i |
| | Olive oil | 30 | ℥ i |

Tate (1885) recommended the application of copper sulphate, 2 drams in water, 8 ounces, to stop the pain and burning.

At least seven remedies were published by different authors in 1886. Of these, an anonymous author recommended an infusion of sweet fern (*Comtonia asplenifolia*) to be applied locally. Barnes (1886) recommended this compound to be taken internally:

| | | Gm. or c.c. | |
|---|---|---|---|
| ℞ | Sodium phenol sulphonate................ | 6 | ʒ iss |
| | Fluid extract of gelsemium ............... | 4 | ʒ i |
| | Water, sufficient to make.................. | 120 | flʒ iv |

Sig.: One teaspoonful every two hours.

Brown published this modification of his 1878 remedy:

| | | Gm. or c.c. | |
|---|---|---|---|
| ℞ | Bromine................................ | | ♏x–xx |
| | Olive oil or oil of sweet almond........... | 30 | flʒ i |

L. D. M. gave as a remedy the following:

| | | |
|---|---|---|
| ℞ | Pulverized borax........................ | ℥ ii |
| | Phenol................................. | ℥ i |
| | Morphine sulphate...................... | gr. x |
| | Compound powder of acacia............. | ʒ iv |
| | Water, sufficient to make................ | ℥ viii |

In criticism of this mixture, he stated that phenol and borax "help to kill the poison," and the gum acacia helps to allay irritations and pruritis. Regensburger (1886) recommended Russian baths in the treatment of *Rhus diversiloba* dermatitis.

In 1887, Baldwin announced a remedy in phenol ointment U.S.P., and recommended as local California remedies an infusion of *Grindelia robusta*, bay berry bush, eucalyptus, and buckeye. Couch in the same year recommended frequent and thorough washing with hot soapsuds, and asserted that this treatment removed the irritant.

Hawley, in 1890, stated that the use of oil of palustre ledum 3x if administered when the eruption first appeared would cause all symptoms to disappear within forty-eight hours.

Aulde used whitewash externally in 1890. Kite used black mercurial lotion similarly in 1891. Other external applications recommended in 1891 were a decoction of chestnut leaves (*Castanea fagus*) by Straley, thymol iodid by Levick, concoction of fluid extract of serpentaria (Virginia snakeroot), Walker.

In 1894, Cantrell used full strength solution of chlorinated soda (Labarraque's solution) with good results in seven cases.

An anonymous author, in 1895, recommended the juice or infusion of the touch-me-not (*Impatiens fulva*). Cantrell recommended phenyl salicylate (salol) and Labarraque's solution. Witmer in the same year published, as a topical application, lead water and opium, to be used during the acute stage with ½ grain of mercuric chlorid internally, every three hours.

Brown, two years later (1897), considered a mixture of equal parts of lime water and linseed oil a good external application; and Clarke recommended a solution of borax. During the same year Smith recommended lime water as effective; Todd prescribed black mercurial lotion; Gilpin, fluid extract of serpentaria; Cloyd, the juice of the wild touch-me-not; Winfield, a paste of 0.5 to 1 per cent ichthyol, with magnesium carbonate, olive oil, and simple ointment; Bartley, sodium bicarbonate or lye water; and Hunt, red mercuric iodid.

Next year (1898) Frank prescribed baths followed by antiseptic emulsions containing calamine, glycerine, lime water, and the like.

In 1903, Klotz used one part icthyol to three parts of water as an application for the inflamed area; Thudichum, three drops of tincture of *Rhus* to two-thirds glass of water, a teaspoonful of the mixture to be taken three times daily, and boric acid to be used as a dusting powder. Thudichum said his daughter, having used lemon juice to remove freckles, tried it for poison ivy, and a cure resulted within thirty-six hours. Pollard used a decoction of California "buckbrush" leaves locally. Hughston (1905) applied with unvarying success lead acetate 10 grains, mixed with spirit of nitrous ether, 1 ounce.

In 1906, Daniel considered a mixture of quinin sulphate in water a *specific*, and it cured more rapidly than calomel, 16 grains mixed with 4 ounces of lime water. Milton believed immunity to Rhus poisoning resulted from a few doses of European anacardium.

Lindley, in 1908, recommended a solution of lead acetate and tincture of deodorized opium preferable to alcohol, hydrogen peroxid, boric acid, and potassium permanganate. An anonymous writer used a calamine and lead lotion.

Ellis (1910) considered the best remedy sodium bicarbonate, when used as a dusting powder and covered with lime liniment. This he believed to be better than a saturated solution of sodium thiosulphate, a saturated solution of borax, a lead and opium wash, talcum powder phenol ointment (1:30), iodine ointment, camphorated phenol ointment, lead acetate solution, zinc sulphate solution and thymol iodid.

### RATIONAL REMEDIES

Rational topical remedies are considered as based on general therapeutic principles and more or less erroneous conceptions of the chemical nature of the poison and its pharmacologic action. The list of these remedies seems to begin with Horsfield in 1798. Owing to the incomplete chemical analyses of Khittel, in 1857, and Maisch, in 1865, by which the poison was first considered a volatile alkaloid and then a volatile organic acid, more remedies were produced. Burrill, in 1882, believed the disease to be caused by a specific parasite that infests the *Rhus* (a view supported by Hubbard in 1885, and Frost, in 1916), and introduced disinfectants among the list. The work of Pfaff, in 1897, which resulted in the poison's being considered a non-volatile oil, was the cause of still other remedies. Acree and Syme by their discovery, in 1906, of a supposed toxic glucoside of fisetin, rhamnose, and gallic acid in *R. Toxicodendron* made further alterations in the list necessary. Despite the successive discoveries as to the nature and cause of Rhus dermatitis, the list of remedies, instead of decreasing, increased with each successive experiment. There were physicians who until 1908 (two years after the work of Acree and Syme) still believed the active principle to be the toxicodendric acid of Maisch and others who insisted upon its being the toxicodendrol of Pfaff.

If those substances and methods which have been used to allay the pain, itching, and systemic effects, as well as those that assist involution, are excluded the list of remedies is not nearly so long as those of the empirical or inductive type.

The first substance used in an attempt at rational treatment was mercuric chlorid. This was employed by Horsfield (1798) with the hope that by its corrosive action on the skin the poison would be thrown off the affected area.

The next attempt at rational treatment involved the employment of those chemicals which when added to the poison in laboratory glassware might be expected to produce non-toxic compounds. To my present knowledge, the first experimenter in this line was Maisch (1865). In this connection he says:

> As remedies against it, I have tried subacetate of lead, permanganate of potassa and ammonia, the last, I believe, with the best success. Alkaline solutions were first recommended by Professor Procter, I believe, and, as my experiments show, they are the remedies which a priori might be expected to afford the greatest relief, just as in the case of formic acid. The eruption produced by this acid is very similar in its nature to the one produced by toxicodendric acid, and its effects yield readily to alkaline lotions. It is not unlikely that, like the formates, the toxicodendrates are without any ill effects, if applied externally. The reactions of our new acid show, likewise, the reason why permanganate of potassa, subacetate and even acetate of lead may be valuable remedies for this eruption. While the former completely decomposes it, the last named salts produce nearly insoluble precipitates with it; at least, toxicodendric appears to be stronger in its affinities than acetic acid.

Dr. James White, writing in 1873 and again in 1887, considered the poison to be the toxicodendric acid of Maisch. With this idea in mind, he says:

> We have to deal with an acid, and the antidote for an acid is an alkali, that is, provided the salts thus formed are not equally poisonous. In poisoning by oxalic acid, for instance, potash is not an antidote, because the combination formed is nearly as poisonous as the acid itself. Whether the salts formed with toxicodendric acid by ammonia, potash, and soda are likewise poisonous, Professor Maisch leaves us somewhat in doubt as the result of experiment, but speaking clinically, he leads us to believe that they are not; for he says that the application of solutions of ammonia seemed to be most effective in counteracting the action of the acid. This is consistent with the popular reputation of solutions of saleratus and soda as remedies, and will explain the action of the soft-soap. These are true antidotes, but they can be of benefit only from their chemical action, and in this way.

Of the other writers who believed the poison to be the volatile toxicodendric acid of Maisch, Park, in 1879, recommended the use of a camphor-chloral mixture (equal parts of each allowed to stand in the open air and liquefy); Brandt, in the same year, used a saturated solution of sodium thiosulphate, externally and internally, and aborted the worst cases in from twenty-four to forty-eight hours. He also used alkaline bicarbonates and lime water locally and internally with "fair success." Ward (1879) prescribed Labarraque's solution, concentrated when the skin was unbroken and diluted with from three to six parts of water when the skin surface was broken. Johnson (1886) used externally a formula of sodium thiosulphate, 1 ounce, distilled water, 8 ounces, phenol, 1.5 drams, glycerine, ½ ounce. Internally he used potassium iodid, 2 drams, distilled water, 7 ounces, syrup, 1 ounce, a tablespoonful four times a day. Beringer (1896) used granular sodium thiosulphate, 1 dram. glycerine, ½ fluidounce, camphor water, sufficient to make 4 fluidounces; also he used hot soda baths, and, as a preventive treatment, washing the face and hands with a solution of hydrogen peroxid. Davis (1897) considered as a remedy a warm bath for from fifteen to twenty minutes at blood heat to which 4 ounces of borax had been added. The cuticle was dried and cosmolin applied. In one hour a strong solution of lead acetate, a weak ammonia water, sodium carbonate, alum curd, or a tincture of *Grindelia squarrosa* (?) was applied. Hadden prescribed, in 1906, Labarraque's solution as better than alcoholic lead acetate; Conner (1907) used sodium thiosulphate mixed with glycerine and phenol, or a solution of benzoic acid and solution of formaldehyd with an equal amount of saturated solution of sodium thiosulphate. He considered quinin solution of little value; and Ward (1908) used as a lotion a saturated solution of aluminum acetate, or if this is not to be had, he used phenol from 2 to 4 per cent, sodium bicarbonate, sodium sulphite, lead acetate, lotion of lead and opium, or black mercurial lotion.

When the poison was found to be a non-volatile oil by Pfaff (1897), a modified method of treatment was prescribed. He recommended the precipitation of the poison with lead acetate, copper, or iron. Ordinary oxidation, he says, is very slow, but may be slightly accelerated by a solution of sodium carbonate. He does not recommend the use of oxidizers, however.

Of the physicians who followed the discovery of Pfaff, Schwalbe, in 1903, recommended the use of alkalies to destroy (saponify ?) the oil; he accordingly prescribed a 0.1 to 0.5 per cent solution of potassium carbonate or a 1 to 1.5 per cent solution of ammonium chlorid. McKee (1906) believed a formula consisting of alcohol, 53 per cent, distilled water, 47 per cent, and lead acetate, sufficient to make a saturated solution, would give relief for from six to eight hours. Guernsey (1913) considered a saturated solution of magnesium sulphate best, although he also recommended the use of strong soap and water to "neutralize the acidity of the oil," a 50 per cent alcohol solution of lead acetate, from 2 to 4 per cent potassium permanganate, 1.5 per cent ammonium chlorid, hydrogen peroxid, 1 teaspoonful of sodium carbonate to a quart of water, sodium thiosulphate, 1 part of household ammonia to 2 parts of water, a solution of alum, and thymol iodid or alum dusting power.

Syme (1906) considered the poison a glucoside of rhamnose, fisetin, and gallic acid. In counter-distinction to Pfaff, he recommended the use of an oxidizer, namely potassium permanganate.[1] Syme said in part:

> The best example of the latter was obtained with the ether solution from the extraction of the lead precipitate in the Soxhlet apparatus. After removing the ether, a small drop of the residue was applied to the wrist as described. An itching red spot about the size of a dime was noticed in thirty-six hours, and it steadily increased in size. Nearly two days after the application of the poison, a dilute solution of potassium permanganate containing a little caustic potash was rubbed into the spot until the pimples were destroyed. A little black spot was left wherever there had been a pimple, showing that the permanganate had been reduced to oxid in the skin. The place was washed and nothing more was thought of it until the morning following, when it was noticed that the wrist had commenced to swell during the night, and the characteristic watery secretion was running from the poisoned spot. More permanganate solution was applied without potash and the wrist was bandaged, thinking that this would prevent the spreading of the eruption, but it really facilitated spreading by becoming saturated with the poisonous fluid and keeping it in contact with a larger surface of skin. In the meantime the swelling and inflammation had extended nearly to the elbow. The arm now had the appearance of having been bitten by a snake. To reduce the swelling it was immersed in hot water. This seemed to bring out the eruption very quickly and the blisters were treated with permanganate as fast as they appeared. The swelling was reduced, but returned during the night. On the evening following, the forearm was immersed in a bowl of hot permanganate solution containing a little caustic potash. The solution was kept as hot as could be borne for about half an hour.

[1] This substance was used as early as 1865 (Maisch, 1865), and in 1894 (Campbell, 1894), see also p. 155.

After this bath, the poison was completely oxidized, for the swelling was reduced and did not return, nor was there any fresh eruption. What appeared to be a severe case of poisoning was thus cured very quickly. The use of hot water not only reduces the swelling, but also helps to destroy the poison. The action of permanganate is also more rapid at high temperatures.

The oxidizing power of permanganate, as is well known, is greater in acid solution than in alkaline, five atoms of oxygen being available in the former and three in the latter, according to these equations:

$$2\ KMnO_4 + 3\ H_2SO_4 = K_2SO_4 + 2\ MnSO_4 + 3\ H_2O + 5O.$$
$$2\ KMnO_4 + H_2O = 2\ MnO_2 + 2\ KOH + 3O.$$

Permanganate was used as a remedy in some cases mixed with dilute sulphuric acid, and in others, with zinc sulphate; also with lime water. It was found to be satisfactory whether used alone or with any of the substances mentioned, provided it was well rubbed into the skin. The concentration of the solution used was varied according to the location and condition of the eruption. Where the skin was thin or already broken, dilute solutions (1 per cent) were used. In one case, the eruption appeared in the palm of the hand where the skin was so thick that it was necessary to open it before the remedies could reach the poison. The difficulty of getting the remedy in contact with the poison in the skin is the reason why the eruption is hard to cure.

Syme also opposed the use of an alcoholic solution of lead acetate as a remedy:

This remedy is unsatisfactory for the reason that its action consists in depositing an unstable lead compound of the poison in the skin where the conditions of moisture and temperature are favorable for its decomposition, liberating the poison with all its irritant properties. Moreover, alcoholic preparations should not be used because the alcohol dissolves the poison and, on evaporation, lets it spread over a larger surface like a varnish. Potassium permanganate, however, oxidizes the poison completely. The only objection to the use of permanganate of which the writer is aware is that it stains the skin. The stain can be removed by vigorous scrubbing with soap, or it will wear off gradually in a few days. It can be removed at once by certain acids, but these should not be used by persons not familiar with their action.

Baird on the strength of this knowledge recommended a 2 to 4 per cent solution of permanganate in 1909.

According to my present knowledge, the next person who attempted to find an antidote through a search for a chemical neutralizer was von Adelung, in 1912. He believed the poison to be the glucoside of Acree and Syme. His experiments in that line were as follows:

Experiment 14: Ammonia water.—Equal parts of ammonia and tincture of rhus were mixed and tested on the skin. The mixture is toxic, from which it is evident that ammonia does not destroy the poison.

Experiment 15: Peroxid of hydrogen.—Because it is a strong oxidizer, it was presumed that hydrogen peroxid would have some curative property. But when tested by adding it in equal quantity to the rhus tincture, it failed to inhibit the toxicity, and when tested, with control, on the patch of dermatitis, it was found inert.

Experiment 16: Aristol.—The left of two artificial patches of dermatitis was treated during five days with a solution of aristol in cottonseed oil. The control received no treatment. Both were scratched. Result: The untreated patch recovered first.

Experiment 17.—The same test was made on the left of two spots produced by green leaves. The aristol in oil was applied five times in four days and protected by gauze held in place by plaster. Result: No difference could be noted. Aristol therefore appears to be of no value.

Experiment 18: Castor Oil.—A mixture of equal parts of 10 per cent tincture of *Rhus* and castor oil was rubbed on the arm. In thirty-six hours there was a slight itching, but no eruption.

Experiment 19: Cedar Oil.—A similar mixture with cedar oil was applied to the arm. After thirty-six hours, a slight eruption appeared which later developed into a fair patch of itching dermatitis.

Experiment 20: Cottonseed Oil.—A similar mixture with cottonseed oil was applied to the thin skin of the wrist. After eight days no dermatitis had appeared.

Experiment 21.—Cottonseed oil in which green leaves had been soaked for twenty-four hours was applied to the arm. The result was slight dermatitis. This, repeated on another person, gave the same result.

Experiment 22.—Some cottonseed oil in which green leaves had been heated was applied to the arm. After four days, itching began, and, in five days, a slight eruption.

Experiment 23.—A mixture of equal parts of tincture of rhus and cottonseed oil was applied to the arm. No dermatitis was detected in eight days.

These results raised the question whether cottonseed oil did not combine chemically with the toxin, destroying the toxicity. To test this point, the mixture of oil and tincture was allowed to stand a few days, when the tincture formed a layer above the oil. This supernatant fluid was toxic, producing dermatitis.

Experiment 24.—A mixture of equal parts of tincture of rhus and of tincture of green soap was applied to the arm and protected by gauze. After twenty-four hours only a slight eruption was noted.

Experiment 25.—A mixture of tincture of rhus, 25 parts, and tincture of green soap, 5 parts, was applied to arm and protected with gauze. Only slight dermatitis resulted.

Experiment 26.—After allowing tincture of green soap to dry on a spot, tincture of rhus was applied. A control spot was made with the rhus alone. Both spots were protected with gauze. The control took well, while the soaped spot showed a slight dermatitis. Thus it appears that soap deters the poison of rhus.

Experiment 27: Ichthyol Collodion.—The worse of two patches of dermatitis, three days old, was painted with a 5 per cent ichthyol collodion daily. In twenty-four hours, distinct improvement was noted in the treated patch, and this patch recovered earlier. This was confirmed in treating hospital cases.

Experiment 28: Hyposulphite of Sodium.—Tests with this substance were also negative. It failed to inhibit the toxicity when added in large proportion to the tincture of rhus; and it failed to show curative effect on dermatitis patches compared with controls.

Experiment 29: Iodid of Potassium.—This substance in strong solution, added to an equal part of tincture rhus, failed to inhibit the toxicity as tested on the skin.

Experiment 30: Tincture of Iodin.—Full official strength tincture of iodin when mixed with an equal quantity of tincture of rhus destroys the poison; for when this mixture is tested on my arm no dermatitis results. If, however, the strength is reduced to less than 5 per cent of the mixture, by addition of water or alcohol, the toxicity is not destroyed completely.

Experiment 31.—Tincture of iodin also has curative property. To one of two patches of dermatitis, official tincture of iodin was applied. The application burned. But the treated patch recovered earlier than the control. Itching quickly subsided and healing followed. The spot remained discolored and tender, presumably from iodin burning.

Experiment 32.—The right of two patches of dermatitis was rubbed with 90 drops of water mixed with 10 drops of tincture of iodin. The control was rubbed with alcohol. The application of iodin caused a burning sensation, not severe. In twenty-four hours the rhus dermatitis had disappeared, but was replaced by an iodin burn. The control ran a normal course.

Experiment 33: Potassium Permanganate.—A mixture of equal parts of potassium permanganate (0. 56 gm. in 120 c.c.) with tincture rhus, when tested on the arm, was found to be absolutely non-toxic.

Experiment 34.—One of two patches of dermatitis was painted with potassium permanganate in the above strength. The treated patch healed earlier than the control.

Experiment 35: Magnesium Sulphate.—Chemical Tests: A fresh rhus leaf macerated with a saturated solution of magnesium sulphate remained toxic, as proven by testing on my arm.

Experiment 36.—Saturated solution of magnesium sulphate (Squibb's), added in equal quantity to tincture rhus, does not inhibit the toxicity, for dermatitis results when the mixture is applied to the skin.

Making use of the solubility of Rhus poison, therapeutic experiments have been based on the remedial value of solvents as well as chemical agents. Maisch and White considered the poison soluble in water and recommended that parts exposed to *Rhus* be immediately washed or bathed for a considerable time in water. Pfaff prescribed the mechanical removal of the poison as soon as possible after exposure by vigorously washing the affected and exposed parts with soap, water, and a scrubbing brush. As the poison is soluble in alcohol, Pfaff likewise believed in thoroughly washing with alcohol and a scrubbing brush, or in washing the exposed parts with an alcoholic solution of lead acetate. He also recommended the use of oils, including petrolatum, if quickly removed and repeatedly used so as not to spread the poison. Syme, as previously quoted, believed the poison would be spread by the use of alcoholic lead acetate. Stevens (1906) obtained the best results by rubbing the surface with a little petrolatum, which he scraped off with a knife, and washing the surface with a weak solution of sodium hydroxid or carbonate. He also recommended alcohol, petroleum benzine, ether, or kerosene as washes to remove the poison. As heretofore quoted, von Adelung experimented with castor, cedar, and cottonseed oils.

In the belief that the poison was Pfaff's toxicodendrol, Balch (1906) said:

> The use of soap and water and a good hand brush is the simplest method of getting rid of the oil. The action is entirely mechanical and is perfectly efficient. Alcohol dissolves and removes the oil, but successive portions must be allowed to flow over the part as after contact the alcohol may contain sufficient oil to spread the irritation. Ordinary alcohol must be used and not 50 per cent alcohol as the latter does not dissolve the oil. The action is purely a solvent one and not one of neutralization.

Guernsey (1913), also a follower of Pfaff, recommended the use of a wash of alcohol, whiskey, or ether to remove the poison.

Many physicians have made clinical comparisons of various popular remedies, with or without taking into consideration the chemistry of the poison. Such comparisons of remedies, which were made successively on the same patient and therefore in different stages of the disease, are considered untrustworthy and are therefore eliminated. The earliest of these comparisons is that of Dr. Bigelow (1820). He says:

The acetate of lead is perhaps as useful as any external palliative, and it should be used in solution rather than in the ointment, that it may be applied as cold as possible. The late Dr. Barton speaks highly of a solution of corrosive sublimate externally applied in this disease, but from trials of the two remedies made at the same time and in the same patient, I have found the lead the more beneficial of the two.

Cantrell (1898), who carried his experiments over a long period of time and who had an abundant opportunity for experimental work, summed up the relative values of certain drugs in the treatment of ivy poisoning in order of preference, as follows: First, Labarraque's solution (dilute in erythematous and concentrated in vesicular); second, phenyl salicylate (salol) 0.5 dram to the ounce of petrolatum liquefied or ether, because both produce a cure in less than a week's time; third, bromine (10 grains to the ounce of some oily substance) cures in about ten days; fourth, boric acid (saturated or dilute solution) cures in about two weeks; fifth acetanilid ($\frac{1}{2}$ dram to 1 dram to the ounce of liquid petrolatum) cures in about two or three weeks, because they may be relied on to produce no ill effects; sixth, *Grindelia robusta* (fluid extract 2 drams to the pint of water, more concentrated irritates) cures in about two weeks. This can always be relied on to produce a cure, but it is long delayed and may, if not watched carefully, produce a higher grade of inflammation.

Von Adelung in 1912 carried on comparative therapeutic tests as follows:

Though magnesium sulphate fails to destroy the toxicity of rhus when mixed with its tincture, or its juice, it, nevertheless, possesses definite therapeutic value.

Experiment 37.—Test 1: In one of two patches of dermatitis, saturated solution of magnesium sulphate was rubbed three times at hour intervals. By the next morning the treated patch was better than the control. Three more similar applications were made during the forenoon and by noon a very marked improvement was noted. The treated patch recovered earlier than the control.

Test 2.—To one of two patches of dermatitis, saturated solution of magnesium sulphate (Squibb's) was applied on gauze, covered with rubber tissue, and a bandage. A similar dressing was applied to the control, using water in place of magnesium. After twenty-four hours, while the first patch was not healed, it was free from itching, it was not tender, and not edematous, thus contrasting with the control, which remained tender for six days.

HOSPITAL CASES

A. B., male, aged 23, was poisoned four days previously. Whole face was edematous and the right eye closed. On Oct. 25, 1911, in the afternoon, hot applications of 2 per cent permanganate were begun, but applied on to the right side of the face. In thirty hours the right eye was in good condition. The left side recovered tardily.

B. C., male, March, 1912, face and hands severely poisoned. The right side of the face and the right arm were treated with the hot permanganate, while the opposite side was treated with hot standard photographers' solution of sodium hyposulphite. In addition, both arms were bandaged in their respective solutions. After twenty-four hours the patient stated that the permanganate side felt distinctly better than the other. The right side recovered the earlier.

E. U., male, aged 25, was poisoned four days previously. Both arms showed marked edema, vesicles and pustules. He had already applied cold permanganate six or seven times. Hot permanganate was applied frequently by the nurse. There was no improvement in forty-eight hours. When the solution was changed to hot mercuric chlorid, and bandaging begun with the same, recovery began.

This case illustrates the uselessness of permanganate when the vesicles become infected.

A. E., male, aged 45. Dermatitis one day old. The whole face was swollen. The eyes half closed by edema of both lids. The right ear was much swollen. Thirty hours after the dermatitis began, hot permanganate saturated solution was applied to all areas. The application burned severely, especially the eyelids. Recovery occurred in five days, though this man had always been two weeks getting well. A weaker solution of permanganate would have been better.

Besides the results of Bigelow, Cantrell, and von Adelung little can be attempted in summarizing the comparative values of these remedies, as the results obtained by different physicians with the same remedy are so often conflicting.

One of the chief reasons for this unsatisfactory condition is the fact that many physicians in treating a case of Rhus dermatitis will first use a so-called remedy for a few applications; failing to secure a satisfactory result this remedy will be replaced by another. This process may continue until finally convalescence, delayed or accelerated by the use of the various remedies, occurs, and the remedy used in the last stages of the disease is considered the best.

This remedy may then be used by another physician or the same physician in the initial stages of another case with failure as a result. A condition of disputation and uncertainty results. In support of this explanation there are the published cases of Batlett (1838), French (1903), Matheson (1874), Morris (1897), and Stone (1874).

A further discussion of remedies will be taken up in chapter xv.

RHUS DERMATITIS "CURES" AND "REMEDIES" FROM MEDICAL LITERATURE

| | Approvals as Remedy | Disapprovals as Remedy |
|---|---|---|
| Acids: | | |
| Boric | 2 | |
| Boric acid, phenol, morphine, gum arabic | 1 | |
| Boric acid, phenol, vaseline | 1 | |
| Nitric | 1 | |
| Nitro-hydrochloric | 1 | |
| Sulphuric acid, ferric sulphate | 1 | |
| Alkalies: | | |
| Ammonia water | 3 | |
| Calcium hydroxid | 6 | |
| Calcium hydroxid, galvariam | 1 | |
| Calcium hydroxid, linseed oil | 1 | |
| Calcium hydroxid, mercuric chlorid | 2 | |
| Calcium hydroxid, phenol, fld. *Grinelia* | 1 | |
| Calcium hydroxid, phenol, olive oil | 1 | |
| Potassium hydroxid | 2 | |
| Alum (potassium aluminum sulphate) | 1 | |
| Ammonium chlorid | 11 | 1 |
| Ammonia water | 3 | |
| Ammonia water, ethyl nitrate, and Tr. *Lobelia* | 1 | |
| Arsenic sulphid (internally) | 1 | |
| Borax | 1 | |
| Borax, glycerine | 1 | |
| Borax, phenol, morphine sulphate, *acacia* | 1 | |
| Borac acid | 2 | |
| Borac acid, phenol, morphine, gum arabic | 1 | |
| Boric acid, phenol, vaseline | 1 | |
| Bromid of sodium | 1 | |
| Bromine | 1 | 1 |
| Bromine, olive oil | 4 | |
| Calamine, lead acetate | 1 | |
| Calcium carbonate, Tr. *Lobelia* | 1 | |

| | Approvals as Remedy | Disapprovals as Remedy |
|---|---|---|
| Calcium hydroxid | 5 | |
| Calcium hydroxid, galvariam | 1 | |
| Calcium hydroxid, linseed oil | 1 | |
| Calcium hydroxid, mercuric chlorid | 2 | |
| Calcium hydroxid, phenol, fld. *Grindelia* | 1 | |
| Calcium hydroxid, phenol, olive oil | 1 | |
| Chlorid of sodium, kerosene | 1 | |
| Chlorinated soda (Labarraque's solution) | 4 | |
| Copper sulphate | 5 | |
| Copper sulphate, lard, red oxid mercury | 1 | |
| Ferric chlorid | 1 | |
| Ferric chlorid, conchonidine sulphate (internally) | 1 | |
| Ferric sulphate | 1 | |
| Ferric sulphate, quinin sulphate | 1 | |
| Ferric sulphate, sulphuric acid (Monsel's solution) | 1 | |
| Fowler's solution (internally) | 1 | |
| Fowler's solution magnesium sulphate (internally) | 1 | |
| Gunpowder, cream | 1 | |
| Gunpowder, water | 0 | 1 |
| Iodine, tincture | 1 | 1 |
| Iodine tincture, phenol, glycerine, morphine sulphate | 1 | |
| Iron (*see* Ferric) | | |
| Lead acetate | 7 | 3 |
| Lead acetate, calamine (zinc carbonate, zinc silicate) | 1 | |
| Lead acetate, ethyl nitrite | 1 | |
| Lead acetate, opium | 1 | |
| Magnesium silicate | 1 | |
| Magnesium sulphate | 1 | |
| Magnesium sulphate, Fowler's solution (internally) | 1 | |
| Mercuric chlorid | 6 | 1 |
| Mercuric chlorid, calcium hydroxid | 2 | |
| Mercuric chlorid, sodium salicylate, phenol, glycerine | 1 | |
| Mercuric oxid (red), copper sulphate, lard | 1 | |
| Mercuric chlorid, zinc oxid, salicylic acid | 1 | |
| Mercurous chlorid | 0 | 1 |
| Monsel's solution | 1 | |
| Nitric acid | 1 | |
| Nitro-hydrochloric acid | 1 | |

| | Approvals as Remedy | Disapprovals as Remedy |
|---|---|---|
| Potassium aluminum sulphate | 1 | |
| Potassium arsenite (*see* Fowler's solution) | | |
| Potassium chlorate | 3 | |
| Potassium nitrate | 1 | 1 |
| Potassium permanganate | 6 | 1 |
| Silver nitrate | 1 | |
| Sodium bicarbonate | 4 | |
| Sodium borate (*see* Borax) | | |
| Sodium bromid | 1 | |
| Sodium chlorid | 4 | |
| Sodium chlorid, kerosene | 1 | |
| Sodium chlorinated (Labarraque's solution) | 4 | |
| Sodium salicylate, mercuric chlorid, phenol glycerine | 1 | |
| Sodium sulphate, glycerine, camphor | 1 | |
| Sodium sulphite, glycerine, camphor water | 1 | |
| Sodium sulphite, phenol | 1 | |
| Sodium sulphite, phenol, olive oil | 1 | |
| Sodium thiosulphate | 4 | 1 |
| Sodium thiosulphate, glyco-phenique | 2 | |
| Sodium thiosulphate, phenol | 1 | |
| Sodium, thiosulphate in 95 per cent alcohol | 1 | 1 |
| Starch | 0 | 1 |
| Starch, oxid of zinc | 1 | 1 |
| Sulphuric acid, ferric sulphate (Monsel's solution) | 1 | |
| Sulphid of arsenic (internally) | 1 | |
| Zinc oxid | 9 | 0 |
| Zinc oxid, mercuric chlorid, salicylic acid | 1 | |
| Zinc oxid, starch | 1 | 1 |
| Zinc sulphate | 3 | |
| Zinc sulphate, sweet clover | 1 | |

NON-PHYTOLOGICAL ORGANIC

| | Approvals as Remedy | Disapprovals as Remedy |
|---|---|---|
| Acetanilide | 1 | |
| Alcohol (95 per cent), $Na_2S_2O_3$ | 1 | |
| Alcoholic menthol, $Na_2S_2O_3$ | 1 | |
| Antiphlogistine, nuclein solution | 1 | |
| Butter, fresh | 1 | |
| Butter, milk | 1 | |
| Campho-phenique, sweet oil | 1 | |
| Chloral hydrate, camphor, vaseline | 1 | |

| | Approvals as Remedy | Disapprovals as Remedy |
|---|---|---|
| Cream and marshmallows | 1 | |
| Creolin | 1 | |
| Ethyl alcohol (95 per cent), $Na_2S_2O_3$ | 1 | |
| Ethyl ether | 1 | |
| Ethyl nitrite | 6 | 1 |
| Ethyl nitrite, $NH_4OH$, Tr. *Lobelia* | 1 | |
| Ethyl nitrite, lead acetate | 1 | |
| Ethyl nitrite, wormwood | 1 | |
| Glycerine, fld. belladonna | 1 | |
| Glycerine, borax | 1 | |
| Glycerine, camphor, $Na_2SO_3$ | 1 | |
| Glycerine, camphor water, $Na_2SO_3$ | 1 | |
| Glycerine, phenol | 1 | |
| Glycerine, phenol, $H_2O_2$, $NaHS_2O_3$ | 1 | |
| Glycerine, phenol, $HgCl_2$, Na salicylate | 1 | |
| Glycerine, phenol, Tr. I, morphine sulphate | 1 | |
| Glyco-phenique | 1 | |
| Glyco-phenique, olive oil | 1 | |
| Glyco-phenique, $Na_2S_2O_3$ | 2 | |
| Guiaicol | 2 | |
| Ichthyol, dolomel | 1 | |
| Kerosene | 1 | |
| Kerosene, sodium chlorid | 1 | |
| Lard, copper sulphate, red oxid Hg | 1 | |
| Lard (hog's), *Rhus* charcoal | 1 | |
| Menthol alcoholic, $NaS_2O_3$ | 1 | |
| Milk (butter) | 1 | |
| Nuclein solution, antiphlogistine | 1 | |
| Phenol, borax, morphine sulphate, acacia | 1 | |
| Phenol, boric acid, morphine, gum arabic | 1 | |
| Phenol, glycerine | 1 | |
| Phenol, glycerine, $H_2O_2$, $NaHS_2O_3$ | 1 | |
| Phenol, glycerine, $HgCl_2$, Na salicylate | 1 | |
| Phenol, glycerine, Tr. I, morphine sulphate | 1 | |
| Phenol, olive oil, Ca $(OH)_2$ | 1 | |
| Phenol, olive oil, sodium sulphite | 1 | |
| Phenol, $Na_2SO_3$ | 1 | |

| | Approvals as Remedy | Disapprovals as Remedy |
|---|---|---|
| Phenol sodique | 1 | |
| Phenol, sweet oil | 1 | |
| Phenol, vaseline, boric acid | 1 | |
| Phenol, vaseline, cocain | 1 | |
| Protonuclein (internally) | 1 | |
| Salicylic acid, ZnO, $HgCl_2$ | 1 | |
| Vaseline, camphor, chloral hydrate | 1 | |
| Vaseline, phenol, boric acid | 1 | |
| Vaseline, phenol, cocain | 1 | |
| PHYTOLOGICAL | | |
| Acacia, morphine sulphate, phenol, borax | 1 | |
| *Allium* (*see* Onion) | | |
| *Aristolochia serpentaria* (Virginia snakeroot) | 3 | 3 |
| *Artemisea* (*see* Wormwood) | | |
| *Atropa belladonna* (*see* Belladonna) | | |
| Bark of elder (*Sambucus*), buttermilk | 1 | |
| Bark of white oak (*Quercus alba*) (fld.) | 2 | |
| Belladonna (fld.) glycerine | 1 | |
| Belladonnae unguentum | 3 | |
| Benzoin (*see* Unguentum) | | |
| Bloodroot (*see Sanguinaria*) | | |
| Boneset (*see Eupatorium*) | | |
| Bugbane (*Cimicifuga*) (Tr.) | 1 | |
| Buttonbush (*Cephalanthus occidentalis*) (fld.) | 1 | |
| Camphor, chloral hydrate, vaseline | 1 | |
| Camphor, glycerine, sodium sulphite | 1 | |
| Camphor (spirits) | 1 | 1 |
| Camphor water | 0 | 1 |
| Camphor water, sodium sulphite, glycerine | 1 | |
| Camphor wood shavings (aqua) | 1 | 1 |
| Capaiba | 1 | |
| Cedar oil | 1 | |
| *Cephaelis* (*see* Ipecac) | | |
| *Cephalanthus occidentalis* (Buttonbush) (fld.) | 1 | |
| *Chlorogallum pomeridianum* (Indian snake root) | 1 | |
| Cimicifuga (Tr.) | 1 | |
| Cinchonidine sulphate (*Cinchona*), iron chlorid (internally) | 1 | |
| Citric acid | 1 | 1 |
| Clearweed (*see Pilea*) | | |
| Clover (sweet) (*Melilotus*), zinc sulphate | 1 | |

| | Approvals as Remedy | Disapprovals as Remedy |
|---|---|---|
| Cocain (*Erythoroxylon coca*), carbolized vaseline | 1 | |
| Cocain hydrochlorid | 1 | |
| Coffee (*Coffea*) (fld.) | 1 | |
| *Comptonia asplenifolia* (sweet fern) | 1 | 1 |
| Conaflower (*see Echinaceae*) | | |
| Cottonwood (*Populus monilifera*) leaves (fld.) (internally) | 1 | |
| *Cruciferae* (*see* Mustard) | | |
| *Cypripedium* (Lady's slipper) (internally) | 1 | |
| *Diervilla canadensis* (Bush-honeysuckle) (fld.) | 1 | |
| *Echinaceae* (Purple coneflower) (fld.) (internally) | 1 | |
| *Echinacea* (Tr.) | 1 | |
| Elder (*Sambucus*) bark, buttermilk | 1 | |
| *Erythroxylon coca* (*see* Cocain) | | |
| Eucalyptol | 1 | |
| *Eupatorium perfoliatum* (thorough wort, Boneset) (fld.) | 1 | |
| Fern (sweet) | 1 | 1 |
| Foxglove (*Gerardia*) (fld.) | 1 | |
| Galvariam, lime water | 1 | |
| *Gelsemium* (Yellow jessamine) (fld.) | 4 | 2 |
| *Gerardia* (*see* Foxglove) | | |
| Goldenrod (*Solidago canadensis*) | 1 | 1 |
| *Grindelia robusta* (gum plant) (fld.) | 13 | 2 |
| Gum arabic, morphine, boric acid, phenol | 1 | |
| *Hedeonia puleioides* (American pennyroyal) | 1 | |
| Hellebore (*see Veratrum*) | | |
| Honeysuckle (*see Diervilla*) | | |
| Houseleek (*see Sempervivum*) | | |
| *Impatiens fulva* (Spotted touch-me-not) (fld.) | 1 | |
| Ipecac (*Cephaelis Ipecacuanha*) tea | 2 | |
| Jaborandi (*Pilocarpus*) (fld.) (internally) | 1 | |
| Jessamine (*see Gelsemium*) | | |
| Lady's slipper (*Cypripedium*) (internally) | 1 | |
| Lobelia (Tr.) | 1 | 1 |
| Lobelia (Tr.), calcium carbonate | 1 | |
| Lobelia (Tr.), ethyl nitrite, ammonia | 1 | |
| *Melilotus* (*see* Clover) | | |
| Morphine, gum arabic, boric acid, phenol | 1 | |
| Morphine sulphate | 2 | |
| Morphine sulphate (*Papaver somniferum*), acacia, phenol, borax | 1 | |

| | Approvals as Remedy | Disapprovals as Remedy |
|---|---|---|
| Morphine sulphate, phenol, glycerine, Tr. iodine | 1 | |
| Mustard (*Cruciferae*), water | 1 | |
| Nettle (*Urtica pumila*) (bruised) | 1 | |
| Oak, white, bark of (fld.) | 2 | |
| Oil of: | | |
| Cedar | 1 | |
| Olive | 2 | |
| Olive (internally) | 1 | |
| Olive, $Ca(OH)_2$, phenol | 1 | |
| Olive, phenol, sodium sulphite | 1 | |
| Olive, glyco-phenique | 1 | |
| Olive, bromine | 4 | |
| Lindseed, $Ca(OH)_2$ | 1 | |
| Sassafras, sweet oil | 1 | |
| Sweet oil, campho-phenique | 1 | |
| Sweet oil, phenol | 1 | |
| Onion (*Allium*) poultice | 1 | |
| Opium (*Pavaver somniferum*) lead acetate | 1 | |
| *Sambucus* (*see* Elder) | | |
| Sambucus bark, buttermilk | 1 | |
| *Sanguinaria* (Tr.) (Bloodroot) | 2 | |
| Sassafras oil (*see* Oil) | | |
| Sassafras root | 2 | |
| *Sempervivum tectorum* (Houseleek) (crushed) | 1 | |
| Snakeroot, Virginia (*Aristolochia serpentaria*) (fld.) | 3 | 3 |
| *Solidago canadensis* (Goldenrod) | 1 | 1 |
| Starch | 0 | 1 |
| Starch, zinc oxid | 1 | 1 |
| *Stramonium* (Thorn apple) | 2 | |
| Strychnine (*Strychnos*), pilocarpine (alternately) | 1 | |
| Sweet clover, zinc sulphate | 1 | |
| Tannin glycerite | 1 | |
| Thorn apple (*Stramonium*) | 2 | |
| Touch-me-not (*see Impatiens*) | | |
| Turpentine (spirits) | 1 | |
| Unguentum (White wax, lard, siam benzoin) | 2 | |
| *Urtica pumila* (Nettle) (bruised) | 1 | |
| *Veratrum viride* (American white hellebore) (fld.) | 1 | |
| White oak bark (fld.) | 2 | |
| Wormwood (*Artemisia*), ethyl nitrite | 1 | |

SUMMARY

1. Remedies are here classified as empirical and rational.

2. Empirical remedies—those that do not take into account the chemical composition of the poison—begin with Horsfield (1798) and are treated historically.

3. Old remedies were still used after the discoveries of Khittel and Maisch as to the chemical nature of the poison.

4. Rational topical remedies are treated historically beginning with Horsfield.

5. The list of remedies instead of decreasing increased with additional discoveries of chemists as to the nature of the poison. Many of the older remedies are still in use.

6. Horsfield attempted to throw off the poison from the skin by the corrosive action on the skin of mercuric chlorid.

7. Maisch sought remedies from the use of chemicals which render the poison non-toxic in laboratory glassware. Many physicians used similar reasoning in search of remedies.

8. Similar reasoning was applied after the discoveries of Pfaff in 1897 and Syme in 1906.

9. Remedies were also sought among the solvents of the poison.

10. Comparisons of remedies were made successively on the same patient in different stages of the disease and are untrustworthy.

11. More reliable comparisons of different remedies were made on anatomically corresponding areas in the same stage of disease on the same patient.

12. One of the chief reasons for conflicting therapeutic results among physicians is the fact that many physicians in treating a case of Rhus dermatitis will first use a so-called remedy for a few applications; failing to secure a satisfactory result this remedy will be replaced by another. This process may continue until finally convalescence, delayed or accelerated by the use of the various remedies, occurs, and the remedy used in the last stages of the disease is considered the best. This remedy may then be used by another physician or the same physician in the initial stages of another case with failure as a result. A condition of disputation and uncertainty follows.

13. Remedies are further considered in chapter xvi.

# CHAPTER XVI

## A CONTRIBUTION TO THE CHEMOTHERAPY OF RHUS DERMATITIS AND TENTATIVE METHOD FOR TREATMENT[1]

The object of chemotherapy in Rhus dermatitis (caused by *Rhus diversiloba*) is to imitate nature's method of overcoming the poison (lobinol) by the aid of substances that destroy the poison while the body cells are left unharmed or only slightly injured. The chemical agent employed, therefore, must possess a much stronger affinity for the toxic substance than for the body cells, that is, it must be more toxitropic than organotropic.

### NECESSARY QUALIFICATIONS FOR THE REMEDY

In order best to accomplish this, the remedy should render the poison harmless, relieve pain, prevent sepsis, and aid in restoring the tissues injured by the poison to a normal condition. It may, therefore, be necessary to use two different formulas to be applied successively: one formula to neutralize the poison physiologically, and another formula to relieve pain, prevent bacterial infection, reduce the subsequent inflammatory changes in the cutaneous tissues, and promote healing.

In order to choose the most fitting substance physiologically to neutralize this poison it is necessary to consider, apart from its chemical action on the poison, many other factors, such as its capacity for irritating the tissues, its toxicity, its solubility, its power of penetrating the tissues and of being absorbed by them, and the manner in which it reacts with the protein and other constituents of the tissues.

### CHEMICAL NATURE OF THE POISON

It has been determined (McNair, 1921*c*) that the principal irritant of *R. diversiloba*, if pure and not a mixture, is probably an unsaturated compound of the aromatic series containing carbon, hydro-

[1] Reprinted from the *Archives of Dermatology and Syphilology*, III (June, 1921), 802–8.

gen, and oxygen. The oxygen may exist combined as hydroxyl. The behavior of the poison is phenolic, and it may contain two hydroxyl groups in the *ortho* position.

### PROPHYLACTIC SUBSTANCES

The first problem in prophylactic treatment is to prevent the penetration of the poison into the skin. This can be considered in regard to the aid of solvents and precipitants.

Lobinol (McNair, 1921*c*) is soluble in ether, chloroform, alcohol, methyl alcohol, benzin (boiling point below 60° C.), benzene, toluene, xylene, ethyl acetate, nitrobenzene, oil of turpentine, glacial acetic acid, and 80 per cent chloral hydrate. The foregoing solvents could be used as washes to remove the poison from the surface of the skin, provided they were not injurious. All of the solvents, however, are deleterious and some of them have a decidedly harmful action on the skin, such as glacial acetic acid, turpentine, benzene, nitrobenzene, and chloral hydrate.

Von Adelung (1913) carried out the following experiments with solvents. Equal parts of 10 per cent tincture of *Rhus* and cottonseed oil, castor oil, and cedar oil were rubbed on separate areas of the arm. In thirty-six hours the cedar oil mixture caused a slight eruption, which later developed into a fair patch of itching dermatitis. After the castor oil mixture had been applied for thirty-six hours there was a slight itching, but no eruption. The mixture containing cottonseed oil produced no dermatitis. In considering these results, von Adelung considered the possibility of cottonseed oil chemically combining with the poison and destroying its toxicity. However, when the mixture of oil and tincture were allowed to stand several days, the tincture formed a supernatant toxic layer. It is probable that the different degrees of dermatitis produced by these mixtures varied in accordance with the solubility of the poison in the oils involved. For instance, when phenol is made up in solutions with water, alcohol, glycerine, turpentine, and cottonseed oil, it has been determined that when fingers are immersed in them the blanching, tingling sensations, and anaesthesia are greatest in the water solution and decrease as follows: alcohol, glycerine, turpentine, and cottonseed oil. The solubility of phenol in these instances varies in the reverse order of its anaesthetic effect. Therefore, if the results of von Adelung with the tincture of *Rhus* are comparable, the solubility of lobinol is greatest in cottonseed oil, less in castor oil, and least in cedar oil.[1]

From a practical standpoint, the removal of the poison from the skin by the use of solvents seems quite futile, for, unless a sufficiently large amount of solvent is used to remove the poison thoroughly, the poison will be spread on the surface of the skin and thus enlarge the diseased area. Then, too, lobinol has the power to form either a physical or chemical compound with the skin of such a nature that it is quite impossible to remove with soap and water (White, 1873; Brown, 1922) or with solvent action.

Lobinol is precipitated from alcoholic solutions by lead acetate, silver nitrate, mercurous nitrate, cupric acetate, ferric chlorid, barium hydroxid, bromine, iodine, platinum chlorid, gold chlorid, uranium acetate, and cupric nitrate. Some of these precipitants, for example, tincture of iodine, must be used in dilute solutions, in order to prevent harmful action on the skin. Some of the precipitates formed by these substances are still toxic, such as the precipitate formed with lead acetate.

It is theoretically possible to remove the poison, before it has penetrated or firmly adhered to the skin, by the combined action of both solvent and precipitant, for instance, by the use of an alcoholic solution of lead acetate.

## CURATIVE SUBSTANCES

If the poison succeeds in penetrating the skin, it should be rendered harmless as quickly as possible. The chemotherapeutic agent, therefore, must have a penetrability and diffusibility greater than the poison.

If lobinol contains a polyhydrophenol group, it has consequently several possibilities of being changed to a non-poisonous substance or substances. Among these processes is oxidation. Some of the oxidizers that have been used are potassium permanganate, potassium bichromate, silver nitrate, hydrogen peroxid, manganese peroxid, barium peroxid, magnesium peroxid, litharge, and man-

[1] See chap. xiv, p. 159, for detailed description of these experiments.

ganese hydroxid. If these substances be added in laboratory glassware to the poisonous sap of the plant, it will be observed that potassium permanganate, silver nitrate, manganese peroxid, barium peroxid, magnesium peroxid litharge, and manganese hydroxid have the power, after a more or less lengthy period of contact, to render the poison harmless. Some of these substances, for instance, litharge and barium peroxid, because of their insolubility and inability to penetrate the skin, cannot be used as remedies. Silver nitrate becomes too irritating when used in sufficiently strong solution. Many substances which enter into the composition of the tissues inhibit its action in a marked manner. The sensitivity to light and the staining property of silver compounds are also objections to their use. Von Adelung (1913) has shown that hydrogen peroxid was without appreciable beneficial effect, while potassium permanganate did have the power to render the poison non-toxic. Potassium permanganate, however, has an injurious action on the skin and is not as efficient a remedy as some other remedies, as will be shown later.

Lobinol has an ability to react with nitric acid, probably due to its phenolic properties, to form a nitrated compound. As is well known, nitric acid, even in dilute solution, stains the skin a bright yellow or yellowish-brown, which makes its use undesirable.

Lobinol evidently has the property of forming compounds with sodium and potassium, but both of these when first formed are poisonous.

Bromine and iodine form compounds with the poison, probably owing to its unsaturated nature. When experimented with in vitro, these halogens reduce the toxicity. When applied to the skin, however, they coagulate the proteins and irritate the tissues. The following five iodine compounds were experimented with: ethyliodid, iodol in alcohol, iothion, iodipin (iodized sesame oil) and colorless tincture of iodine. In trying these substances, five areas of skin, of practically the same thickness, on the flexor surface of the forearm, were inoculated with equal amounts of fresh *Rhus* sap. These different areas were protected by doughnut-shaped corn plasters, and the various iodine preparations were applied. The benefit derived from these substances increased in the following order: colorless iodine, iodipin, iothion, iodol in alcohol and ethyl iodid.

None of these, however, were very beneficial, either in reducing the pain or in promoting healing.

The best success in the search for a remedy was obtained by taking into consideration the body defense against phenolic compounds. Whether or not lobinol has the power to form an ester with glucuronic acid, either within the body or in laboratory glassware, has not been determined. With an idea that glucuronic acid might be formed from glucose by the action of the body cells, a 5 per cent aqueous solution of chemically pure crystalline glucose was applied to an area of Rhus dermatitis. Although glucose has a slight irritant action on the skin, as is exemplified in diabetes mellitus, healing was promoted more rapidly in the area to which the glucose had been applied than in a check patch of dermatitis on which no remedy was used.

The power of lobinol to form a sulphonic ester in the body is quite probable. With this in view the following nine sulphur compounds were used similarly to the iodine preparations: sodium sulphate, sodium ethyl sulphate, sodium pyrosulphate, sodium dithionate, sodium sulphite, sodium ethanol 1, 2-diacidsulphite, sodium pyrosulphite, sodium thiosulphate, and taurin. Of these nine preparations, sodium sulphite and sodium ethanol 1, 2-diacidsulphite gave the best results. These results, too, were superior to any results previously listed in this chapter.

It is likely that iron may be one of the chemical elements enrolled in the body defense mechanism. As a tissue source of this there are the erythrocytes and protein. Whether or not the iron of the body plays a part in the physiologic neutralization of lobinol cannot at present be stated. Ferric chlorid, however, despite its coagulating effect on protein and irritant properties, with the possible exception of sodium sulphite and sodium ethanol 1, 2-diacidsulphite, has been found to be the most efficient remedy for the disease. At my suggestion a 5 per cent mixture of ferric chlorid in 50 per cent aqueous glycerol has been successfully used on bed patients with severe cases at the infirmary of the University of California. Its use there was discontinued on account of the iron staining the bed linen.

If further opportunity presents itself for continued experimentation on the chemotherapy of this disease it is hoped that a preparation may be found which, like those of Ehrlich in syphilis, will be more toxitropic, less organotropic, and have fewer of the disagreeable features of the substances presented herewith.

### CLASSIFICATION OF THE CHEMOTHERAPEUTIC AGENTS ACCORDING TO THEIR ACTION IN VIVO AND IN VITRO

The chemotherapeutic agents in Rhus dermatitis may be classified according to the manner in which they react with lobinol.

1. A substance may render the poison non-toxic when in vitro, but not necessarily exert this effect in vivo. Litharge, for example, although it is able to decrease the toxicity of lobinol when in laboratory glassware, is unable to cure Rhus dermatitis because of its insolubility and consequent inability to penetrate the skin.

2. Some substances capable of therapeutic effect under certain conditions are without effect in others, either in vivo or in vitro. For instance, solvents are ineffective in removing lobinol after it has firmly combined with the skin. Some remedies when too highly diluted also fail.

3. Substances exerting a marked effect in vivo may have no effect in vitro.

Solutions of dextrose, sodium sulphite, or magnesium sulphate in sufficient dilution are without apparent reaction on lobinol in vitro, yet when applied to Rhus dermatitis in its initial stages they have a marked therapeutic value. This effect may be brought about by the remedial substance undergoing some modification in the body cells, so that it is changed into an active agent and unites with lobinol to form a corresponding physiologic neutral ester or other comparatively harmless substance. Like phenolic compounds lobinol may probably form an ester with either glucuronic acid or sulphuric acid. Glucuronic acid probably has its origin in the body from dextrose through the oxidation of its terminal alcohol group. Such oxidation, however, could only take place when the aldehyde group is protected from oxidation.

Magnesium sulphate, which has been found of benefit in this disease by von Adelung (1913), may owe its effect not so much to its chemical action on the poison as to its salutary effect on the nerves. A review of the experiments of Solis-Cohen (1909) with magnesium sulphate on the nervous system points in this direction. Meltzer (1918) has shown the beneficial effect of a 25 per cent solution in experimental first and second degree burns.

An effect in vivo and not in vitro may also be obtained by interference with the toxic function of lobinol without its direct chemical change, for example, substances which harden the skin or increase the thickness of the corium.

Part of the remedial value of iodine, picric acid, and ferric chlorid in Rhus dermatitis may be due to their ability to form a layer of precipitated and denatured protein on the injured surface. This layer acts as a protection, not only against the penetration of the poison, but also against air and traumatic injury. An effect in vivo and not in vitro may possibly occur also merely by a stimulation of the natural protective mechanisms with or without the assistance of either of the foregoing methods.

4. Substances may have a destructive action on the toxicity of lobinol both in vitro and in vivo, for example, ferric chlorid, iodine, and potassium permanganate.

### TENTATIVE METHOD FOR EXTERNAL TREATMENT

Rhus dermatitis, like burns, may be classified into three degrees of intensity as follows:

*First degree* (*hyperemia or erythema*).—The skin has a bright red or purple hue, which disappears temporarily under the pressure of the finger and which gradually blends with the normal color of the skin around. There is a transitory swelling of the poisoned area, with perhaps slight oozing of serum from the surface. The superficial layers of the cuticle usually peel off later.

*Second degree* (*vesication*).—This stage has all the features of the first degree in aggravated extent. Some hours later vesicles appear. No permanent scar remains after the healing of this degree of dermatitis, but the part may show for a time a slight depression or dark-colored pigmentation. Infection by septic bacteria may induce superficial suppuration and so delay repair.

*Third degree* (*destruction of true skin*).—This seldom occurs in Rhus dermatitis. When it does, permanent scars form.

Until further opportunity for experimentation and clinical observation occurs, Barthe de Sandfort's (1914) paraffin treatment of burns is given as tentative for the more severe cases of Rhus dermatitis.

*Equipment.*—(1) A fine varnish brush or, better, a paraffin atomizer (Sherman's type, with double-jacketed, detachable handle, manufactured by H. R. Pierce Co., Philadelphia).

2. A double boiler (cereal boiler) or, better, a "food warmer," pint size, sold for warming babies' milk. Put on a hot plate and turn current on and off as desired. Fill two-thirds full of parowax (Standard Oil Co.). If desired, sodium acetate may be put in the pot surrounding the vessel containing the parowax. The sodium acetate retains heat for a long time, e.g., about one hour at 58° C. (Sollman, 1917).

3. An electric drier. A Shelton electric hot-air draft or a Hamilton-Page fan may be used.

4. Absorbent cotton divided into very thin layers.

*Treatment.*—(1) Remove clothing. Puncture blebs, but do not excise.

2. Bathe all itching parts with 5 per cent ferric chlorid[1] in 50 per cent ethyl alcohol. Protect bed linen by rubber sheet.

3. Dry the treated surface with a current of air from an electric fan or drier.

4. Spray or paint treated surface with "parowax" (Standard Oil Co.).

5. Apply thin layer of sterile sheet wadding of the same shape as the irritated area. Then apply another film of parowax over the wadding and one inch on the uninjured skin beyond. The parowax must adhere to the skin at the edges or the secretions may escape to excoriate the intact skin, soil the dressings, and give a disagreeable odor. Keep the parowax dressing in place with a gauze bandage.

6. Renew dressing daily until the area shows a minimum of secretion. Clean with a spray or cotton balls saturated with M/5 sodium chlorid or boric acid solution.

7. If repair is sluggish or if infection has interfered, clean (Carrel-Dakin method) and reapply parowax. The clinical evidence of

[1] The author makes no claims for originality in the use of ferric chlorid as a remedy for Rhus dermatitis. Ferric chlorid has been used for this purpose by Browning (1886) and was proposed also by Pfaff (1897). See pp. 96, 98, 99, 156, 176, and 178.

infection-oedema, redness, lymphangitis, and free pus, increase in pulse rate, and temperature elevation are poor criteria. Much more reliable evidence can be obtained from bacterial counts from smears from suppurations or leucocyte counts from the blood or from suppurations. Lindemann (1917) has shown that in the treatment of wounds a continued increase in leucocytosis confirmed infection.

### A SECOND TENTATIVE METHOD OF TREATMENT

For those who do not care to apply the paraffin treatment the following is suggested:

1. Immediately bathe entire body with dilute aqueous ferric chlorid to physiologically neutralize all the poison on the body surface. If efficiently done and if the poison has not already penetrated the skin this should prevent spreading of the disease.

2. Require an entire change of clothing, including shoes. The clothing may have some of the poisonous resinous sap on it, and the poison may be transferred from it to the skin and the irritation continued in this way.

3. It is advisable to thoroughly wash the hair in 75 per cent ethyl alcohol to remove possible traces of poison that may have been carried there by the hands or otherwise, and which would be a source of infection.

4. Use no bandages that will slip, for these tend to spread the poison to the adjacent surface. If any protection is necessary let it be a loosely applied dressing of absorbent cotton, kept moist with aqueous ferric chlorid.

5. There must be no scratching (cut patient's finger nails short or require gloves to be worn).

6. Use no ointments for acute stage as fats have a tendency to dissolve and spread the poison.

7. Wash frequently with lukewarm aqueous ferric chlorid.

8. Keep diseased parts surgically clean to prevent bacterial infection.

9. After acute stage is past, when the disorder is considerably abated and a condition of eczema exists, the use of aqueous ferric chlorid may be objectionable and soothing ointments are permissible.

# APPENDIX

## ABSTRACTS OF TYPICAL CASES OF RHUS DERMATITIS FROM MEDICAL LITERATURE

### CASE OF SEVERE R. DIVERSILOBA DERMATITIS, BOIL AS SEQUELA

BALDWIN (1887*a*)

July 31, 10:30 A.M.—Few isolated points: skin natural in color; true skin raised as from within; parts affected, wrists. 4:30 P.M.—Points reddened and elongated; number increased, tendency to coalesce, light burning pain, with slight itching. 10:30 P.M.—Intense itching, greatly increased by rubbing; points running together and presenting reddened, raised borders, points blunted and tendency to flatten; greater area involved toward forearm; surrounding surfaces pinkish tinge; heat local; intensified capillary stasis (deep) and lines of redness well marked, irregular.

August 1, 6:00 A.M.—Anterior forearms to flexure of elbow presenting angry, reddened surface, diffuse over the upper pronators, fading to natural color of skin above median basilic vein; wrists infiltrated and puffy, sensation here of great distension; itching intense, and slowly passing upward.

August 1, 12:00 M.—Tenderness of whole forearm and tendency of points to mass; local heat much intensified; burning sensation of whole forearm; parts very angry and structure deeply infiltrated. 6:00 P.M.—From wrist to elbow parts very much intensified; sense of great fullness and construction; muscles over humerus biceps and brachialis anticus very painful, and pain increased on motion; itching sensation, which has been increasing from close of first six hours is now very annoying, producing nausea through sympathetics; parts begin to show mass of blunted, irregularly shaped points, very much flattened and thinned at apex, with whitening of central core. 10:30 P.M.—The cuticle raised as if by liquid burn, in irregularly shaped masses with tendency to circular form; fluid, limpid, with minute points of brick color exuding, and drying, form a semi-brown, yellowish, scaly scab, thicker in spots and scaling off when rubbed, leaving cutis pink in color and exquisitely sensitive to the air.

August 2, 6:00 A.M.—Arms to median basilic vein very tense, painful, and covered with masses of drying, freshly exuding, and old serum; subcutaneous cellular tissues very tense and excruciatingly painful; portions of cuticle raised and containing two or four drams of serum, clear in part and colored in others; appearance of arm less angry, but dusky red in portions not affected; weight of arm very painful; no indication of spread of condition beyond metacarpus. 12:00 M.—Itching increased, till patient seems beside himself; pulsation of artery very painful; whole forearm tense, hard, and unyielding to the touch like bottom of an overshoe; parts very hot and skin stretched to capacity. 6:00 P.M.—Height of fever passed at about 3:00 P.M. when parts grew less tense and throbbing ceased; great quantities of serum have saturated bandages, and dusky color of skin is changing to pink; sensation of tight band midway between wrist and elbow; local heat somewhat abated.

August 3, 6:00 A.M.—Bandages very much colored (yellow) and stiff with drying serum; pain in axillae; on pressure, cuticle bursts and subsides; substance of cuticle much thinned and shows peculiar transparency of dermoid structures beneath; subcutaneous structures much infiltrated; very tense and great sense of constriction in the entire forearm. 12:00 M.—Bandages scarcely wet through: skin under sloughs red, shiny, and very smooth; pink and merging into roughened corrugated portions of cuticle that still throw off liquid serum; areolar structures less turgid but painful on pressure; pain in axillae intensified; general feeling of pyrexia; functions of accommodation imperfect and uncertain; sympathetic itching of ankles; few isolated points have retained their individuality; cuticle dead over apices and scaling off slowly, bases raised, irregular, and surmounted by small secondary points which rise at various angles from periphery and lower portions of base; pain on pressure very marked midway between elbow and wrist and exudate confined to space from 3 to 4 inches square; itching intense during entire period. 6:00 P.M.—Serum turning brown, containing less water and forming scabs which stick closely to cutis, appearance of skin when this covering is washed away: smooth, shiny, red, with slight corrugations running transversely around the arm.

August 4, 6:00 A.M.—All portions affected covered with thick, brownish scab, which is so intimately mixed with dead and disintegrating cuticle that all comes away together with slight force, showing a serous covering of derma which weeps copiously upon irritation. Glands of inquinal regions involved and swelled to size of English filbert. Axillary glands large and swelling of borders more clearly defined, hard and very painful, structures over and contiguous to lympathic canals somewhat painful, also lymphatics of breasts and cervical region. No symptoms of itching except on removal of bandages and exposure to air; new minute points show through red dermoid surfaces. 12:00 M.—Whole surfaces involved covered with fresh crop of white elevated points, 1/32 inch, filled with creamy thick fluid, isolated and showing when removed a clear serum at bottom which passes through malpighian layer; entire structure of epidermis destroyed and capillary circulation appears impeded in patches, leaving dark-red elongated deposits of haemaglobin. 6:00 P.M.—Between white points another set containing clear fluid and opening at surface of true skin, somewhat smaller, 1/64 inch, with very little elevation, breaking under slight pressure and leaving depression. Interference of functions of accommodation more marked toward evening.

August 5, 6:00 A.M.—Vesicles and points of suppuration have coalesced and form irregularly shaped bodies raised 1/16 inch, and full of yellow matter, serum which twelve hours since was found underlying the drying matter, and decaying scarf skin has formed a thin, scaly structure which cracks and pulls off. Eyelids smeared with yellowish matter, which when hard crumbles into dust easily; pain over and around lymph organs and ducts continued, intensified in axillae and flexure of elbow. Movements of pectoralis muscles, deltoid, biceps, and triceps very painful; itching of arms subsided, prepuce involved, congested, light itching sensations of external and internal malleolus of tibia; functions of accommodation interfered with, ciliary ligament slow to respond to light, and vice versa. 12:00 M.—Scarfskin being entirely destroyed and true skin much corroded and pitted; capillary circulation exceedingly rapid beneath and around former suppurating points exhibits red areas, 1/8–1/4 inch in diameter. Thin flakes of drying serum, constantly falling away from living structure beneath, cause peculiar appearance of short wool between points of new dermoid growth. At intervals intense itching for a few moments.

August 6, 12:00 M.—New structures forming throw off quantities of scarfskin; case rapidly being terminated by lysis.

August 7.—Isolated, elongated raised bodies 1/8 inch long, 1/14 inch wide, appear on inside portion of thighs, over the vastus internus, gastrocnemius, gluteals, and lattissimus dorsi; spots that indicated onset of attack still remain on wrists.

Between this date and August 22, a crop of seven boils appeared on the forearms, and an enormous amount of pus followed; at writing small isolated boils are forming.

As this case ran a natural course, the symptoms may be relied upon as those usually presented when any portion of the body is involved.

### CASE OF SEVERE R. DIVERSILOBA DERMATITIS, BOIL AS SEQUELA

BALDWIN (1887*b*)

May 22, 9:00 A.M.—Burning sensation over regions of inferior maxillary, followed by prickling (very painful) and throbbing of facial arteries; cutis inspissated, reddened, and very warm to the touch; light papular eruptions; points isolated and distinct. After 2:00 P.M.—Itching intense; cheeks and cervical regions becoming involved; lines of redness over lymphatic organs.

May 23, 9:00 A.M.—Entire structures of face and neck involved, subcutaneous cellular tissues tense and unyielding; oedema of lids, patient unable to open eyes, from which a sero-purulent matter slowly exudes; muscles of face, maxillae, cervical regions, and over platysma myoides to collar bone, very sore and painful; patient unable to rotate head or move jaws; angry red surface merging into delicate pink toward surrounding parts; papules filled with serum.

May 24—Exquisite tenderness of parts involved, and tendency of points to mass in irregularly shaped patches; local heat intensified; sensation of hot iron held to face; epidermis destroyed in regions where points are massed, and copious discharge of brownish-colored liquid; itching increased, with increased tension of cellular structures; nausea; functions of the lens imperfect; pupils contracted; pain in eyeballs sharp, shooting from attachment of external rectus to internal paracusis, with slow pains running over structures contiguous to lymphatics of head and neck; liquid serum on drying leaves scab which cracks and falls away, leaving pink vascular tissues beneath; structures involved covered with masses of serum, which dries on exposure; parts very tense, and face swollen till mouth cannot be opened, eyes tightly closed.

May 25—Stenosis of larynx coming on within one half-hour; patient unable to breathe; great weight of parts involved; intense itching; pulsations of arteries produce great pain; quantities of serum, forming scab; continued nausea; vomiting.

May 26—Intense pain in eyes, shooting from side to side, parts involved pass down to upper half of breasts and form a distinct line of separation from healthy structures below; very little exudate from breasts, the right one being affected for a space of 2 inches lower than the left; surface covering back part of neck, and structures over sterno mastoids very red, angry, and tense.

May 27—Lymphatic structures very painful on pressure; stenosis of glotus; old points show gradual introcession, and between basis a fresh crop appears, with white pus at core; these raise slowly, and carry heavy red border, which subsides when central core bursts, leaving clean-cut cavity, which fills with clear serum at bottom; eyes grow more painful with each successive hour; stomach very irritable; general prostration very great.

May 28—Eyes opened sufficiently to show a double which continues for several days. With slight pressure a great quantity of yellow pus flows from right eye. Skin less tense and with softening of structures folds and corrugations appear; new skin shows beneath dead and decaying structures a bright pink tint.

May 29—General subsidence of symptoms; itch continued from the first; stomach irritable; patient unable to retain food. Six days later a large boil developed over the symphysis of lower jaw, with quantities of pus.

CASE OF R. TOXICODENDRON DERMATITIS

BATLETT (1838)

May 2—Exposure to poison ivy.

May 12—Weak $H_2O$ solution acet. plumbi to eruption, nearly whole length of tibia.

May 16—Eruption to scrotum, colorless discharge. $H_2O$ solution opium and unguentum acet. plumbi.

May 17—Eruption completely covered face, trunk, extremities, scrotum, thighs, penis. Discharge. Great restlessness, pulse 120. Tongue slightly furred. Discontinued former medicine. Sponged body with NaCl (one part to eight parts tepid water). Immediate relief to itching and burning.

May 18—More comfortable. Discharge less. Continued sponging six or eight times a day.

May 19—No discharge, swelling gone, general eruption faint. Continued sponging.

May 20—Disappeared except forearms.

CASE OF R. TOXICODENDRON DERMATITIS, ANNUAL RECURRENCE WITHOUT RE-EXPOSURE, BOILS AS SEQUELAE

Beringer (1896)

April, 1883—Writer poisoned in Odd Fellow's Cemetery, Philadelphia, by handling some poison ivy on which the new leaves were just appearing. Although the hands were protected by gloves, the exposed portions, face and hands, were shortly after washed, nearly the entire surface of the body suffered, the face and eyelids being so swollen as to nearly produce blindness. Following the attack came a series of boils, and for several years afterward, about the same time, there appeared the characteristic eruption and sensations when there had been no contact or exposure to the plant.

Poisoned also May, 1894, September, 1894, November, 1894. Series of boils in the summer and fall of 1894.

Conclusion: *R. Toxicodendron* poisonous at all seasons of the year, also dust shaken from roots.

THE VOLATILE TOXIC CONSTITUENT OF POISON IVY

Bessey (1914)

Assistant brought into laboratory a tin box full of plants including many flowering specimens of poison ivy. The day was hot and the assistant had walked in the sun for a mile or more in bringing in the plants. Bessey did not touch the box or contents, but leaned over and looked in the open box.

"In a day or two, usual inflammation appeared; surfaces affected were those only which had been directly exposed when I leaned over the box of plants.

"My face was inflamed all over, except where my beard, mustache, eyebrows, and nose made projecting protections. Above these there were small areas entirely free from inflammation. The underside of my eyebrows (the overhang) was thoroughly poisoned and so was the inside of my nose (the nostrils). My right hand was severely poisoned, but here again the distribution of the inflammation was peculiar, being confined to the parts which were directed downward as I pointed at the various specimens in the box. Thus the proximal and middle joints of the second, third, and fourth fingers, and the underside of the wrist of that hand were badly affected, while the upper side of the hand was not poisoned at all. My left hand was not poisoned and I account for this by the fact that it was kept back and not used in indicating plants to be examined by the assistant.

"Forced to conclude that there is a volatile poison, also, in this plant, poison volatile enough to be carried up apparently in straight lines by the warm air which escaped from the tin collecting box (*vasculum*) when opened in my study."

### EXPERIMENTAL CASE OF RHUS POISONING

BIBB (1914–15)

The poison oak was rubbed vigorously on a sharply delimited piece of cardboard with a hole in the center area of the arm. The area coming in contact with the plant was one-fourth the size of a postage stamp. A vaccination shield of celluloid, but perforated, was fastened by adhesive over the point of application of the *Rhus*. Within twenty-four hours characteristic lesions appeared various places on both forearms and the left upper arm. The area that had been inoculated showed as a red, raised spot. It was suggested that the offending agent had been spread by the shirt sleeve which had been worn rolled up just above the elbow. Under treatment by lead water the lesions rapidly disappeared.

The second person inoculated showed absolutely no reaction at any time.

### DERMATITIS FROM HERBARIUM SPECIMEN THREE YEARS OLD

BOGUE (1894 ?)

*Rhus venenata* deposited in Ohio State University not less than three years.

"About ten days ago I noticed that they were infected with borers—the larva of some beetle. Desiring to study the beetle, the stems were broken a few times so that they would go into a covered glass jar. They were found to be bored through many times, so that they broke easily, and at every breaking the powder from the borings flew freely. I had no fears of being poisoned, but about 3 A.M. the next morning I was awakened by an itching between my fingers as if poisoned. Later developments proved that it was poison, and I can account for it in no other way than that it came from the poison ivy. The epidermis is now coming off the affected part exactly as when having been poisoned with *R. venenata* D.C."

### CASE OF R. TOXICODENDRON DERMATITIS BY INDIRECT CONTACT, ANNUAL RECURRENCE

BUSEY (1873)

In June, 1871, Mrs. V. suffered very severely from a burning and itching eruption covering her entire face, neck, both mammae, external genitals, extending along the inner surface of both thighs, both hands, wrists, and portions of her abdomen. Her husband, at the same time, suffered with a similar eruption, though not so severe, on both hands, and an infant had it very slightly about the mouth and chin. A week previous to the appearance of the eruption, the husband and wife had passed an afternoon at a picnic, and he had fastened his horse to a bush covered with a vine, the character of which he had not observed. The wife did not approach the plant, and the child had been left at home.

The disease returned May 6, 1872, on all localities attacked the previous year, and also returned May 31, 1873.

Busey cites another case of annual recurrence (in summer time). All cases which Busey observed occurred in spring, summer, or autumn months, usually in the spring.

## CASE IN WHICH HANDS TRANSMITTED R. TOXICODENDRON POISON EVEN AFTER WASHING THEM WITH SOAP

CANTRELL (1891)

Marg. G., thirty-four years of age, was admitted into the general wards of the Philadelphia Hospital on September 24, 1890, and was removed on October 26 to the maternity ward, where she was delivered of a male infant. She continued well until September 29, when she complained of an itching and burning sensation of the abdomen, which showed an inflamed surface, covered with vesicles and bullae.

Two nurses, one from the surgical and the other from the maternity ward, left the hospital at 2:00 P.M. on September 26, taking a stroll through an adjacent cemetery, gathering leaves and bringing a number back with them. Among the leaves were a number of ivy leaves, but this fact was not known by the nurses at the time. The nurse stated that after her return her hands were washed several times with ordinary soap and water, but when dressing the young mother her hands came in contact with the skin of the abdomen, and this probably conveyed the ivy poison to the spot affected, as her hands, which at this time were apparently not affected, showed the eruption in a day or two. It also appeared on the abdomen of the patient at about the same time.

## CASE OF INTERNAL POISONING BY R. TOXICODENDRON

CONNER (1907)

"Once when attending a funeral early in the spring of the year, while listening to the exercises, I thoughtlessly broke off a tender shoot and chewed it. In about twenty-four hours afterward my lips and mouth began to itch and burn severely, and in a few hours more I had slight nausea which was soon succeeded by diarrhea and escoriation of the tissues surrounding the anus. At first I was at a loss to account for these signs and symptoms, but soon the characteristic papules made their appearance on the mucous membrane of the lips—more especially the lower one, and also of the cheeks. I realized now that I had a case of Rhus poisoning to deal with. The treatment consisted in rinsing the mouth and gargling the throat with a mixture containing boric and benzoic acids, thymol, and glycerine, and, once in awhile swallowing a dose of the medicine. The trouble subsided in a couple of days, leaving me none the worse for wear."

## CASES OF R. TOXICODENDRON DERMATITIS ILLUSTRATING INDIRECT CONTACT AND VARIABLE SUSCEPTIBILITY

CUNDELL (1883)

Stanley. N, who was wont to suffer from the poison three or four times during the summer, now that he is eighteen years of age, handles the weed (poison ivy) with absolute impunity.

Granville R., who, after some years of immunity, laughed at the fears of his companions, again suffered greatly from poison ivy.

James M., aged seventeen, is peculiarly susceptible to the influence of the poison oak. In bathing in early summer, he threw his clothes at the foot of a sycamore tree, where the Rhus was growing. During the night, about twelve hours after bathing, the lad awoke, scratching the loose folds of his scrotum. The usual course of the eruption followed.

### CASE OF R. TOXICODENDRON DERMATITIS ON SCROTUM, PENIS, GROIN, RECTAL AND GENITAL REGIONS

DUNCAN (1916)

C. V., male, living in the country, one evening when defecating in the woods was unfortunate enough to select a spot that was covered with poison ivy. When seen, three days later, he presented the most terrible spectacle of ivy poisoning the writer had ever seen. The cutaneous manifestation was severe, covering the whole scrotum, penis, groin, rectal and gluteal regions. Each testicle appeared to be the size of the fist, and the penis several times its natural size, puffy, and oedematous. He was instructed to return to the spot of evacuation and to select a leaf from this particular plant, a part of which he was instructed to chew and to swallow the juice. This he did. There was a reduction of swelling, and the symptoms of itching and burning rapidly subsided, so that within three days he was able to resume his duties as butler. The reason for instructing him to return to the spot and chew the leaves of this particular plant was that there are several species of ivy and in attempting to treat the patient with the tincture from the fresh plant he might have been given a tincture of some ivy other than the one with which he had been poisoned.

### CASE OF PROCTITIS AND PERITONITIS FROM RHUS POISONING OF THE BUTTOCKS

DUNMIRE (1881)

On August 19, Mrs. C., aged thirty, with her family visited the East Park. In the evening, returning by way of a bridle-path, she had occasion to evacuate her bowels, after which the absence of paper was supplied by the abundance of foliage within her reach. Two days after this the woman's husband came to get a prescription to "kill poison." (I visited the place in the East Park, vicinity of the Dairy, and there found abundance of the *R. Toxicodendron.*) August 22, four days after the handling of the leaves, I was called to see her. She was suffering from an eczematous eruption upon the skin. The sense of burning, the violent itching and swelling at times peculiar to it, with the pain, heat, fever, and vesication attending, she characterized as "awful."

It had begun near or about the nates, extending over the vulva, which was greatly tumefied and painful, with a purulent discharge from the vagina. From these parts it spread all over the body, first on the face, evidently owing to the discharge from the primary trouble being carried by the hands. The face and lips were swollen so as to change the features, and what seemed new to observation was that the mucous membrane of the mouth and throat was inflamed and painful. From all these annoyances, so restless did she become that scarcely for a moment could she be still, much less sleep.

Notwithstanding, the remedies, which gave some relief, on the morning of September 1 (twelve days after the exposure) the poisonous action was still active, but had taken on a slow erysipelatous condition, particularly upon the hands, arms, and hips, and would not be headed off by frequently repeated applications of tincture of iodine. At this time the patient complained of an uneasy feeling in the rectum, and also of bearing down, as if wanting to have an evacuation. This feeling was not relieved even after a large enema of sweet oil. So violent did the tenesmus become during the day that a neighboring woman insisted that she must be pregnant and aborting and the doctor must be sent for. Hypodermic injections of morphia and suppositories of extract of hyoscyamus and opium had to be repeated to control the symptoms through the night.

On the morning of September 2, the patient was found lying on her back, totally indifferent to her other trouble, with thighs flexed upon the pelvis. There was great pain and tenderness over the bowels, particularly so on the left side, which afterward extended over the abdomen. The lightest pressure would produce pain. The pulse and temperature were high, having had a chill in the night. Opium was freely given, and locally turpentine stupes and poultices of oatmeal made with acetic acid and alum were applied constantly.

On third day of this abdominal trouble the pulse was quick and small, temperature lower, some anxiety of countenance, and sick stomach. These symptoms occasioned some fear for the result of the case. After more than five weeks from the beginning of the Rhus poisoning, the patient recovered.

Was this not a case of proctitis and peritonitis by contiguity of tissue by way of the pelvic organs, and resulting from the poisonous toxicodendric acid?

### CASES OF INTERNAL POISONING

Escafet (1847)

First Observation—Joseph Baron, aged seven years, Parish of Reynes, ate the berries of sumac of corroyeurs at 9:00 A.M., August 14, 1831. The father of the child, seeing him suffer, went to Ceret two hours after noon, sought Mr. Slabet, health officer, who arrived within three hours and found him in the following condition: in a complete faint, paralyzed tendons, haggard eyes, sightless, jaws set; it was impossible to get even liquid to his stomach. At 11:00 P.M. he collapsed, and he died at 8:00 A.M., August 15.

Second Observation—Françoise Mas, called Selve, aged nine years, and Angelique Figueras, called Tarice, aged seven years, ate some berries of this bush on August 20, 1844, at 2:00 P.M.; fifteen minutes after eating them, they commenced to be depressed, they retained their senses, their movements were uncertain, and they were obliged to have assistance during their walk. The mother of Mas called Dr. Claret, and the mother of Figueras, Mr. Marty, health officer. They gave them sugar water, which provoked abundant vomiting, and the toxic substance was ejected. It was a cerise red, mixed with black seeds. At 3:30 they were given a cup of infusion of camomille. Dr. Claret, having been called by another patient, told the mother of Mas to call me during his absence, in case of new symptoms; in fact, she came to my drug store and told me that her little child, also the Figueras child, were found in a heavy stupor; I had given them, in small cups, a strong infusion of coffee and took them for a walk; on their return Angelique Figueras had a feeble vision which they had not previously noticed. At 10:00 P.M. all the symptoms of poisoning had disappeared, and they gave him a bouillon. August 21, no toxic phenomena being present, the two children returned to their usual habits, and after this day enjoyed perfect health.

Third Observation—André Brausse, aged six years, a native of Saint-Jean-Pla-de-Coro (Orientales Pyrenées), ate some berries of this bush on August 10, 1846. The child went home, and they gave him soup; at that time nausea and vomiting began; the soup was ejected mixed with a red liquid, deep cerise color; convulsions and tetanus followed; the parent, attributing these symptoms to an illness, gave him salt water. Mr. Negre, health officer, was called three hours after and observed the following: complete depression, paralyzed tendons, general convulsions, dilated pupils, loss of vision, haggard eyes, jaws set one against the other, sardonic grin. It was with great difficulty that he placed a piece of wood between the jaws; impossible to get a spoonful of emetic potion to the stomach, which the professional man attributed to the spasmodic state of the pharynx; great swelling of the abdomen; complete retention of urine; died at 6:00 P.M.

Fourth Observation—Bonaventure Rodar, aged five years, with Brausse, the subject of the preceding observation, ate some sumac berries of the currier; fifteen minutes after he began to vomit a part of the poison, red in color, mixed with some black seeds; on returning home he told his parents he had no appetite; at 5:30 P.M. some symptoms of poisoning presenting themselves, Mr. Negre was called; he gave lukewarm water; and a quantity of red liquid, deep cerise color, was vomited; at 8:00 P.M. enemas provoked three stools; the child urinated, passed the entire night in a deep stupor; on August 11 all toxic symptoms disappeared and the child enjoyed perfect health.

The autopsies on the bodies of the first and third observations not having taken place, Mr. Escafet with the professional men had only been able to observe the results which this poison produced in domestic animals; he had only observed that according to the phenomena in the second observation it ought to act like the acrid narcotic poisons.

### CASE OF SEVERE R. TOXICODENDRON DERMATITIS

FARQUAR (1888–89)

J. S., a light mulatto girl of seventeen years of age, had always been healthy except in childhood when she suffered from cervical adenitis. The patient, while walking, pulled some leaves which grew along the fence, and, not knowing their poisonous character, played with them by rubbing them on her face and about the left ear. In a short time, the characteristic vesication, associated with the usual itching, appeared. In a few days there was considerable oedema about the face and the eyes were almost closed. The family became alarmed, and summoned me to take charge of the case. Five days after the first contact with the poison I found the following conditions: The face, ears, part of the neck and forehead were almost entirely converted into a mass of yellowish crusts, from beneath which, and from the vesicles upon the remainder of the affected area, a serious discharge exuded. There was distinct constitutional disturbance, a slight rise in temperature, coated tongue, constipated bowels, a sense of fullness in the head, and insomnia; menstruation was delayed; the throat was considerably swollen and tense, and the patient suffered from dyspnaea and dysphagia.

Successful treatment was recommended by the United States Dispensatory with the addition of $KMnO_4$ as there was an offensive odor, and later the employment of bismuth and laudanum to relieve the intense itching.

Process continued four weeks with complete recovery ensuing.

### CASE OF PROBABLE TRANSMISSION OF R. TOXICODENDRON POISON BY SMOKE OF BURNING PLANT

FINCH (1897)

A conductor of a wrecking train, on Thursday, December 10, from 2:00–7:00 A.M., was engaged in removing a wrecked freight train from track. It was a bitter cold night, and the patient came down and made a fire near the embankment. He says he noticed a very peculiar pungent odor arising from the burning shrubbery, but paid no attention to it. Thinks now that it was *R. Toxicodendron.* By Monday noon he noticed a slight eruption on edge of neck and upon dorsal aspect of hands. On Wednesday, December 16, his face was swollen, and eyes nearly closed, arms swollen; burning and itching of the parts were severe; pustules of clear serum on arms.

A physician was called December 17. He gave cocain hydrochlorid 20 grains, aquae distil 3 ounces M. A tablespoon of this was added to one-half pint of warm water and applied to parts with sponge; the itching and burning was relieved immediately.

### CASE IN WHICH THICK SKIN PREVENTS PENETRATION OF R. TOXICODENDRON POISON

FONTANA (1795*a*)

"I let several large drops of this milk (fresh sap) fall on the hands of two gardeners, who at the end of three days had black spots on their hands where the sap had fallen, but were not sick." This he attributes to the callous on the hands resisting the penetration of the poison.

### CASE IN WHICH SMALL AMOUNT OF POISON CAUSES DERMATITIS

FONTANA (1795*b*)

"I scarcely touched the back of my hand with a leaf of the toxicodendron which I had cut near the stalk and could with difficulty perceive the skin to be wet at a place where I had applied it.

"Three days after there appeared a dark spot, my whole face began to swell, particularly the eyelids and tips of the ears. I experienced a terrible smart for fifteen days, and an intolerable itching for fifteen more; even the hands smarted and itched, above all betwixt the fingers, which were become red, and were covered here and there with small vesicles filled with a transparent and sharp humour: I had no fever, but my pulse was very quick. The skin of my face, particularly about the eyes and eyelids, was extended and filled with an aqueous fluid, and easily retained the print of anything that touched it. The epidermis fell off in small scales, and I felt a most troublesome itching through the whole process of the disease."

### CASE OF SEVERE R. VENENATA DERMATITIS

FRENCH (1903)

Autumn leaves of *R. venenata* were gathered unrecognized, and no precautions taken. About twenty-four hours after symptoms of itching, burning, and vesiculation developed. Itch began at wrists which had not been covered by gloves. Saturated solution of lead acetate in 50 or 75 per cent alcohol frequently repeated for several days, but absolutely useless. Then used solution of sodium hyposulphite, sweet spirits of niter, and fluid extract of grindelia robusta in turn, using each thoroughly for several days—no benefit.

Third day, lesions increased on wrists, and appeared upon the neck and in the genitocrural region. On the fourth and fifth days hands and face involved, left side of face so badly swollen as nearly to close the left eye. Fifth day general symptoms most severe and the disease seemed to have reached its climax. At this time considerable fever, headache, and general malaise, but at no time confined to bed. After this a gradual decline in severity, although the lesions continued to spread, affecting in turn nearly all portions of the body, especially the flexor surfaces of the limbs and the region of the joints, in addition to those already mentioned.

The first application which gave noticeable relief was camphophenique, or carbolated camphor; there was temporary cooling, but the odor was unpleasant, and action on the skin unfavorable.

Intense itch temporarily relieved by lotion of $\frac{1}{2}$ ounce ZnO, 2 drams of glycerine, one-half dram $C_6H_5OH$, and 8 ounces of lime water, also when parts immersed in hot saleratus water. Itch worse at night than day and worse when quiet in bed than when up and moving about.

Symptoms lasted for five or six weeks. Attack gave increased susceptibility for a time which wore away in course of two or three years if exposure not repeated. In his case no recurrence and no constitutional disturbance.

CASE IN WHICH GLOVES TRANSMIT R. TOXICODENDRON POISON

FROST (1826)

A medical man was present at the gathering of the leaves of the plant (*R. Toxicodendron*), in the month of June. He took up some to examine their botanical characters, having taken the precaution of putting on his gloves previously to so doing. After a few minutes had elapsed, the weather being extremely warm, he took off his hat, and wiped the perspiration from his forehead with one of his gloves, which had imbibed a portion of the juice of the plant, not recollecting at the moment that he had but just been handling the foliage of *R. Toxicodendron.* Dermatitis resulted.

QUESTIONABLE CASE OF RECURRENT R. TOXICODENDRON DERMATITIS

HORSFIELD (1798)

Cause—smoke of *R. radicans.*

First appearance—two months after exposure "when small vesications were seen on the shoulder, which were easily cured by very simple remedies. Twelve months after this, the disease returned upon the same part. The succeeding year it first appeared on his legs; it traveled up his thighs to his arms and shoulders, and finally affected his back and face. This was in the month of May, 1797. The disease now was in a state of ulceration; the ulcers, however, were superficial, and did not appear to extend beyond skin; they very much resembled a certain cutaneous affection, which sometimes occurs in consequence of the venereal disease. His eyes were also affected at this time by a serous discharge, which was followed by a defective vision in one of his eyes, and almost total loss of sight in the other. The blindness was relieved by a slight salivation and by several other remedies."

CASE OF R. TOXICODENDRON DERMATITIS BY DIRECT CONTACT

HUMPHREYS (1874)

Remedy—$ZnSO_4$, ℥ ss to ag. Oj, bathe parts frequently. Used in twelve to fourteen cases. Speedy relief from itching and burning.

A man forty years of age was poisoned with *Rhus.* He was delirious, with considerable fever, pulse 110, tongue thickly coated, bowels constipated; and an eruption of an erysipelatous nature on face. A few days previous, while in the woods, he had come in contact with poison oak, and upon returning home remarked that he would again be poisoned; it shortly did make its appearance, first upon the nose, thence spreading over the cheeks and eyes. The inflammation had extended over the forehead and into the scalp, both eyes were quite closed, both ears, cheeks, and lips were very much tumefied and pitted on pressure, and the patient's features were so much disfigured that he was not at all recognizable.

In two days after treatment the patient was walking about the house and "feeling quite well." Oedema about eyes had nearly disappeared.

### CASE OF POSSIBLE POISONING FROM SMOKE OF RHUS

HUNT (1897)

A railway train stopped near where the workmen were clearing off a swamp and burning the bogs and brush, which would in this latitude pretty certainly contain a considerable amount of both poisonous varieties of *Rhus*. The smoke came in through the open car windows, and in about twenty-four hours I began to feel as if I had been sunburned, and swelling and vesication rapidly appeared, so that by the third day I was completely blind from the tumefaction closing my eyelids.

### CASE OF ANNUAL RECURRENCES OF RHUS DERMATITIS WITHOUT RE-EXPOSURE: CAUSED BY ANOTHER PLANT

HURLBURT (1869)

I have attended Professor Babcock several times for what was supposed to be *Rhus* poisoning; the symptoms are identical with those of *Rhus*. He says in his letter to *The Pharmacist:* "Working botanists have so often been poisoned by *R. Toxicodendron* that many of them have come to regard it as their special bane. In five seasons, commencing with 1868, I was particularly careful not to touch this poisonous plant, not to pluck a specimen growing in its immediate vicinity, not to receive from the hands of another person a freshly gathered plant, for fear it might have come in contact with *Rhus*. In spite of these precautions in the latter part of May or the first of June in each year, I was poisoned so severely as to be confined to my room for several days. In June, 1872, after gathering many specimens of *Cypripedium spectabila*, I observed that my hands were stained with the purplish secretion of the granular hairs with which its stem and leaves are densely clothed, and shortly after experienced a peculiar irritation about the eyes. The next day my whole face presented the appearance of a severe case of Rhus. In reviewing my notes of the previous years, I found in each season the poisoning had appeared on the day after I had collected *Cypripedium spectabila* or *C. pubescens*. In 1873 and 1874 I collected more extensively than ever before, but suspecting that my previous sufferings had been caused by these two specimens of *Cypripedium* rather than the *Rhus*, took no unusual pains to avoid the latter, but refrained from touching either of the former with the bare hand. The result was what I expected, for I escaped entirely the poisoning that I had begun to regard as inevitable, and am now convinced that upon myself, at least, *Cypripedium spectabila* and *C. pubescens* are capable of producing effects similar to those caused by *R. Toxicodendron.*"

### CASE IN WHICH R. TOXICODENDRON POISON PENETRATES RUBBER GLOVES

KUNZE (1883)

The juice from the bruised leaves of *R. Toxicodendron* made indelible stains on the light-colored rubber, gauntlet gloves, and combined with the rubber and then inoculated the hands within. The black stains were visible even in the lining of the gloves.

### CASE IN WHICH COAT TRANSMITS R. TOXICODENDRON POISON FOUR WEEKS AFTER CONTACT WITH PLANT

KUNZE (1883)

"The sleeves of the flannel coat I had on in the woods were to some extent a hiding place for the fine particles of detached ivy roots, and whenever I wore it in the house I was immediately re-inoculated for a period of four weeks after the first exposure. The new crop of eruptions appeared on the dorsal surface of the arms and fingers."

### R. TOXICODENDRON ROOTS POISONOUS IN WINTER

KUNZE (1883)

On November 26, 1876, I started for Long Island in order to dig up some roots of *Apocynum cannabinum*, near Coronna. My assistant dug up the ground, and I, provided with rubber gloves, pulled them out of the soil. We had worked several hours in a drizzling rain before I discovered the fact that the *Apocynum* grew in the midst of a lot of other long fibrous roots which were constantly in the way and had to be torn out with much force. Finally I traced a long runner to a fence-post conveniently near, and here I found myself again in the embrace of my arch enemy. I quit work at about 3:00 P.M., and before leaving saw many of the poison vines trailing through the long, wet grass, devoid of all foliage, of course. At 5:00 P.M. a slight itching was observed in the left eyelid and palmar surface of hands where the *R. Toxicodendron* had first inoculated me through the gloves used. By 10:00 P.M. those parts looked red, and were covered with shining vesicles. Other portions of the hands, wrists, and face now exchanged their natural color for that of a modest blush; slight smarting supervened. The next morning the face and hands were quite inflamed, itched, and accompanied with tumefaction of the features so as to obliterate all contour of the same; vesicles everywhere, scrotum swollen.

### TREATMENT OF R. TOXICODENDRON DERMATITIS WITH LINSEED OIL AND LIME WATER

MATHESON (1874)

Exposure of September 1; eruption began on September 3. Physician called on afternoon of September 6. Sugar of lead lotion had been tried but symptoms increased in severity, with some fever.

Led from the resemblance between the eruption and that of a scald from steam, linseed oil and lime water equal parts were prescribed. The prescription was spread upon old linen, the affected parts were completely covered, and frequent brushings over the cloth from the outside without exposure of inflamed surface. Pain less. Entirely relieved on the fifth day of treatment (eleven days after exposure).

### CASE OF INTERNAL POISONING FROM R. TOXICODENDRON FRUIT

MOORMAN (1866)

"The subjects of these cases were children, one six and the other eight years of age. The quantity eaten was nearly a pint. In a few hours the children became drowsy and stupid, and in a short time vomiting commenced, first of the partially digested fruit, afterwards of a thick, tenacious fluid of a wine color. Then convulsions of different parts of the body followed, accompanied by slight delirium. Respiration was hurried, pulse at first full and strong, but slow, afterward small, frequent, and compressible; pupils dilated. Warm water was given to promote emesis and thus clear the stomach of the poisonous matter; afterward large quantities of carbonate of soda in solution, under the belief that it was an antidote to the poison. Otherwise they were treated on general principles. Both cases recovered, though the youngest convalesced very slowly."

### GUAIACOL IN RHUS DERMATITIS

MORRIS (1897)

The patient, male, forty-five years old, was suffering from face swollen to such an extent as to wholly obliterate the features, and the eyes were entirely closed.

Treatment: ZnO ointment, and ordered application of $Na_2CO_3$ ʒ ii in aqua ℥ iii on absorbent cotton. Result negative.

Third day after onset made application of pure guaiacol, freely painting it over inflamed area with a camel's hair brush, and then covering the parts. Next day marked amelioration and fourth day after inaugurating guaiacol treatment the inflammation had entirely disappeared.

### CASE OF ANNUAL RECURRENCE OF R. TOXICODENDRON DERMATITIS APPARENTLY WITHOUT RE-EXPOSURE UNTIL SOURCE DISCOVERED

NICHOLSON (1899)

The hands were covered on backs with scattered red spots varying from the size of a pin's head to that of a split pea, and a few on lower forearms; the face was much more extensively affected with redness much more uniform, considerable swelling, so that eyes could scarcely be opened. Almost all face and forehead invaded by the rash, which had a fairly sharp margin, and there were a few scattered islets beyond on the healthy skin. There was a tendency to form vesicles, especially on the face; rest of body entirely free. Temperature was normal, tongue clean, no feeling of ill-health beyond local discomfort. At first sight the face presented the appearance of an ordinary case of erysipelas of moderate severity.

Past history—six or seven similar attacks, all of which occurred during the preceding five years, during which period she had lived in the same farmhouse with her parents, and the attacks had all occurred when she was home, most of them in August.

Cause—a poison ivy vine on the farmhouse.

ACTION OF R. RADICANS ON DOMESTIC ANIMALS

ORFILA (1883)

Experiment I.—A small dog was made to swallow 12 grams of dry powder of *R. radicans;* the animal was not sensible of it.

Experiment II.—Ten grams of the aqueous extract of *R. radicans* was applied to the cellular tissue on the back of a little dog. Three days later the animal presented no remarkable phenomena.

Experiment III.—At 7:00 A.M., 16 grams of the same extract was applied on the cellular tissue of the interior side of the leg. At 10:00 A.M., the animal was sensible of nothing; the same condition existed at 6:00 P.M. The next day at 10:00 A.M. he commenced to be a little low spirited. At 10:30 P.M. he was insensible and motionless, he scarcely breathed; it was impossible for him to stand upright; a quarter of an hour later he took two or three deep breaths and died. He was opened the next day. The digestive canal was empty and scarcely damaged; the wound was slightly irritated, and the member operated upon presented an infiltration of bloody serum.

Experiment IV.—At 8:00 A.M. 16 grams of aqueous extract of *R. radicans* was introduced into the stomach of an average-sized dog and the esophagus was tied. The next day at 10:00 P.M. did not appear to be incommoded. The following day at 7:00 A.M. he began to be low spirited; however, he retained the free use of his senses and movements, and he scarcely groaned. At 10:00 A.M. he was very dizzy, and he fell whenever he tried to walk; his head was heavy, his pupils a little dilated; his vision and hearing were good; his respiration was slow and a little labored; he had no convulsions, and did not groan. At 1:00 P.M., he was found dead, and was opened. The stomach contained a large quantity of the brown and viscous fluid; the mucous membrane was a bright red, evidently inflamed, no change in the intestinal canal; the blood in the heart cavities was a rich red and fluid; the lungs red, very crepitatious and contained a little blood.

Experiment V.—Four grams of the same extract dissolved in 12 grams of water was injected into the jugular vein of a very vigorous dog. An hour and a half later the animal had vomited six times a bilious mucous matter and he had had a stool. The next day he was unexpectedly well. One gram, 60 centegr. injected in the jugular vein of a little dog, gave analogous results.

Experiment VI.—The same experiment was repeated on a small dog with 4 grams, 30 centegr. of the extract dissolved in 10 grams of water. The animal panted very much and seemed suffocated; he was put on the ground and he became so insensible that he was thought dead. He expired a minute later in the middle of marked trembling of all the muscles of the body. They opened him in the field. The heart blood was fluid, and of a rich red in the left ventricle; the lungs were in their natural state.

I quote the different facts which I intend to prove: (1) that the most active part of *R. radicans* or *Toxicodendron* is that which is released as a gas when not exposed to the sun's rays (Van Mons); (2) that it acts like the acrid poisons; (3) that the aqueous extract administered internally or applied to the cellular tissue determines a local irritation, followed by an inflammation more or less intense, and which exercises a stupifying action on the nervous system after having been absorbed; (4) that it seems to act in the same manner when it has been injected into the jugular vein.

### CASE OF AN ANNUAL RETURN OF R. TOXICODENDRON DERMATITIS

Parrish (1851)

Mentions a young lady of twenty-two years of age who was exposed in the summer of 1838 to *R. Toxicodendron*, which resulted in dermatitis. In 1839 and about the same time in the year disease again returned and continued to do so every year except the last (viz., 1838, 1839, 1840, 1841, 1842, 1843, 1844, 1845, 1846, 1847, 1848, 1849, 1850, 1851). She was then on a visit to Virginia. She took a preventative treatment of potassium iodine daily for several weeks before the expected attack.

### EXPERIMENTAL CASE OF POISONING WITH R. VENENATA

Pfaff (1897)

October 13, 1894, 5:00 P.M.—On the anterior surface of the left forearm, 3 inches from the wrist, some of the oil extracted from *R. venenata* was placed with a glass rod. The forearm was then wrapped with absorbent cotton and bandaged. 11:00 P.M.—Left forearm has a very slight burning sensation. An area the size of a cent about the point of application of the oil was reddened, and a new dressing put on.

October 14, 7:00 A.M.—Burning sensation slightly increased. The area which was inflamed last night has now about ten vesicles dotted over it, and the redness has increased to the size of a dollar. P.M.—The area of inflammation now about 1 1/2 inches in diameter. The vesicles seen in the morning have become confluent and appear as one large blister the size of a ten-cent piece.

October 15, 5:00 A.M.—The left forearm itched considerably during the night. Redness now 2 inches in diameter and becoming somewhat swollen. P.M.—The arm is now considerably swollen and slightly painful.

October 16, 7:00 A.M.—Arm more painful and tender. The photograph taken this A.M. (Pfaff, Plate X, Fig. 1) gives a good idea of the distribution of the vesicles and the degree of swelling. Applied a paste of zinc oxide ʒ ss, amyli, vaseline āā ℥ ss at 12:00 M. and again at 7:00 P.M. 7:00 P.M.—The vesicles are larger and redder than this morning. There are a few (six or seven) vesicles on index finger and a few scattered all around the forearm. 9:00 P.M.—Swelling extends now from knuckles to the elbow. Pronation and supination painful, feels very uncomfortable. Paste used with light bandage, instead of the heavy bandage of absorbent cotton as heretofore.

October 18, A.M.—Blisters began to break down yesterday and considerable watery fluid ran from the arm. Dressed the arm several times with the above-named paste. Last night applied a mixture of 2 per cent carbolic vaseline and boracic acid ointment. The swelling extends now from between the fingers to above the elbow. The area first affected does not look so red now, nor is it so tender as yesterday. On the edge new vesicles are coming out. The whole arm throbs and burns considerable. 11:00 P.M.—Removed the point of infection, an area 1 inch by 3/7 inch which had become black and necrotic; it was about 1/8 inch in depth. Arm dressed with carbolic vaseline.

October 19, 10:00 A.M.—Arm is considerably swollen to 5 inches above elbow, and some small vesicles here are quite visible. The extent of the swelling can be seen from the second photograph (Pfaff, Plate X, Fig. 2), which is blurred somewhat with the zinc paste. Yet it can be seen that even the finger-joints were noticeably swollen. The whole arm has been oozing since October 17, and required dressing several times a day. The vesicles are now becoming confluent and form blisters the size of a dollar all over the arm.

Two days ago two small blisters appeared on the index finger of the right hand; they have been washed most thoroughly with soap and water and the scrubbing brush, and have not spread much in the last twenty-four hours. During the daytime have carried the arm in a sling since October 16. At night supported arm on a pillow outside of the sheets and blankets, with only an ointment bandage covering it.

October 20, at Dr. Pfaff's suggestion, I stopped applying any ointment and began to scrub the whole arm with soap and water. Although it burned some when rubbed, it was not very painful, and the relief obtained from such treatment was as soothing as after applying the carbolic vaseline. The arm was treated thus several times a day. Went in town today, and as it was painful to bend the elbow, I did not carry the arm in a sling; as a result of this and the car ride, the oedema of the arm became very great, and this caused considerable pain. Supporting it upon a table while sitting in a low chair for several hours gave much comfort and caused an oedematous swelling to collect in the axilla, which disappeared the next day. The vesicular eruption is now at a standstill.

October 23.—From October 21 the swelling gradually disappeared, and today arm is back to normal size. The blebs continued to fill with serum in places until today, the parts first affected drying up three or four days ago. An interesting point is that from the time that water and the scrubbing brush were used, and the ointment stopped, the spreading also stopped, and it left patches on the back of the hand unaffected.

At the height of the inflammation in the arm an intense pruritus ani started up, but two or three days' treatment with soap and water caused it to disappear.

October 27.—After October 23 desquamation began, and by today this process is complete. Now new tissue covers the whole surface that was covered with blisters. The time taken for the healing of the arm from the beginning of the inoculation was just two weeks. There were never any general symptoms, excepting one day a slight fever.

CASE OF SEVERE R. VENENATA DERMATITIS AND CONJUNCTIVITIS

PRICHARD (1891)

A tree (*R. venenata*) was cut for a short time every day for a week, at the end of which time the tree was felled. The sap made the hands black. On October 23 some of juice touched the patient's face, and was wiped off with gloved hand. On October 24 he had three lines of redness on his cheek, which developed in two or three days into facial erysipelas, and grew worse. On October 30 he was ill in bed, arms, genitals, and thighs attacked, first by a red rash, then bullae, suppurated and burst; large crusts formed, exudation profuse from under them. Temperature never over 103° and pulse not over 112. Bowels constipated, required purgatives, urine scanty, but not albuminous.

On October 5 in bed, face, throat, and neck a mass of scabs, some of which were partly loosened by the copious purulent exudation underneath them; unable to see on account of the stiffness of his closed lids, and unable to masticate from the same condition of his cheeks; could protrude tip of tongue, swallow, and speak. On raising the lids, pus poured from his eyes, the conjunctivae were swollen but the corneae bright and the sight good. Forearms, hands, and front and inside of the thighs, and lower part of abdomen were in somewhat the same condition as his face, covered with large crusts surrounded by a pink rash; but the crusts not so black as on face. Genitals much swollen. Effluvium foul and peculiar. Thirsty. Mind clear. Very querulous, complaining most of the itching of his eyes, or the burning of his skin; but he was able to sleep.

This was the day after his worst day. During the next week slowly improved, crusts softened and came off—those of face last—and the conjunctivitis lessened. Able to sit up on October 9. By October 16 convalescent: eyes had ceased to discharge, able to read and walk, face and arms peeling, no pitting; moustache had to be shaved off, as it was impossible to free it from scabs; and a fortnight later he went away for a change.

Treatment—Tonic and antiseptic. Digestion good. Kept up by sustaining nutriment, stimulants, and large doses of tincture $FeCl_3$, strong aperients given when necessary, local applications—eucalyptol, iodoform and oil, and poultices to the scabs. Eyes treated with boracic acid lotion.

CASE OF RHUS CONJUNCTIVITIS, STOMATITIS, AND VULVULITIS

SEABROOK (1891*a*)

In September, 1890, a woman, forty-seven years old, took a wreath which had been hanging on the wall for months and threw it into the fire. While it was burning she noticed some irritation of her throat. Within a day she began to have trouble with the throat and to suffer from general malaise. On her arrival in this city (New York) membrane was found in the fauces and mouth, and later an infiltration of mucous membrane of the genitals and patches of eruption made their appearance on the palms where she had grasped the wreath.

Membrane grayish and not very deep, as it came away readily, leaving a rather dry looking excoriation. Temperature slightly elevated, never above 102° F. and this quickly declined. Lastly, on the fourth day of the attack, the eyes were affected. On the following day a dense membrane had glued together the edges of the eyelids and the lids to the eyeball, but they could be separated. There was but little swelling of lids, which were extremely hard as in diphtheria. In diphtheria conjunctivitis primary secretion serous and infiltration extends through all the tissues of the lids; in this case the infiltration was not apparently in tissues of lids, but mostly upon lower portion of eyeball, with deepest infiltration just within margin of the lower lid, which might possibly be explained by the hands rubbing the eye without getting under the eyelid. Membrane closely attached here, but could be separated, leaving bleeding points on the conjunctival surface of lid. The patches of infiltration on the eyeball had apparently extended deeper than the posterior or anterior conjunctival circulation, for the proper substance of the cornea had been cast from the lower half of the left eyeball. There had been perforations of both corneae, but no infiltrations.

Eyes first treated by atropine and the constant use of hot bichlorid compresses, but they did not do well, and accordingly about the ninth day, the treatment of the left eye was changed for eserin and cold. This stayed the process somewhat. In the diphtheric form the membrane generally lasts about ten days; in this case two days. Perforation on the right had taken place on the tenth day, and on the left about one month from the beginning of the trouble. Shortly before this it had seemed as though it would escape this; for, although there had been an enormous corneal ulcer which had become infiltrated with pus, this had been absorbed, first from the cornea and then from the anterior chamber, showing abscess of the tissues of the iris. But after this, when the tissues of the cornea were regaining their transparency, perforation had occurred. By the use of eserin the lens had not been affected and a fair amount of vision had been obtained.

Diagnosis—Dr. C. S. Bull agreed with Dr. Seabrook in classifying it diphtheric conjunctivitis. Dr. LeRoy M. Yale had case of similar throat symptoms and constitutional disturbances in patient poisoned by inhalation of fumes of burning poison ivy.

Dr. Seabrook in answer to questions agreed that the symptoms had not been those of ordinary diphtheric conjunctivitis and the lesion of the eye had been the last to appear.

## R. TOXICODENDRON THE CAUSE OF FIBRINOUS INFILTRATION OF PREPUCE

SEARBROOK (1891*b*)

Dr. R. F. Weir had case of ivy poisoning in which the prepuce had been the seat of fibrinous infiltration.

## CONJUNCTIVITIS AND KERATITIS FROM POISON IVY

SHERER (1916)

Patient was first seen July 26, 1915 (courtesy of Dr. R. M. Schauffler). Had sustained severe dermatitis venenata from a poison ivy vine several days before. The skin over the left side of left malar eminence was violently inflamed. There was extensive formation of confluent vesicles. Considerable serous oozing occurred, which dried into a soft yellow crust. The inflammation then extended into the ocular structures proper. The conjunctiva became violently inflamed, reddened, swollen, and chemotic. Both palpebral and bulbar conjunctiva were involved, including the transitional folds, which, on everting the lids, appeared like rolls. A number of minute punctate hemorrhages in the conjunctiva were discernible with the magnifying lens. No purulent secretion was discharged at any time. Lachrymation, photophobia, and blepharospasm were present. The pain was very severe. It increased rapidly and became so very bad that an opiate had to be ordered with instructions to use in sufficient amount to control the suffering. By no other means could the pain be subdued.

During the first week of the invasion of the eye the cornea did not exhibit any irritative symptoms. The more painful symptoms had begun to subside already when the first signs of corneal disease appeared in the form of minute gray dots of opacity varying in size from 1/2 to 1 1/2 millimeters in diameter. These first were discovered by focal illumination near the lower border of the limbus. Three days later several appeared near the upper border of the limbus. As many as ten or twelve developed, all deep in the substantia propria. All were confined to the peripheral portion of the cornea and the apical region was never invaded. A faint violaceous circle surrounding the cornea indicated the degree of ciliary injection, although the iris was constantly kept under the influence of atropine. The keratitis, which thus developed relatively late in the course of the disease, persisted correspondingly late after all other symptoms had disappeared.

Focal illumination revealed several small areas of cloudiness of the surface over the deep points of corneal opacity, but no actual desquamation of the corneal epithelium occurred at any place so there was no open ulceration nor cicatrization to contend with. The entire attack lasted about seven weeks, the occurrence of the keratitis prolonging the attack at least three weeks. The areas of gray opacity are to be regarded as accumulations of large numbers of leucocytes which have wandered into the cornea after escaping from the limbic loops of the anterior ciliary and conjunctival blood vessels. These leucocytes correspond to what was originally described by Recklinghausen as "motile corneal corpuscles."

This pathological process occurs whenever any irritant of sufficient intensity is present. The character and amount of the irritant will also determine the quantity of the leucocytic accumulation and whether this inflammatory exudate shall eventually be resolved and absorbed with little or no damage to the corneal tissue or whether a liquefaction shall occur. In the latter case the overlying layers of substantia propria break down, while the epithelium exfoliates and Bowman's membrane gives way and the more dangerous sequel of abcess and ulcer supervene with the possibility, always, in a deep-seated keratitis like this one was, of perforation and eventual loss of the globe.

In this case all the symptoms proved easily controllable and no permanent lesions developed. The strongest mydrialic, atropine, was used throughout. Regular flushings with boric solutions and daily applications of silver were made. Hot applications and the free use of morphine controlled the pain. No iridic exudate formed and the iridic congestion disappeared under the steady dilatation.

As Nuel says, "every pronounced keratitis is dangerous." Uhthoff's statistics show 27 per cent of all blindness to be due to corneal lesions. The prognosis is necessarily serious.

## CASE OF DERMATITIS FROM R. TOXICODENDRON ROOTS, AND RESULTANT HYPERSENSITIVITY

STIRLING (1913)

D. W., aged thirty-four, a strong, healthy, temperate, though temperamentally somewhat nervous man, who works for me as under-gardener, was digging up daffodil bulbs on Thursday, February 20, 1913, from a bed into which the roots of a poison ivy plant, growing on an adjacent bank, had penetrated. In lifting these bulbs, and in ignorance of the presence among them of some of these roots, he happened to handle, in order to throw out, some broken pieces of the latter. The broken ends of the roots exuded a milky juice—a common characteristic of the group to which the poison ivy belongs—and in this plant the juice turns black on exposure in a minute or two. For reasons that will appear, he was afraid of the consequences when he became aware of the nature of the roots he had touched, and when he went home to his mid-day dinner, some two or three hours after contact, he soaked the hand with which he had touched them in a solution of Condy's fluid. On the following morning he experienced some itching pain in that hand (the left), on the back of the proximal phalanges of the first, second, and third digits, and in the inter-digital clefts between these fingers. On the next day, Saturday, February 22, he showed me his hand, and there were then considerable redness and swelling of the parts mentioned, and a few small, clear vesicles exactly like those of herpes. Happening to have antiphlogistine in the house I gave him some to use as an application. On Sunday, February 23, he came from his home to see me, saying that the eruption was much worse, and that it had extended to his left leg. On examination, I found that the redness and swelling of the parts first affected had increased in intensity and area, the vesicles had increased in number, while many of them had, by coalescence, become converted into bullae of about the size of a sixpence, and, in some of the largest of these, the contents had become slightly sanguineous. There were, also, several small isolated patches of similar vesicles of small size, and with clear contents, on the outside of left thigh, the groups being surrounded by areas of reddened and inflamed skin, and there was also a red and slightly swollen patch on, and below, the left lower eyelid. He described the sensation as that of "painful itching" character, and said the antiphlogistine had given no relief. I asked Dr. Hodson, his lodge doctor, who happened to be at my house at the same time, to see him, and take charge of the case, and we advised the use of lead and opium lotion.

I did not see him again until Saturday, March 2, when I visited him at his home, and the conditions were then as follows: The previously mentioned fingers, the back of the hand, the back and radial side of the forearm, as far as the elbow joint, were red, inflamed, and greatly swollen, and almost the whole of this area was so closely covered with contiguous bullae with faintly yellow, serous contents, and of a size varying from that of a sixpence to that of a florin, that scarcely any intervening, unraised epidermis remained. Many of the larger bullae that had ruptured spontaneously were discharging their contents fully, and, at the peripheral edge of this bullous tract, there was a zone of small, clear, herpetic vesicles, some being so small as to be almost punctiform in character. The ulnar border of the forearm was free from redness or bullae. There was also a red area with small vesicles on the front of the right forearm. The vesicles of the isolated patches on the inside of the left thigh, that had become apparent a week previously, had shrivelled, but in their place, the whole of the inside of the thigh had become swollen and red and covered with minute clear vesicles. The right thigh was also similarly affected, to an even severer extent. There was also a patch, showing a little reddening and some small vesicles at the bend of the right elbow, and a faint similar indication on the abdomen. The patient reported that the pain and itching were very severe, that he was unable to get any rest in consequence, and that he felt really ill; but he said that all these symptoms were rather less severe than on the previous day. On one night during the previous week he had had shivering fits, which had so alarmed him that he had sent for Dr. Hodson. There had also been a temporary patch of redness, without vesiculation, on the scrotum. The pulse was good, and the tongue was clean, but he had no taste for food, and had got perceptibly thinner. Unfortunately I can give no record of his temperature. He said that the lead and opium first ordered had done no good, but that he had experienced considerable relief from a cyllinlotion (m. xii to 6 ounces of water) subsequently given by Dr. Hodson on that day; also he was ordered a bromid mixture, which proved effective in giving him some rest. Although the fact was not apparent at the time of my visit, Dr. Hodson told me that he noticed at one time that the red base, from which the bullae were raised, was sharply separated from the unaffected skin by a distinct line of demarcation.

I saw the patient a week later, Sunday, March 9. On the left forearm, in which the condition had been most severe on the previous Sunday, the swelling had subsided and the greater number of the blebs on the radial side and back had disappeared, some of them having been punctured either by Dr. Hodson or himself, under instructions, and some having ruptured spontaneously. The area on which the blebs had existed was of a dark-red color, and there still remained several large blisters on the upper part of the forearm, two or three of these being as large as a crown piece, and elevated to the extent of 1/4–1/3 inch above the general surface of the skin. In most of these bullae the contents were still serous and liquid, but in several they had become sero-sanguinolent and consequently reddish in appearance. In some, the raised epidermis was red, while the contents of the bleb were still serous. None had suppurated. The peripheral zone of small or punctiform vesicles had disappeared, and the ulnar surface still remained unaffected, except for the presence of a few bullae toward the elbow. The "itching pain" had gone, but the patient said there was an "aching pain," like that of rheumatism, in the forearm from wrist to elbow. The blebs in the interdigital clefts had all coalesced into one large blister, extending halfway up to the joint between the proximal and middle phalanges, which was ruptured and discharging. There had been an area of small vesicles just above the elbow, but these had not become confluent, nor had the patches extended; these had now subsided.

On the pulmar aspect of the right forearm from about 3 inches above the wrist to about the same distance below the elbow, there was a crop of mostly unruptured serous bullae, the majority of which were about 1/3 inch in diameter. Some were as large as a florin; and all were elevated to the extent of about 1/4 inch. The larger ones were confined to the front and radial side, and the bullae had encroached, only on one place, on the ulnar side. It was noticeable that, while on the left arm the extensor surface was the most affected, in the right it was the flexor side that suffered most severely, and on both sides the ulnar surface had almost entirely escaped invasion. On the back of the forearm, a little above the wrist, there were about one half dozen blebs. The contents of the blebs were as on the other arm, mostly serous; in a few, however, they had become sanguinolent. In this arm he experienced the same kind of itching pain as he had previously felt in the other, but less severe. There had previously been some swelling but this had almost subsided by the time I saw him. The redness, previously noticed in the lower eyelid, had also subsided without vesiculation. On the inside of the thighs from knees to within 6 inches of the groin there was some redness, diffuse in some parts, in others muscular in character, and suggesting the appearance of eruption of measles. Throughout these areas, there were signs of the antecedent existence of small vesicles which had subsided without coalescence. The patient said there had previously been considerable swelling of both thighs, but this had now subsided, and there were a few small red spots on both calves. The patient was now free from severe pain, could sleep and eat better, looked better, and could walk. It was evident that the right arm was following the left toward recovery, the conditions of the former being, with less intensity, those presented by the latter about five days previously.

The patient presented himself again on March 19, by which date all pain, redness, and bullae had disappeared, and the skin of the previously affected parts had assumed its normal appearance. There still remained, however, a slight tenderness of the hands, and there were a few itching papules on the chest and abdomen, but I am not sure that these were connected with the original trouble. The general health was re-established, and he said he felt quite fit to come back to work. He had, however, been incapacitated from his duties for a period of four weeks, during one of which he was confined to bed.

Ever since the first attack his skin has been excessively susceptible to various irritants, to which he was previously not sensitive. He cannot, e.g., touch the leaves of ordinary ivy without getting a slight vesicular erythema, though previously he could handle this plant with impunity; and, on a recent occasion a very short exposure to the sun, while paddling in the sea, caused a violent dermatitis of the legs with some blistering of the exposed parts, to which effects, also, he said he was not previously liable.

### TREATMENT FOR POISONING BY R. TOXICODENDRON

STONE (1874)

Eruption appeared on the hands the third day after exposure, then scrotum and various parts of the body. Used lead acetate lotion without good results. Followed in forty-eight hours by phenol ʒ iij, glycerol, ℥ ij, water g. s. to make Oj mixture. Almost instant relief.

### CASE OF CHRONIC POISONING FROM CONTACT WITH R. DIVERSILOBA LEAVES

TREILLE (1904)

February 17, 1903—Patient by name of Holl, American sailor, embarked on a trip from Trieste, is entered at the St. Joseph ward, in the service of foreign maladies.

He was a young man twenty-three years of age, originally of the state of Colorado, blond, lymphatic temperament, but of a robust constitution maintained by a strong muscularity. He had never had the malady in infancy or adolescence, until the moment in which the events occur which form the object of this observation, and which run back to 1899. But since this date he has had frequent trouble with his health, and he had just landed in Europe when he had smallpox, in spite of previous vaccination of which legitimate traces remained.

Coming from Trieste to Marseilles seeking embarkment which would permit him to return to the United States, he passed several weeks in this town. Toward the end of January he was seized with a pustular eruption on the neck, shoulders, in the ankle region, and finally in the region of the umbilicus.

Convinced, by having been infected with similar eruptions, which had disappeared after several days of care and rest, he remained at his boarding-house. But the eruption did not stop aggravating him and he decided to seek admission in the hospital. He was then directed to l'Hotel-Dieu, where he was admitted into our service February 17.

We ascertained, the same day, the presence of pustulous blisters and ecthynnosic pustules on the neck and arms, the former on the way to recovery, the others of recent evolution. There existed about fifteen unequally distributed among the regions above mentioned. Between crusty pustules the skin was dry like scurvy-skin; and besides there existed numerous small pimples, sufficiently similar if not identical to lichen tropicus, irregularly distributed over the upper part of the thorax and on the shoulders. The eruption ceased from two sides above the elbows. On the legs the same pustulous eruption appeared at the knee, where it surrounded the limb like a ring. The ulcerated blisters are nearly confluent and their blackish crusts, a little hemorrhagic, assemble on the borders.

But it was in the abdominal region, between the pubis and the umbilica, that the eruption was most characteristic; there it produced real injury. There, in fact, the pustules were jagged in cups, their edges were ulcerated, a corroded process invaded it, and it was no more than a vast serpigineus sore. If there did not exist still more of these, that is to say entirely isolated and conforming normally, one could not know at first sight to what origin to attribute this sore which extends from one hypochondriac to the other, uniting all the region upon the subpubic and descending to the root of the penis. This is ulcerated in a ring; the furrow is deep, spongy; the covering of the penis, even to the end of the prepuce, is the seat of a considerable oedema. Pain exists in the passage of urine, as in certain very sharp phimosis.

The lymphatic system acknowledges its infection by the swelling of the ganglions of the groin, of the arm pit, and of the neck; not of epitrochliens ganglions.

The liver presented nothing odd, neither to the stroke nor at the palpation. The spleen is normal. The stomach is a little enlarged; not sensible to pressure. The caecum and the large intestine as far as the level of the hepatic channel are obstructed; there are coprostase, and besides constipation is a rule after several months. The tongue is plainly saburral, the breath bad; the diseased complains of lack of appetite and nausea. The heart beats are normal. The pulse is weak, depressed, at 114, in contradiction to the temperature which does not exceed 38.5°. Questioned as to his antecedents, and especially on the point as to whether he had had a venereal disease, the diseased affirmed categorically that he never had, and besides he had never even been sick until the moment when he had been touched by the poison oak.

At this point, we demanded him to tell us the circumstances to which he alluded, and here is the account he gave us, which for more certitude we had him commit to writing, and of which this is the literal translation:

"One day in the summer of 1899, I took my gun, and crossing San Francisco Bay, I went into the Berkeley Hills with the aim of hunting squirrels. I walked, to begin from this moment, continually, crossing underwood comprising poison oak, and the branches of this bush rubbed my hands and my face at every moment. Thus I was poisoned. The next morning my face was all red and inflamed; I felt an itching and brisk burning. In the evening of the same day my eyelids swelled so that I could not open them and could not see. My hands, arms, neck, and face burned. These accidents aggravated, and finally my whole body, but most particularly my chest and my back, became the seat of pimples and of insupportable itching. They gave me a special remedy for poison oak; it did not succeed unless to diminish the itching. They then recommended me to take a remedy for purifying the blood, and I tried two kinds. The one had no effect; but the other (Clarke's blood mixture) worked very well, and I believe that this remedy finally cured me, inasmuch as it stopped the fever and the swelling of the skin. This was accomplished with two flagons; and the druggist told me then that I ought to take four more, which would suffice for my entire recovery. But I expected that the progress already obtained would continue by itself, and I ceased to take care of myself.

"Shortly afterward I left California for Australia. During this journey they set salt provisions for us to eat and immediately I felt ill. The skin of my face, neck, chest, and arms which had not been entirely cured were covered again with pimples, blisters, and from this time the eruptions have never ceased.

"This poison oak is a vine of which the wood is dark yellow; its leaves are thick, and, if I remember well, almost figured like those of roses. In winter they are green, but in autumn they turn red and there exist here and there on their branches, small bunches of red (white?) berries. The plant buds like a tree there, or where it is isolated; but as soon as it has a tree for support on which to attach itself it develops a vine and climbs. I have seen it climbing thus on certain trees (redwood?) to a height of 200 feet.

"Certain persons can touch the leaves of poison oak without being in the least discommoded; to certain others, on the contrary, it suffices to breathe of it to be infected.

"The woods and the forests of California are filled with this plant, and each year a number of people are poisoned by it. Many remedies exist for poison oak, and in San Francisco there are numerous calls in this sense. But the effect of these remedies is only temporary.

"I have known of persons who were poisoned by the fumes of stems of poison oak when they were being burned."

Such is the history of this man.

What I know of the properties of *R. Toxicodendron*, called poison oak, poison ivy, trailing poison oak by Americans and the English, agrees perfectly with the account of Holl. There are many cases of poison oak dermatitis among the forest clearers of West America, and also among the river-residents of Vancouver and of the Maritime States on the border of the northern Pacific as far as Alaska and the immensities of the Dominion of Canada. We are evidently in the presence of a dermatitis of this latter origin, subscribed exteriorly of a general infection.

The treatment adopted cannot be symptomatical, in the absence of one essential pathological causality. I confined myself also entirely at first to provoking the cicatrization of the ulcers and to prevent, if possible, the evolution of new blisters or pustules.

I applied locally compresses wet with a solution of ferrico-potassium, an old remedy which I had used in Newfoundland in similar cases; and when at the end of several days the pimples were sufficiently advanced I powdered all the surfaces again with dermatol. In less than fifteen days the cicatrization of the sore at the base of the stomach was complete. In the same time the digestive functions, watched and improved by some laxatives as well as by a proper diet, were re-established little by little; the first day of March the patient could get up and walk, not showing more than several baffling pustules along the anterior surface of the forearm, and some dry nodes, crusts, some of which, in the lower pubic region looked of cicatricial organization.

I ought to indicate here that since the first days I have undertaken by Mr. Chambrau, interne in pharmacy of the office, to analyse the urine which resulted in obtaining the following:

| | |
|---|---|
| Quantity of urine.......................... | 2,000.00 c.c. |
| Very acid.................................. | |
| Urea....................................... | 38.40 gr. |
| Phosphates................................. | 4.46 |
| Chlorids................................... | 14.8 |
| Albumin.................................... | 0.40 |
| Sediment negative.......................... | |

To summarize there is a certain degree of demineralization and besides albuminuria.

At the same time examinations of the contents of the phlycten and of the ulcerated blisters were made by Dr. Gauthrer which gave indications that the staphlococci alone had been constant. The blood analysis furnished proof of the existence of a hyperleucocytosis with abundant polynuclear leucocytes, about 75 per cent, with a relative amount of mononuclear.

Summarizing, if one reckons that this blood character is shown in a large number of infections, its significance in the case which is mentioned remains as much less positive because three months before Holl had had smallpox, and had besides at this moment a pyogenic eruption.

The re-establishment of the disease followed its course until March 4, when suddenly he had a feverish pulse which lasted three days. The morning of the seventh it completely abated to 36.5°; the eighth the temperature rose again to 37.7° (in order to come down to normal); the morning of March 10 until March 14, total intermission. But on March 14 there was a new pulse which lasted just twenty-four hours. To begin from this moment it lowered to normal and remained there. Now during this period of ten days, disturbed by three rises in temperature above 38°, he had gastric trouble, nausea, and constipation. At the same time there was outlining the wrists and the chest in the region of the lower clavical a light eruption of new pustules. But this phenomena stopped short and seemed to have ceased by means of administrations against gastric trouble; milk and eggs, saline purgatives. I would not mention this episode, at first view insignificant and sufficiently common among patients of hospitals in course of treatment or of convalescence, if on the one hand there had only been the one remarkable coincidence between the gastric trouble, the paroxysm of fever, and the new eruption of pimple blisters; and if, on the other hand, I had not employed there to tie up a new morbid manifestation, entirely unexpected, and which seemed to act together in a particularly grave manner.

In fact, the morning of March 18, Holl discovered that he was not able to support himself on his legs. On my visit, he complained of great feebleness and when I asked him to state exactly how he felt, he told us that this was not the first time, and that before in 1901 he had been in like manner very feeble, and that walking had been very difficult for him for many days in consequence of an eruption.

I had him get up, and ascertained, in fact, that he could not place his feet perpendicularly, that he trembled, and that he was obliged to support himself on his bed in order to stand. I had him go to bed, and had inquiry made of the reflexes of the knee pan and the plantar surface of the foot. They were preserved, but the sensibility was injured. He was sensible to pain of the prick of a pin on the sole of the feet, the legs, and the thigh.

To begin from this moment the infirmity increased from day to day, and toward March 30 the paralysis was complete. The patient absolutely could not move his legs. The mere effort that he made met with a contraction of the vastus exterior and of the sartorius of each side so that he was unable to support himself. At the same moment, the reflexes of the knee pan and plantar surface were stopped. It is important, moreover, to note that micturition and defecation were perfectly preserved. It is legitimate to consider it as one of the forms of paralysis of the inferior members, most frequently transitory, which one observes occasionally in the course of certain infectious diseases.

Nevertheless, in the presence of this complication, we ask ourselves what has happened. In spite of the perfect quiet of the patient who repeated always that he had already had feebleness in the legs after a strong eruption—as he well remembered that this time he had incomparably more feeling than previously—one could doubt, justly, a progressive development of the process toward the medulla.

And, besides, the suspicion of a forgotten syphilis presents itself again to the mind. I therefore requested Drs. Boinet and Perrin to come and see my patient. The examination made, and, in spite of the affirmation that the existence of syphilis was impossible, especially in the presence of the cicatrization of the pustules and of the ganglionic resolution, we judged, however, that it was prudent to make an experimental treatment. I prescribed, therefore, a syrup of Gilbert. But, from the fourth spoonful to mouth, the fourth day, a violent stomatitis broke out, and we had to immediately cease administering the syrup of Gilbert.

It was a curious case and what caused a greater surprise in this succession of clinic facts was that at the precise moment in which the administration of the mercury salt had been begun—perhaps the same day or two before—I have thought to remark of the signs of returning activity from the side of the paralyzed members. Still toward April 9 or 10, Holl could move his great toes, and afterward, with great effort, it is true, succeeded in displacing his heels.

This sign of improvement was not noticeable until the first days of May; very slowly, almost insensible, but regularly the facility in moving the legs progressed. Nevertheless, Holl could not move at this last day more than to get out of his bed and stand a few moments on his feet. His legs were soft, uncertain, and it was necessary that he hold tightly to his bed to keep from falling. At the least step which he tried to take his legs awkwardly caught on each other.

Nevertheless, the paralysis has disappeared, the reflexes ever re-established, the sensibility again restored although still weak.

I abridge, from that time, this clinic history; it is hereafter without interest. Holl, at the end of a month, was in a condition to leave the hospital, and the consul of the United States made him go out in view of reconciling him. After five weeks I learned that he had disembarked at New York in good health.

Dr. Treille believes that the repeated relapse of the dermatitis was due to an awakening of the poison.

### CASE IN WHICH PILLOW-CASE TRANSMITS R. TOXICODENDRON POISON

WALKER (1891)

Miss E. W. spent the night with her sister, Mrs. C., whose husband was obliged to be absent on business. Mr. C. had been poisoned about the head and neck with ivy a few days before leaving home. The pillow-case on which he slept was not changed, and his sister-in-law, using it, became poisoned about the face and neck in consequence thereof, no other opportunity for contracting the disease existing.

### DEATH OF CHILD FROM R. TOXICODENDRON POISONING

WHITE (1887*a*)

My wife's brother, of Brookline, a child of six years, died of poison by ivy in the autumn of 1819, having been twice before poisoned during the previous summer. The circumstances were these.

A servant-boy living in the family, being insuspectible of poison by ivy, had been employed in pulling up all the vines of that plant found growing in the grounds about the house. When his task was finished, he was made to wash his hands thoroughly with hot water and soap, and afterward with vinegar. Mrs.—, who feared that the boy, notwithstanding his supposed invulnerability, might possibly be injured by so much handling of the poisonous stuff, stood by to enforce the operation. In the afternoon, at his own request, he was allowed to take little R.—— to Jamaica Pond for a bath. Having stripped the child, he immersed him, holding him with his hands under the armpits, and afterward rubbed his back with his open palm.

After two or three days the child was taken ill, and grew rapidly worse. Deep ulcers made their appearance under the armpits, and the skin of the back exhibited in aggravated form the usual marks of poisoning by ivy. He died at the end of the third week of his sickness. The attending family physician was the late Dr. Wilds.

The child had been healthy, although not robust. Perhaps the two previous poisonings, from which, however, he seemed to have perfectly recovered, had weakened the power of resistance in the constitution, and so contributed to the fatal result of the last attack. He died on October 6.

### CASE OF MILD DERMATITIS FROM R. VENENATA

WHITE (1887*b*)

On September 28 I picked a large bunch of the gorgeously tinted leaves of *R. venenata* from a tree some 10 feet high, growing in a swamp in Dedham. It was a warm and sunny afternoon, and, my botanical box being filled with other specimens, I brought them home in my hand, from the palm of which the epidermis had been torn in several places a few minutes before by falling upon the uncut, splintered portion of a stump. They were carried in this hand at least an hour and a half, and during the evening were repeatedly handled while arranging them for the herbarium. Some of the still green and unchanged leaves were also picked. The conditions were thus as favorable as possible for the absorption or action of the poison. Not the slightest effect was produced upon the skin, however. I thought I felt during the evening, while working over them, directly beneath the heat of an argand gas-burner, a sensation of irritation or acridity about the eyes and throat. They were subsequently handled freely for ten days every morning, while changing the driers in the press.

October 6—I picked at Fresh Pond a large quantity of *R. Toxicodendron* specimens changed to autumn tints, and others still of a glossy green, from plants running over stone walls and climbing high trees. Both leaves and stems were collected. These, too, were handled freely on a warm afternoon, and repeatedly afterward in the press. It was absolutely inactive upon my skin.

October 10—I again visited the swamp where the poison sumach, or dogwood, grows in abundance, after specimens of the fruit, but failed to obtain them. I picked many of the brilliant leaves, however, and twigs and branch with foliage still unchanged in color. The juice, which exuded freely from the broken wood, was rubbed upon my hands in several places and allowed to dry there, and the leaves touched my face repeatedly while gathering them. I again thought I perceived in my air-passages and eyes at the time, and later in the evening again while pressing the specimens, the same impression of acridity.

Nothing was noticed upon the skin indicating any action upon its tissues until two days later (October 12) a single vesicle, with the peculiar thick cover and somewhat dark look so often seen, appeared upon the back of a finger, but accompanied by no sensation.

October 13—The third day, a single and similar, though somewhat larger, vesicle appeared upon my left wrist; to which two others joined themselves on the following or fourth day, thus making a very small group. At the same time —that is, October 14—a single additional vesicle showed itself some three-fourths inch from the first-comers upon the finger and wrist.

October 17—One of the vesicles which appeared last upon the knuckle, without any external irritation, increased to three times its original size, with burning and itching sensations. The other efflorescences quiescent or receding.

October 19 (no specimens having been handled for a week)—A new and very large vesicle of irregular shape appeared on the back of the last phalanx of the right thumb, covered with so thick a roof as to appear untransparent, as if the effusion had taken place in the lowest layer of the rete mucosum.

October 21—Two new vesicles, one on the back of the left forefinger, the other on the thumb near its base.

October 23—All the groups, old and new, have become enlarged by the appearance of new vesicles at the peripheries (excepting those upon the wrists, which had been opened for the purpose of an experiment described below), and one new cluster appeared on the back of the right middle-finger. All itch and burn extremely.

October 26—The original vesicles and papules have, in many of the clusters, resolved themselves apparently into two or three times their number of smaller efflorescences, the whole patch flattening down and assuming a darker brown tinge.

October 27—A large, single vesicle, with the thick and opaque covering peculiar to its seat, has struggled up into distinct prominence in the palm of the right hand, near its ulnar border; a fresh one also at the base of the nail of the left thumb. At this date there are seven single or groups of efflorescences on different parts of the hands, in all stages of development or involution.

November 1—Another small vesicle has appeared in the right palm, half an inch from that of October 27. The earlier vesicles have nearly all flattened down to the level of the general surface.

November 3—A single vesicle shows itself upon the internal lateral surface of the left thumb. This was the last to appear, and from this date all the effects present gradually subsided and after a fortnight were no longer perceptible. At the present time, November 26, their seats are still defined by the more glossy look of the new epidermis which covers them.

This may be taken as a description of the effects of the poison upon the human skin in its mildest form. The changes, however, as described, are typical of the peculiar efflorescence in all cases. In what respects it falls short of the manifestations in its severest forms may be learned by comparison with the histories of the following cases.

### CASE OF SEVERE R. TOXICODENDRON DERMATITIS

WHITE (1887*c*)

Several years ago I was called to see a young lady who a few days previously had come in contact with poison ivy while gathering autumn leaves. Her whole head was greatly swollen, and the features were so distorted that no one could recognize her. On close inspection, the skin of the face and neck was felt to be deeply oedematous, and was largely covered with vesicles of all sizes, many of which were seated on an erythematous base, others being still in their papular stage of development. There were also numerous large excoriations, from which fluid was freely exuding, stiffening in places on drying and forming soft crusts. The ears were much thickened, and were dripping with the escaping serous exudation. The hands were also affected, being thickly covered upon their backs with groups of small vesicles, while upon the palms numerous vesicular exudations were dimly seen beneath the thickened epidermal coverings, trying to push themselves above the level of the general surface. The other parts of the body were unaffected. The subjective symptoms were great itching and burning of the parts affected, with the feeling of local discomfort consequent upon so great swelling of the features. The eyes were nearly closed. There was a slight general febrile action.

New efflorescences continued to appear for several days; but the course of all the cutaneous manifestations was abbreviated, and the oedema immediately reduced, by the local treatment which was employed.

The following year, the same patient, then nineteen years old, was bathing at the seashore in August, and, while climbing up from the water over the rocks, her bare knee and leg came in contact with the poisonous vine. I saw her a few days afterward. There was then a long strip of reddened skin, several inches in width, covered with vesicles and a few papules, running upward and downward from the knee. The chin was occupied by a large group of papules, a few of which had already advanced to the vesicular stage. The skin beneath one eye was also puffed and reddened. The further progress of the affection was quickly checked by local applications, and, as in the previous attack, the effects of the poison at the end of some two weeks had entirely disappeared.

Three years afterward, at New Year's time, I was again called to see this young lady. Her face and hands were affected in a manner similar to that first described, though the inflammatory process was less severe. The parts were less swollen, but there was an abundant eruption of the vesicles and flow of serous exudation from the excoriated parts. The appearances were wholly characteristic of ivy poisoning, yet she had not been out of the city, and it was midwinter. On inquiry, I found that a box of Christmas greens had been received from the country, which she had used in decorating the house. Among them were sprigs of poison ivy leaves, the cause and explanation of the attack.

CASE OF SEVERE R. TOXICODENDRON DERMATITIS

WHITE (1887*d*)

Late in October, 1871, I was called to see a gentleman who, in cleaning up his grounds at the seashore a few days previously, had handled the poison vine which grew upon the place in great abundance. His hands, especially the lateral surfaces of the fingers, were then thickly covered with vesicles, and his face and genitals were badly swollen. The following day the eruption appeared upon the arms, and about the thighs and abdomen, and continued to spread for several days, until at last it presented the following appearances.

The face and ears were of a lurid red color, greatly swollen, and dripping with fluid exudation. The neck, chest, and abdominal wall were also reddened, and occupied by large patches of flattened papules and vesicles, and by moist excoriations. The genitals were enormously distended by oedema, and the scrotum was running with serum. The arms and legs were also oedematous, and largely occupied by fields of the peculiarly characteristic vesicles of the affection. The patient was of a highly nervous temperament, and suffered tortures from the severe itching which accompanied the eruption. The skin was so universally irritable that no clothes could be worn for forty-eight hours when the affection was at its height, and a sheet or blanket was the only covering tolerated during this time. Sleep without powerful anodynes was impossible for several nights in succession. There was but little fever or constitutional disturbance, however. Applications were almost constantly made to the whole surface, and after the seventh or eighth day from the first appearance of the eruption there were no new manifestations, and the skin rapidly returned to its natural state.

# BIBLIOGRAPHY

The bibliography is divided into classifications as follows: Botanical References; Chemical References (fat formation—carbohydrates to fat in animals, carbohydrates to fat in plants, protein to fat in animals; Japan wax; chemistry of the poisonous principle of *Rhus;* laccase); Pathological References; Remedies. This list of references makes no claims of being complete but it may serve as a beginning for anyone interested in the subjects. By far the greater part of the list was given to me a number of years ago by Mr. L. E. Warren, associate chemist for the American Medical Association. The original bibliography of Mr. Warren is now in Lloyd's Library in Cincinnati, Ohio, and Mr. John Uri Lloyd has kindly given the author permission to print it here.

## BOTANICAL REFERENCES


ABRAMS, LEROY

1911. *Flora of Los Angeles and Vicinity.*

ADANSON, M.

1763. *Familles des plantes*, Part II, p. 342. Paris.

AGUILAR, ALONZO RAEL VALVORDE Y COSIO DE (ANTONIO).

1719. *Diario y Derrotero.* In Bancroft Collection, University of California, Berkeley, California.

AITON, W.

1787. *Hortus Kewensis*, I, 366, 367. London.

1905. *Index Kewensis*, Supp. 2, p. 158, *Rhus Rydbergii.* Oxford.

ALDEN, J. B.

1892. *Manifold Cyclopedia of Knowledge and Language*, Vol. XXXVI, art. "Sumach." New York.

ANDERSON, C. L.

1870. "Catalogue of Nevada Flora," *Nevada State Mineralogist* (third biennial report), p. 119.

ANDREWS, E. F.

1903. *Botany All the Year Around*, p. 87. New York, Cincinnati, and Chicago.

ANNANDAB, C., and SPOFFORD, A. R. (editors).

1901. *Twentieth Century Cyclopaedia*, VIII, 151. New York and Philadelphia.

APGAR, A. C.

1891. *Pocket Key of Trees*, p. 18. Trenton.

1892. *Trees of the Northern United States*, p. 90. New York, Cincinnati, and Chicago.

APPLETON.

1904. *Medical Dictionary*, p. 1703. New York and London.

Arthur, J., and MacDougal, D. R.
1898. *Living Plants and Their Properties*, p. 162. New York.
Atkinson, G. F.
1905. *College Botany*, pp. 416, 707. New York.
Bailey, L. H.
1906. *New Cyclopedia of American Horticulture*, V, 1529, 1530. New York.
1907. *Cyclopedia of American Agriculture*, II, 114. New York.
Bailey, W. W.
1873. "Our Poisonous Plants," *American Naturalist*, VII, 4, 5. Salem.
1896. *Among Rhode Island Wild Flowers*, p. 25. Providence.
Baillon, H. E.
1892. *Dictionnaire de botanique*, IV, 129. Paris.
Baker, E. D.
1883. *A Partial List of the Native Flora of Waltham, Massachusetts*, p. 5. Waltham.
Bancroft, Hubert Howe.
1889. *History of Arizona and New Mexico*, p. 236. San Francisco.
Barton, W. P. C.
1818. *Compendium, Florae Philadelphicae*, I, 154. Philadelphia.
Beal, W. J.
1892. *Michigan Flora*, p. 81. Lansing.
Beck, L. C.
1848, 1856. *Botany of the United States North of Virginia* (2d ed.), pp. 72, 75. New York.
Beckwith, Florence, and Macauley, Mary E.
1896. *Plants of Monroe County, New York*, p. 55. Rochester.
Beddome, R. H.
1873. *The Flora Sylvatica for Southern India*, III, 78, Fig. 3. Madras.
Behr, H. H.
1889. *American Druggist and Pharmaceutical Record*, XVIII, 201. New York.
Bennett, J. J.
1838. *Plantae Javanicae Rariores*, p. 60.
Bennett, J. L.
1888. *Plants of Rhode Island*, p. 8. Providence.
Bentham, G.
1861. *Flora honghongencis*, p. 69. London.
Bigelow, J.
1817. "*Rhus vernix*," *American Medical Botany*, I, 96. Boston.
1820. "*Rhus radicans*," *ibid.*, III, 20.
Bergen, J. Y.
1901. *Bergen's Botany, Key and Flora Northern and Central States*, p. 138. Boston.
*Florula Bostoniensis* (3d ed.), pp. 126, 127.

BISHOP, J. N.
1885. *A Catalogue of All the Phaenogamous Plants at Present Known to Grow in the State of Connecticut*, p. 6. Hartford.

BLACKWOOD, A. L.
1906. *A Manual of Materia Medica, Therapeutics, and Pharmacology*, pp. 433–35. Philadelphia.

BOERHAAVE, H.
1720. *Indexalter plantarum quae in Horto academico Lugduni-Batavo aluntur*, II, 229. Lugduni Batavorum.

BOLANDER, H. N.
1863. "*Rhus diversiloba*," *Proceedings of the California Academy of Science* (1st. ser.), III, 78. San Francisco.
1867. *Names of California Plants*, p. 7. San Francisco.

BOSSER, N., and FORSTER, J. R.
1771. *Travels through that Part of North America Formerly Called Louisiana*, II, 30. London.

BRAINERD, E., JONES, L. R., and EGGLESTON, W. W.
1900. *Flora of Vermont*, p. 58. Burlington.

BRANDEGEE, TOWNSEND S.
1889. "A Collection of Plants from Baja California," *Proceedings of the California Academy of Sciences* (2d ser.), II, 140.
1890. "The Plants of Santa Catalina Island," *Zoe*, I, 110, 134. San Francisco.

BRANDIS, D.
1874. *The Forest Flora of Northwestern and Central India.* London.

BRENDEL, F.
1860. *The Trees and Shrubs in Illinois*, p. 19. Springfield.
1882. *Flora Peoriana*, p. 60. Budapest.

BREWER, W. H., WATSON, S., and GRAY, A.
1876. *Botany* (2d ed.), pp. 110 (In J. D. Whitney, *Geological Survey of California*, Vol. I). Cambridge, Massachusetts.

BRITTON, N. L.
1889. *Catalogue of Plants Found in New Jersey*, p. 79. (*Geological Survey of New Jersey.*) Trenton.
1893–94. *Contribution in List of Pteridophyta and Spermatophyta Growing without Cultivation in Northeastern America*, p. 216. New York.
1901. *Manual of the Flora of the Northern United States*, p. 601. New York.

BRITTON, N. L., and BROWN, A.
1897. *An Illustrated Flora of the Northern United States and the British Possessions*, II, 388. New York.

BRITTON, N. L., and SHAFER, J. A.
1908. *North American Trees*, pp. 604, 609 ff. New York.

BROOKS, H., and DAME, L. L.
1902. *Handbook of the Trees of New England*, p. 136. Boston.

Brown, A., and Britton, N. L.
1897. *An Illustrated Flora of the Northern United States and the British Possessions*, II, 338. New York.
Brown, R. J.
1881. "Catalogue of the Medicinal Flora of the State of Kansas," *Proceedings of the American Pharmaceutical Association*, XXIX, 440. Philadelphia.
Browne, P.
1789. *The Civil and Natural History of Jamaica*, pp. 177, 186. London.
Brunton, T. L.
1885. *A Textbook of Pharmacology, Therapeutics and Materia Medica*, p. 755. Philadelphia.
Buck, C. H. (& Co.)
1894. "Wild Flowers of America," *Botanical Fine Art Weekly*, I, Plate 168. New York.
Burgess, T. J. W.
1880. "On the Beneficent and Toxical Effects of the Various Species of *Rhus*," *Canadian Journal of Medical Science*, V, 327–34. Toronto.
1881. *Pharmaceutical Journal*, XI, 858.
1892. *Journal and Proceedings of the Hamilton Association*, VIII, 119. Hamilton.
1893. *Proceedings of the American Pharmaceutical Association*, XLI, 625.
Busch, A. H.
1901. *A Reference Handbook of the Medical Sciences*, III, 424. New York.
Cameron, R.
1895. *Catalogue of Plants Found Growing without Cultivation in Niagara Falls Park*, p. 14. Toronto.
Campbell, D. F.
1907. *University Textbook of Botany*, pp. 363, 410, 437. New York.
Candolle, A. P. de
1825. *Prodromi systematis naturalis, etc.*, II, 67, 68, 69. Paris.
Carter, J. M. G.
1881. *Synopsis of the Medical Botany of Illinois*, p. 12. Chicago.
1888. *A Synopsis of the Medical Botany of the United States*, p. 21. St. Louis.
Cash, N.
1910. *Medical Advance*, XXXVIII, 115–16. Batavia.
Castiglioni, L.
1790. *Viaggio negli Stati Uniti dell'America Settentrionale*, II, 356. Milan.
Catesby, M.
1731. *Natural History of Carolina, Florida and the Bahama Islands*, I, 40. London.

CHAPMAN, A. W.
1897. *Flora of the Southern United States* (3d ed.), p. 72. Cambridge, Massachusetts.

CHESTNUT, V. K.
1897*a*. *American Druggist*, XXXI, 307. New York.
1897*b*. *Yearbook of the United States Department of Agriculture* (*1896*), pp. 139 ff. Washington.
1898*a*. *Principal Poisonous Plants of the United States* (United States Department of Agriculture, Division of Botany, Bulletin No. 20), pp. 35 ff. Washington.
1898*b*. *Thirty Poisonous Plants of the United States* (United States Department of Agriculture, Farmer's Bulletin No. 86), pp. 19 ff. Washington.
1902. "Plants Used by Indians of Mendocino County, California," *Contributions from United States National Herbarium*, VII, 364.

CHRISTY, T. (& Co.)
1899. *New and Rare Drugs* (8th ed., No. 312). London.

CLAPP, A.
1852. *A Synopsis or Systematic Catalogue of the Medicinal Plants of the United States*, p. 70. Philadelphia.

CLAPP, A., *et al.*
1852. "Report on Medical Botany," *Transactions of the American Medical Association*, V, 754. Philadelphia.

CLARK, J.
1852. *Catalogue of the Flowering Plants and Ferns Observed in the Vicinity of Cincinnati*, p. 21. Cincinnati.

CLAYTON, J.
Translation of J. F. Gronovius, *Flora virginica*.

CLUTE, W. G.
1898. *Flora of the Susquehanna*, p. 27. Binghamton.

COLE, Emma J.
1901. *Grand Rapids Flora*, pp. 101, 102. Grand Rapids, Michigan.

COLEMAN, N.
1873. *Catalogue of Flowering Plants of the Southern Peninsula of Michigan*, p. 11. Grand Rapids, Michigan.

COLLETT, H.
1902. *Flora Simlensis*, p. 105. Calcutta and Simla.

COLLINS, F. S., and DAME, L. L.
1888. *Flora of Middlesex County, Massachusetts*, p. 21. Malden.

COLLINS, S. H.
1883. *Cincinnati Lancet and Clinic*, L, 223. Cincinnati.

CONGDON, J. W., and GREEN, F. H.
1857. *Analytical Classbook of Botany*, p. 146. New York and London.

CONKEY, W. B. (publisher).
1896. *The American Encyclopaedic Dictionary*, III, 3463. Chicago.

CONWENTZ.
1887. *Annales des Sciences Nat. Botanique* (7th ser.), VI, 297.
COOPER, J. G.
1859. *Annual Report of the Smithsonian Institution for 1858*, pp. 250, 264. Washington.
1861. *Annual Report of the Smithsonian Institution for 1860*, p. 440. Washington.
COOPER, S.
1906. *Proceedings of the Indiana Academy of Science*, pp. 51–63. *Pharmaceutical Journal*, LXXVI, 227.
CORNATUS, J.
1635. *Plantarum Canadensium, etc., Historia*, p. 96. Paris.
COULTER, J. M.
1885. *Textbook of Western Botany* (with *Gray's Lessons*), p. 49. New York and Chicago.
COULTER, J. M., and OTHERS.
1881. *Flora of Indiana*, p. 6. Crawfordsville.
COULTER, J. M., and PORTER, T. C.
1874. *Synopsis of the Flora of Colorado*, p. 19. Washington.
COULTER, J. M., and WATSON, S.
1890. *Gray's Manual* (6th ed.), p. 119. New York and Chicago.
COVILLE, FRED. V.
1893. "Botany of Death Valley Expedition," *Contributions from United States National Herbarium*, V, 81.
CREEVEY, CAROLINE, A.
1897. *Flowers of Field, Hill and Swamp*, pp. 478, 480. New York.
CUNDELL-JULER, DR.
1883. *Cincinnati Lancet and Clinic*, L, 344. Cincinnati.
CURTIS, M. A.
1867. *Geological and Natural History Survey of North Carolina*, III, 15. Raleigh.
DAME, L. L., and BROOKS, H.
1902. *Handbook of the Trees of New England*, p. 136. Boston.
DAME, L. L., and COLLINS, F. S.
1888. *Flora of Middlesex County, Massachusetts*, p. 21. Malden.
DANA, W. S.
1900. *How to Know the Wild Flowers*, pp. 114, 116. New York.
DARBY, J.
1866. *Botany of the Southern States*, Part 2, pp. 254, 255. New York.
DARLINGTON, W.
1847. *Agricultural Botany*, p. 24. Philadelphia and New York.
1853. *Florula Cestrica* (3d ed.), p. 44. Philadelphia.
1859. *American Weeds and Useful Plants*, pp. 79, 80. New York.
DAVIDSON, ALICE M.
1898. *California Plants in Their Haunts*. Los Angeles.

DAY, D. F.

1883. *Plants of Buffalo, New York, N.Y., and Vicinity*, p. 26. Buffalo.

1888. *A Catalogue of the Flowering and Fern-like Plants Growing without Cultivation in the Vicinity of Niagara*, p. 20. Troy, New York.

DEANE, W.

1896. *Flora of the Blue Hills (and Other) Reservations*, p. 18. Boston.

DESFONTAINE, R.

1809. *Histoire des arbres et abrisseaux qui peuvent être cultives en pleine terre sur le sol de la France*, II, 325. Paris.

1815. *Tableau de l'école de botanique, du jardin de roi* (2d ed.), p. 227. Paris.

1829. *Catalogus plantarum, horti regii Parisiensis* (3d ed.), p. 329. Paris.

DEWEY, L. H.

1899. *Yearbook of the United States Department of Agriculture (1898)*, p. 197. Washington.

DIELS, L.

1898. "Die Ephermose der Vegetationsorgane bei Rhus L.," *Engler's botan. Jahrbücher*, XXIV, 568–647.

DIETRICH, N. F. D.

*Synopsis plantarum*, II, 1002–3.

DON, G.

1831. "A General System of Gardening and Botany," *Miller's Gardener's Dictionary*, II, 70, 71, 72. London.

DOWD, A. M.

1906. *Our Common Wild Flowers of Springtime and Autumn*, p. 154. Boston.

DRAGENDORFF, G.

1898. *Die Heilpflanzen der verschiedenen Völker und Zeiten*, pp. 398, 400. Stuttgart.

DUCHESNE, E. A.

1836. *Répertoire des plantes utiles et des plantes vénéneuses du globe*, p. 293. Paris.

DUDLEY, W. R.

1886. *The Cayuga Flora*, p. 22. Ithaca.

DUDLEY, W. R., and THURSTON, C. O.

1892. *Catalogue of the Flowering Plants and Vascular Cryptogams Found in and near Lackawanna and Wyoming Valleys*, p. 14. Wilkesbarre, Pennsylvania.

DULAMEL, H. L.

1804. *Traité des arbres et arbuster*, II, 48, 107, 163, 165. Paris.

DUROI, J. P.

1772. *Die Harbkesche wilde Baumzucht*, II, 306. Brunswick.

EATON, A.

1833. *Manual of Botany for North America* (6th ed.), pp. 302, 303. Albany, New York.

EATON, A., and WRIGHT, J.

1840. *North American Botany*, p. 392. Troy, New York.

EATON, D. C., WATSON, S., and OTHERS.

1871. "Botany of the Fortieth Parallel," *United States Geological Exploration of the Fortieth Parallel*, p. 53. Washington.

EDGWORTH, M. P.

1879. *Pollen.* London.

EDITORIAL.

1903. *American Botanist*, IV, 80.

1909. *Midland Druggist and Pharmaceutical Review*, LIII, 397. Columbus.

1910. *Pharmaceutical Journal and Pharmacist*, LXXXV, 316. London.

EGGLESTON, W. W., JONES, L. R., and BRAINERD, E.

1900. *Flora of Vermont*, p. 58. Burlington.

ELLIOT, S.

1821. *Sketch of the Botany of South Carolina and Georgia*, I, 361–03. Charleston.

Cited by Bigelow in *American Medical Botany*, I, 96.

ELLIS, J.

1757. *Philosophical Transactions*, XLIX, 866. London.

1758. *Philosophical Transactions*, L, 441–56. London.

ENGELMANN, G.

1848. *Sketch of the Botany of A. Wislizenus' Expedition from Missouri to Santa Fe, Chikuahua, Parras, Saltillo, Monterey, and Matamoros*, p. 4. Washington.

ENGLER, A.

1883. De Candolle's *Monographias phanerogamiarum*, IV, 397. Paris.

"Über die morphologischen und die geographische Verhältnisse Verbreitung der Gattung Rhus, wie der mit ihr verwandten labenden und ausgestorbenen Anacardiacrae," *Bot. Jahrbuch für System pflanzenschichte und pflanzengeographie*, I, 365–427. Leipzig.

ENGLER, A., and PRANTL, K.

1897. *Die natürlichen Pflanzenfamilien*, Part 3, No. 5, pp. 168–70. Leipzig.

ESSER, P.

1910. *Die Giftpflanzen Deutschlands*, p. 115, Table 62. Braunschweig.

FERNALD, M. L.

1892. *The Portland Catalogue of Maine Plants* (2d ed.), p. 48. Portland.

FISCHER, B., and HARTWICH, C.

1905. *Hager's Handbuch der pharmaceutischen Praxis für Apotheker, Ärzte, Drogisten und Medicinalbeamte*, I, 692; II, 268, 740, 472. Berlin.

FISHER, W. R.
1903. Translation of A. F. W. Schimper, *Planzen-Geographie auf physiologischer Grundlage*, p. 539. Oxford.
FITZPATRICK, T. J.
1899. *Manual of the Flowering Plants of Iowa*, p. 32. Lamoni.
FLINT, W. T.
1880. *Botanical Gazette*, V, 42. Madison.
FOGEL, E. D., and PAMMEL, L. H.
1907. "Catalogue of the Poisonous Plants of Iowa," *Proceedings of the Iowa Academy of Science*, XIV, 164. Des Moines.
FORBES, F. B., and HEMSLEY, W. B.
1886. *Journal of the Linnean Society*, XXIII, 147 ff. London.
FORSTER, J. R., and BOSSER, N.
1771. *Travels through that Part of North America Formerly Called Louisiana*, II, 30. London.
FROST, C., and TUCKERMAN, E.
1875. *A Catalogue of Plants Growing without Cultivation within Thirty Miles of Amherst College*, p. 7. Amherst.
GAERTNER, J.
1788. *De fructibus et seminibus plantarum*, I, 205. Stuttgart and Leipzig.
GALEN, J.
1884. *Flora of Lancaster County, Pa.*, p. 9. Rawlinsville.
GAMBLE, J. S.
1902. *A Manual of Indian Timbers* (2d ed.), pp. 209–10. London.
GATTINGER, A.
1901. *The Flora of Tennessee*, p. 114. Nashville.
GEDDES, W. N.
1904. *A Brief Flora of the Eastern United States*, p. 87. New York, Cincinnati, and Chicago.
GIBBONS, W. P.
1871. "Medicinal Plants of California," *Proceedings of the American Pharmaceutical Association*, XIX, 300. Philadelphia.
GIFFORD, T.
1883. *Cincinnati Lancet and Clinic*, L, 274. Cincinnati.
GOING, MAUD.
1903. *With the Trees*, pp. 199, 265. New York.
GRAY, ASA.
1849. "Plantas Fendlerianae Nori-Mexicanae," *Memoirs of the American Academy of Arts and Sciences* (new series), IV, 28. Cambridge, Massachusetts.
1850. "Plantae Lindheimerianae," *Boston Journal of Natural History*, VI, 159. Boston.
1853. *Plantae Wrightianae Texano-Neo-Americanae*, Part II, p. 27. Washington.

1854. "Plantae norae-Thurberianae," *Memoirs of the American Academy of Arts and Sciences* (new series), V, 301. Cambridge, Massachusetts.

1859*a*. *Catalogue of the Phaenogamous and Acrogenous Plants Contained in Gray's Manual of the Northern United States, Adapted for Marking Desiderata in Exchanges of Specimens*, p. 11. New York.

1859*b*. *Proceedings of the Boston Society of Natural History*, VII, 143, 146. Boston.

1860. *Reports on Explorations . . . . for a Railroad* (United States War Department), XII, Part 2, 41. Washington.

1868. *Manual of the Botany of the Northern United States* (5th ed.), p. 111. New York and Chicago.

1873. Excerpt in E. Hall, *Plantae Texanae*, p. 5. Salem.

1876. *Botany*, p. 110. (*Geological Survey of California*, Vol. I.)

GRAY, ASA, and SPRAGUE, I.

1849. *The Genera of the Plants of the United States*, II, 159. New York.

GRAY, ASA, and TORREY, J.

1838, 1843. *Flora of North America*, I, 217, 218, 681. New York and London.

GRAY, ASA, WATSON, S., and ROBINSON, B. L.

1886–87. "Studies in the Botany of California and Parts Adjacent," *Bulletin of the California Academy of Science*, II, 393.

1897. *Synoptical Flora of North America* (2d ed.), I, Part 1, 383. New York.

GREEN, F. H., and CONGDON, J. W.

1857. *Analytical Classbook of Botany*, p. 146. New York and London.

GREENE, EDWARD LEE.

1886–87. "Notes on the Botany of Santa Cruz Island," *Bulletin of California Academy of Sciences*, II, 393.

1894. *Manual of Botany*, p. 73. San Francisco.

1903–6. *Leaflets of Botanical Observation and Criticism*, I, 119. Washington.

GRIBBLES, H.

1875. *Handels-Bericht vom Monat April*, p. 25. (Gehe & Co.) Dresden.

1876. Reprint, *Archiv der Pharmacie*, VIII, 374.

GRISEBACH, A. H. R.

1864. *Flora of the British West Indian Islands*, p. 175. London.

1866. *Catalogus Plantarum Cubensium*, p. 67. Lipsiae.

GRONOVIUS, J. F.

1762. *Flora virginica* (2d ed.), p. 148. Leyden.

GUIBORT, N. J. B. G.

1876. *Histoire naturelle des drogues simples* (7th ed.), III, 480, 489. Paris.

HALE, P. M.
1883. *The Woods and Timbers of North Carolina*, p. 151. New York.
HALL, HARVEY MONROE.
1902. *A Botanical Survey of San Jacinto Mountains*, pp. 1–140. (University of California Publications—Botany, Vol. I.)
1912. *A Yosemite Flora*, p. 151.
HALL, J., and WRIGHT, J.
1836. *A Catalogue of Plants Growing without Cultivation in the Vicinity of Troy*, p. 33. Troy, New York.
HAMILTON, W.
1846. *Pharmaceutical Journal and Transactions*, V, 60. London.
1848. *Pharmaceutical Journal and Transactions*, VII, 270. London.
HARRISON, W. H.
1905. *Garden and Forest*, VIII, 268. New York.
HARTWICH, C., and FISCHER, B.
1905. *Hager's Handbuch der pharmaceutischen Praxis für Apotheker Ärzte, Drogisten und Medicinalbeamte*, I, 692; II, 268, 740, 742. Berlin.
HAVARD, V.
1885. *Proceedings of the United States National Museum*, VIII, 458, 511. Washington.
HELLER, A. A.
*Catalogue of North American Plants North of Mexico*, p. 129.
HEMSLEY, W. B.
1873. *Handbook of Hardy Trees, Shrubs, and Herbaceous Plants*, p. 112. Boston.
HEMSLEY, W. B., and FORBES, E. B.
1886. *Journal of the Linnean Society*, XXIII, 147 ff. London.
HENKEL, ALICE.
1906. *Wild Medicinal Plants of the United States* (United States Department of Agriculture, Bureau of Plant Industry, Bulletin No. 89), p. 58. Washington.
HENSINGER, H.
1809. *Observata quaedam sistens circa Rhoa toxicodendron et radicantem.* Helmstadii.
HILDEBRANDT, F.
1883. "Über einige Fäble von verborgenen Zweigknospen," *Bot. Zentralbl.*, XIII, No. 6, 207–12, 6 figures.
HIGLEY, W. H., and RADDIN, C. S.
1891. *The Flora of Cook County, Illinois, and a Part of Lake County, Indiana*, p. 26. Chicago.
HOBBS, C. E.
1876. *Botanical Hand-Book of Common English, Botanical and Pharmacopocial Names*, pp. 91, 206, 207. Boston.

HOLMES, E. M.
1908. *Pharmaceutical Journal*, LXXXI, 231. London.
1909. *Chemical Abstract*, III, 225.
HOOKER, J. D.
1879. *The Flora of British India*, II, 11, 12. London.
HOOKER, J. D., and JACKSON, B. D.
1895. *Index Kewensis*, Part IV, p. 714. Oxford.
HOOKER, W. J.
1831. *Flora boreali americana*, I, 126, 127, t. 46. London.
1834. *Journal of Botany*, I, 202. London.
HOOKER, W. J., and ARNOTT, G. A. W.
1832. *The Botany of Captain Beechey's Voyage*, Part III, p. 137. London.
HOUGH, R. B.
1907. *Handbook of the Trees of the Northern United States and Canada*, pp. 310, 311. Lowville.
HOWELL, THOMAS.
1898. *A Flora of Northwest America* (1st ed.), I, 119. Portland, Oregon.
1903. *Ibid.* (2d ed.), p. 119.
HOYT, P. B.
1859. *North American Journal of Homoeopathy*, VII, 59. New York.
HUNTINGTON, ANNIE O.
1908. *Poison Ivy and Swamp Sumac.* Jamaica Plain, Massachusetts.
HUETT, J. W.
1897. *Essay toward a Natural History of La Salle County, Illinois*, p. 61. Ottawa.
HUSEMANN, T.
1892. *Handbuch der Arzneimittellehre* (3d ed.), p. 440. Berlin.
HYATT, J. B.
1875. "Climbing Plants," *Torrey Botanical Club*, Bulletin VI, p. 47.
1894. "Exhibit of Transverse Section of Stem of Poison Ivy *Rhus Toxicodendron*," *New York Microscopical Society Journal*, X, 61.
INVISON and PHINNEY (publishers).
1859. *Catalogue of the Phaenogamous and Acrogenous Plants Contained in Gray's Manual of the Northern United States Adapted for Marking Desiderata in Exchanges of Specimens*, p. 7. New York.
JACKSON, J.
1894*a*. *Flora of Worcester County, Massachusetts*, p. 15. Worcester.
1894*b*. *Through Glade and Mead*, pp. 85, 171, 190, 194, 322. Worcester.
JACKSON, J. R.
1871. *Pharmaceutical Journal and Transactions* (3d ser.), II, 61. London.
JADIN, F.
1888. *Origine des sécrêteurs* (Thèse). Montpellier.
1893. "Observations sur quelques térébinthacées, *Journal de Bot.*, VII, 382–90.

JAMES, J. F.

1879. *Catalogue of the Flowering Plants, Ferns and Fungi Growing in the Vicinity of Cincinnati*, p. 6. Cincinnati.

JEPSON, W. L.

1901. *A Flora of Western, Middle California* (1st ed.), p. 250. Berkeley.

1902. *A School Flora for the Pacific Coast*, p. 38. New York.

1911. *A Flora of Western, Middle California* (2d ed.), p. 249.

JESUP, H. G.

1891. *Flowering Plants of Hanover, New Hampshire*, p. 10. Hanover.

JOHNSON, G. W.

1877. *Gardener's Dictionary*, p. 694. London.

JOHNSON, LAWRENCE.

1876. "Eccentricity of the Pith of Rhus Toxicodendron," *Torrey Botanical Club*, Bulletin, VI, 117–21.

JONES, L. R., BRAINERD, E., and EGGLESTON, W. W.

1900. *Flora of Vermont*, p. 58. Burlington.

JUSSIEU, A. L., DE.

1789. *Genera plantarum*, p. 369. Paris.

KAEMPFER, E.

1712. *Amoenitatum exoticarum politico-physico-medicarum*, V, 791–94. Lemgoviae.

KALM, P.

1772. *Travels into North America* (English translation, 2d ed.), I, 53, 60–64, 139; II, 20. London.

1812. *Travels into North America;* etc. Trans. into English by John Reinhold Forster in John Pinkerton, *A General Collection of the Best and Most Interesting Voyages and Travels*, XIII (1812), 402–3, 434. London, 1808–14.

KEELER, HARRIET, L.

1900. *Our Native Trees*, p. 94. New York.

1903. *Our Northern Shrubs*, pp. 82, 84, 86. New York.

KELLOGG, J. H.

1881. *The Home Hand Book of Domestic Hygiene and Rational Medicine*, Plate 17, opp. p. 1394. Battle Creek, Michigan.

KLEINSTÜCK, O.

1890. *Chemiker-Zeitung*, XIV, 1303. Cöthen.

KNOBEL, E.

1894. *Guide to Find the Names of All Wild-Growing Trees and Shrubs of New England by Their Leaves*, p. 35. Boston.

KRAEMER, H.

1907. *A Textbook of Botany and Pharmacognosy* (2d ed.), p. 319. Philadelphia and London.

LAMARCK, J. B. A. P. M.

1791. *Illustration des Gênères*, II, 346. Paris.

LAMARCK, J. B. A. P. M., and POIRET, J. L. M.
1806. *Encyclopédie méthodique Botanique*, VII, 505–9. Paris.

LANDERER, X.
1851. "Über die in Griechenland und Macedonien vorkommenden Getreide-Arten, Futter, Kräuter und Giftpflanzen," *Archiv der Pharmacie*, CXV, 41 (2d ser., LXV, 41). Hanover.
Reprint in *Pharm. Chem. Central-Blatt*, XXII, 320.

LAPHAM, I. A.
1875. *A Catalogue of the Plants of Minnesota*, p. 9. St. Paul.

LAWES and GILBERT.
1859. *Philosophical Transactions*, Part 2.

LEA, T. G.
1849. *Catalogue of the Plants, Native and Naturalized, Collected in the Vicinity of Cincinnati During the Years 1834–1844*, p. 10. Philadelphia.

LEBLOIS, A.
1887. "Recherches sur l'origine et le développement des canaux sécréteurs et des poches sécrétrices," *Ann. Sci. Nat. Bot.* (Sér. 7), VI, 247–330.

LEE, C. A.
1848. *A Catalogue of Medicinal Plants Indigenous and Exotic Growing in the State of New York*, p. 16. New York.

LEE, J.
1745. *An Introduction to Botany*, p. 323. London.

LESQUEREAUX, L.
1860. In *Owen's Second Report of a Geological Reconnaissance of the Middle and Southern Counties of Arkansas*, p. 853. Philadelphia.

LINDLEY, JOHN.
1831. *An Introduction to the Natural System of Botany*, p. 127. New York.
1838. *Flora medica*, pp. 284, 285. London.
1845. "Rhus diversiloba. Various-Leaved Poison Oak," *Edward's Botanical Register* (new series), XVIII, 38. London.

LINDLEY, J., and MOORE, F.
1866. *The Treasury of Botany*, Part 2, p. 979. London.

LINNAEUS, C.
1737. *Hortus cliffortianus*, p. 110. Amsterdam.
1748. *Hortus upsaliensis*, p. 68. Stockholm.
1772. *Materia medica*, p. 50. Leipzig and Erlangen.
1778. *Species plantarum*, pp. 265, 266. Stockholm.

LINNEY, W. W.
1882. *Report on the Botany of Madison (and Other) Counties, Kentucky*, p. 31. (*Geological Survey of Kentucky*.) Frankfort.

LONDON, J. C.
1844. *Arboretum et fruticetum Britannicum*, II, 552, 555, Fig. 230; 556, Fig. 231. London.

1850. *Hortus Britannicus* (2d ed.), pp. 110, 509, 598. London.
1855. *Encyclopedia of Plants*, p. 226. London.

LOUNSBERRY, ALICE.
1899. *A Guide to the Wild Flowers*, pp. 53, 261. New York.
1901. *Southern Wild Flowers and Trees*, p. 308. New York.

LUMMERT.
*Pflüger's Archiv*, Vol. LXXI.

LYONS, A. B.
1898. *Proceedings of the American Pharmaceutical Association*, XLVI, 275. Baltimore.
1907. *Plant Names: Scientific and Popular* (2d ed.), pp. 397, 398. Detroit.

LYON, WILLIAM S.
1886. "The Flora of Our Southwestern Archipelago. II," *Botanical Gazette*, II, 333.

MACAULEY, MARY E., and BECKWITH, FLORENCE.
1896. *Plants of Monroe County, New York*, p. 55.

MCCARTHY, G., and WOOD, T. F.
1887. *Wilmington (N.C.) Flora*, p. 18. Raleigh.

MACDOUGAL, D. T., and ARTHUR, J.
1898. *Living Plants and Their Properties*, p. 162. New York.

MACFADYEN, J.
1837. *The Flora of Jamaica*, I, 225. London.

MACMILLAN, C.
1892. *Metaspermae of the Minnesota Valley*, p. 346. Minneapolis.
1899. *Minnesota Plant Life*, pp. 310, 562. St. Paul.

MCNAIR, JAMES B.
1918*a*. "Secretory Canals of Rhus Diversiloba," *Botanical Gazette*, LXV, 268–73.
1921*a*. "A Study of *Rhus diversiloba* with Special Reference to Its Toxicity," *American Journal of Botany*, VIII, 127–46.
1921*b*. "The Morphology and Anatomy of *Rhus diversiloba*," *American Journal of Botany*, VIII, 179–91.

MACOUN, J. M.
1883, 1886. *Catalogue of Canadian Plants*, Part 1, p. 100; Part 3, p. 505. Montreal.

MANN, H.
1868. *Catalogue of the Phaenogamous Plants of the United States East of the Mississippi and of the Vascular Cryptogamous Plants of North America, North of Mexico*, p. 11. Cambridge.

MARSHALL, H.
1785. *Arbustum americanum*, pp. 130, 131. Philadelphia.

MATHEWS, F. S.
1901. *Familiar Trees and Their Leaves*, p. 221. New York.
1902. *Field Book of American Wild Flowers*, p. 252. New York and London.

MEARNS, E. A.
1902. "Two New Species of Poisonous Sumachs from the States of Rhode Island and Florida," *Proceedings of the Society of Washington*, XV, 147–49. Washington.

MEEHAN, THOMAS.
1899. "The Eccentricity of the Annual Wood Circles in *R. Toxicodendron*," *Proceedings of the Academy of Natural Science*, IL, 113–15. Philadelphia.

MEDIKUS, F. K.
1783. *Botanische Beobachtungen des Jahres 1782*, pp. 223, 225. Mannheim.

MICHAUX, A.
1803. *Flora boreali-Americana*, I, 182–83. Paris.
Cited by Bigelow in *American Medical Botany*, I, 96.

MILLER, E. S., and YOUNG, H. W.
1874. *Catalogue of the Phaenogamous and Acrogenous Plants of Suffolk County, Long Island*, p. 6. Port Jefferson.

MILLER, P.
1756. *Philosophical Transactions*, XLIX, 161. London.
1758. *Philosophical Transactions*, L, 430–40. London.
1807. *The Gardener's and Botanist's Dictionary*, Vol. II, Part 2, Article, "Sumac." London.

MILLIGAN, J. M.
1879. *Botanical Gazette*, IV, 219. Madison.

MILLSPAUGH, C. F.
1892. *Flora of West Virginia*, p. 346. Charleston.

MILLSPAUGH, C. F., and NUTTALL, L. W.
1896. *The Flora of West Virginia*, p. 215. (Publications of the Field Columbian Museum, Vol. I.) Chicago.

MÖBIUS, M.
1897. *Berichte deutschen botanischen Gesellschaft*, XV, 435.

MÖBIUS, M. A.
1899. "Der Japanische Lackbaum, Rhus vernicifera D.C.," *Abhandlungen Herausgegeben von der Senckenbergischen Naturforschenden Gesellschaft*, XX, Part 2, 201–47. Frankfort.

MOHR, C. T.
1901. "Plant Life of Alabama," *Contribution from the United States National Herbarium* (Alabama edition), VI, 600. Montgomery.

MUIR, JOHN.
1911. *My First Summer in the Sierra*, pp. 34, 35. Boston and New York.

MULDREW, W. H.
1901. *Sylvan Ontario*, pp. 17, 42. Toronto.

MÜLLER, C.
1890. *Medicinalflora*, p. 372. Berlin.

NEWBERRY, J. S.

1857. *Reports of Explorations . . . . from the Mississippi River to the Pacific Ocean, 1854–55* (United States War Department, Botanical Report), VI, 69. Washington.

1860. *Catalogue of the Flowering Plants and Ferns of Ohio*, p. 15.

NEWHALL, C. S.

1897*a*. *Shrubs of Northeastern America* (1st ed.), p. 74. New York.

1897*b*. *The Vines of Northeastern America*, p. 34. New York and London.

1900. *Shrubs of Northeastern America* (2d ed.), p. 198. New York.

NEWMAN, J. B. (editor).

1896. *Illustrated Botany*, I, 224. New York.

NUTTALL, L. W., and MILLSPAUGH, C. F.

1896. *The Flora of West Virginia*, p. 215. (Publications of the Field Columbian Museum, Vol. I.) Chicago.

NUTTALL, T.

1818. *Genera of North American Plants*, I, 203. Philadelphia. Cited by Bigelow, in *American Medical Botany*, I, 96.

OWEN, MARIA L.

1888. *A Catalogue of Plants Growing without Cultivation in the County of Nantucket, Mass.*, p. 20. Northhampton.

OYSTER, J. H.

1888. *Catalogue of North American Plants* (2d ed.), p. 18. Paola.

PAINE, J. A.

1864. *Catalogue of Plants Found in Oneida County (New York) and Vicinity*, p. 17. Utica.

PAMMEL, L. H.

1910. *A Manual of Poisonous Plants*, I, 122–23. Cedar Rapids, Iowa.

PAMMEL, L. H., and FOGEL, E. D.

1907. "Catalogue of the Poisonous Plants of Iowa," *Proceedings of the Iowa Academy of Science*, XIV, 164. Des Moines.

PARKHURST, H. E.

1903. *Trees, Shrubs, and Vines*, pp. 218, 307. New York.

PARRY, C. C.

1852. In Owen's *Report of a Geological Survey of Wisconsin, Iowa and Minnesota*, p. 610. Philadelphia.

PARSONS, MARY E.

1907, 1909. *The Wild Flowers of California; Their Names, Haunts and Habits* (corrected edition), p. 8. San Francisco.

PATTERSON, H. N.

1892. *Numbered Check List of North American Plants North of Mexico*, p. 21. Oquawka.

PAVON, J., and RUIZ, H.

1802. *Flora Peruviana et Chilensis*, III, 29, t. 252. Madrid.

PAXTON, J.

1868. *Botanical Dictionary*, p. 483. London.

PERKINS, G. H.
1882. *General Catalogue of the Flora of Vermont*, p. 10. Montpellier.
PERSOON, C. H.
1805. *Synopsis Plantarum*, I, 324, 325. Paris.
PFEFFER, W.
1900. *The Physiology of Plants* (2d rev. ed., Trans. by A. J. Ewart, 1900), I, 479, 500 (Sec. 90).
PIPER, CHARLES V.
1906. "Flora of the State of Washington," *Contributions from the United States National Herbarium*, IX, 384.
PLANCHON, L.
1904. *Précis matière médicale*, I, 387, 474, 475. Lyon.
PLENCK, J. J.
1790. *Icones plantarum medicinalum*, III, 33, 34, 35, t. 234, 235, 236. Viennae.
PLUKENET, L.
1691. *Phytographia*, t. 145. London.
1696. *Almagestum*, p. 45. London.
POIRET, J. L. M., and LAMARCK, J. B. A. P. M.
1791. *Illustration des Gênères*, II, 346. Paris.
PORCHER, F. P.
1849. "Report on the Indigenous Medicinal Plants of South Carolina," *Transactions of the American Medical Association*, II, 746–49. Philadelphia.
1863, 1869. *Resources of the Southern Fields and Forests*, p. 241. Richmond and Charleston.
PORTER, T. C.
1903. *Flora of Pennsylvania* (Small, J. K., editor), p. 202. Boston.
PORTER, T. C., and COULTER, J. M.
1874. *Synopsis of the Flora of Colorado*, p. 19. Washington.
POTTER, M. C.
1895. Translation of E. Warming, *A Handbook of Systematic Botany*, p. 439. London and New York.
PRANTL, K., and ENGLER, A.
1897. *Die natürlichen Pflanzenfamilien*, Part 3, No. 5, pp. 168–70. Leipzig.
PROVANCHER, L.
1862. *Flore canadienne*, p. 130. Quebec.
PROVIDENCE FRANKLIN SOCIETY.
*Catalogue of Rhode Island Plants*, p. 2. Providence.
PURSH, F.
1814. *Flora americana septentrionalis*, I, 204, 205. London.
Cited by Bigelow in *American Medical Botany*, I, 96.
RADDIN, C. S., and HIGLEY, W. K.
1891. *The Flora of Cook County, Illinois, and a Part of Lake County, Indiana*, p. 26. Chicago.

RAFINESQUE, C. S.
1830. *Medical Flora of the United States*, II, 257. Philadelphia.
RAND, E. S., JR.
1859. *Proceedings of the Boston Society of Natural History*, VII, 155. Boston.
RATTAN, V.
1905. *Popular West Coast Flora*, pp. 30, 104. San Francisco.
REINECKE, F.
*Ber. Schles. Gesells.*, LXXIII, Part 2, 75.
RICE, W. S.
1902. "Suspicious Characters of the Woods," *Outing*, XL, 551. New York and London.
RIDDEL, J. L.
1852. "Florae Ludovicianae," *New Orleans Medical Journal*, p. 758. New Orleans.
RIDLEY, H. N.
1910. *Pharmaceutical Journal and Pharmacist*, LXXXIV, 360. London.
RIECKE, V. A.
1840. *Die neueren Arzneimittel*, pp. 565, 566. Stuttgart.
RIMBACH.
1899. *Berichte der deutschen bot. Gesell.*, XVII, 18. Berlin.
ROBINSON, B. L., GRAY A., and WATSON, S.
1897. *Synoptical Flora of North America* (2d ed.), I, Part 1, 383. New York.
ROBINSON, J.
1880. *The Flora of Essex County, Massachusetts*, p. 42. Salem.
ROEMER, J. J., and SCHULTES, J. A.
1819. *Systema vegetabilum*, VI, 646, 648, 651, 652. Stuttgart.
ROGERS, JULIA E.
1905. *The Tree-Book*, pp. 356–58. New York.
ROHE, G. H.
1899. *Annual and Analytical Cyclopaedia of Practical Medicine*, II, 468. Philadelphia, New York, and Chicago.
ROXBURGH, W.
1832. *Flora Indica; or, Descriptions of Indian Plants*, II, 98. Serampore.
ROYEN, A.
1740. *Florae leydensis prodromus*, p. 244. Lugduni Batavorum.
RUIZ, H., and PAVON, J.
1802. *Flora Peruviana et Chilensis*, III, 29, t. 252. Madrid.
SALOMON, C.
1881. *Wörterbuch der deutschen Pflanzen-Namen*, pp. 54, 144. Stuttgart.
SARGENT, C. S.
1874. *The Woods of the United States*, pp. 25, 145, 154, 156, 159, 161, 163, 168, 170, 174. New York.

1884. "Report on the Trees of North America," *Tenth Census*, IX, 54. Washington.

1892. *Silva of North America*, VIII, 7, 13, 23. Boston and New York.

1894. *Forest Flora of Japan*, p. 33. Boston and New York.

1895. "Rhus Michauxii," *Garden and Forest*, VIII, 404. New York.

1905. *Manual of the Trees of North America*, pp. 603, 608. Boston and New York.

SAUNDERS, CHARLES FRANCIS.

1920. *Useful Wild Plants of the United States and Canada.* New York: McBride & Co.

SAYRE, L. E., and STEVENS, W. C.

1906. *A Manual of Organic Materia Medica and Pharmacognosy*, p. 171. Philadelphia.

SCHAFFNER, J. H.

1904. *Ohio Naturalist*, IV, 69. Columbus.

SCHAFFRANEK, A.

1888. *Floral Almanac of Florida*, p. 23. Palatka.

SCHIMPER, A. F. W.

1898. *Pflanzen-Geographie auf physiologischer Grundlage*, p. 571. Jena.

SCHKUHR, C.

1791. *Botanisches Handbuch*, I, 236. Wittenberg.

SCHMIDT.

1891. *Flora*, LXXIV, 300.

SCHNEIDER, A.

1909. *Pacific Pharmacist*, II, 463. San Francisco.

SCHRENK, JOSEPH.

1878. "The Excentricity of the Pith of Rhus Toxicodendron," *Torrey Botanical Club*, Bulletin VI, 204–6.

SCHULTES, J. A., and ROEMER, J. J.

1819. *Systema vegetabilum*, VI, 646, 648, 651, 652. Stuttgart.

SCRIBNER, F. L.

1869. *Weeds of Maine*, p. 49. Augusta.

1875. *The Ornamental and Useful Plants of Maine*, p. 43. Augusta.

SELBY, A. D.

1906. "Second Ohio Weed Manual," *Ohio Agricultural Experiment Station*, Bulletin 175, p. 339. Wooster.

SHAFER, J. A., and BRITTON, N. L.

1908. *North American Trees*, pp. 604, 609 ff. New York.

SHERARD, W.

1723. *Philosophical Transactions*, XXXI, 147. London.

SHIRASAWA, H.

1900. *Iconographie des essences forestières du Japon*, Vol. I, t. 57, 58. Tokyo.

SIECK, W.

1895. "Die schizolysigenen Secretbehälter," *Jahrb. Wiss. Bot.*, XXVII, 227, Plates 6–9.

SIMMONDS, A. B., and OTHERS.

1885. *Plants of Fitchburg (Massachusetts) and Vicinity*, p. 10. Fitchburg.

SLOANE, H.

1696. "Terebenthus maxima, pinnis pancioribus majoribus atque rotundioribus racemoso sparso," *Catalogus plantarum quae in insula Jamaica sponte proveniunt*, etc., p. 167. London.

SMALL, J. K.

1903. *Flora of the Southeastern United States*, p. 727. New York.

SMITH, J.

1882. *Dictionary of Popular Names of Economic Plants*, pp. 397, 249, 426. London.

SMYTH, B. B.

1892. *Check-list of the Plants of Kansas*, p. 11. Topeka.

SOLLERS, B.

1888. *Check List of Baltimore Plants*, p. 13. Baltimore.

SPACH, E.

1834. *Histoire naturelle des vêgêtaux phanerogames*, II, 211–18. Paris.

SPOFFORD, A. R., and ANNANDALE, C. (editors).

1901. *Twentieth Century Cyclopaedia*, VIII, 151. New York and Philadelphia.

SPRAGUE, I., and GRAY, A.

1849. *The Genera of the Plants of the United States*, II, 159. New York.

SPRENGEL, C.

1825. *Linnaeus Systema vegetabilium* (16th ed.), I, 936, 937, 938. Göttingen.

STEARNS, F.

1859. *Proceedings of the American Pharmaceutical Association*, VII, 276. Philadelphia.

STEVENS, A. B.

1906. "Poisonous Species of Rhus," *Pharmaceutical Era*, XXXVI, 527. New York.

STEVENSON, ROBERT L.

1883. "*The Silverado Squatters' First Impressions of Silverado*, chapter ii, "With the Children of Israel"; chapter iii, "Napa Wine in the Valley."

STRASBURGER, E., and OTHERS.

1898. *A Textbook of Botany* (Translated by H. C. Porter), p. 122. London.

SUDWORTH, G. B.

1897. *Nomenclature of the Arborescent Flora of the United States* (United States Department of Agriculture, Division of Forestry, Bulletin No. 14), pp. 274, 276. Washington.

1898. *Check List of Forest Trees of the United States* (United States Department of Agriculture, Division of Forestry, Bulletin No. 17), p. 88. Washington.

TABATA, S.

1907. "Früchte und Keimpflanzen von Rhus succ.," *Tokyo University College of Sciences Journal*, Vol. XXIII, art. 1.

TATNALL, E.

1860. *Catalogue of the Phaenogamous and Filicoid Plants of Newcastle County, Delaware*, p. 20. Wilmington.

THOMPSON, R.

1900. *Gardener's Assistant*, II, 317. London.

THOMPSON, R., and WATSON, W. (editors).

1904. *Gardener's Assistant*, I, 317. London.

THOMPSON, W.

1892. "Challenger Expedition," quoted by T. J. W. Burgess in *Journal and Proceedings of the Hamilton Association*, VIII, 126.

THUNBERG, C. P.

1784. *Flora Japonica*, p. 121. Leipzig.

THUNBERY, C. C.

1795–96. *Travels in Europe, Africa, and Asia between the Years 1770 and 1779* (3d ed.), I, 171; III, 188; IV, 38, 62, 91, 92, 93. London.

THURSTON, C. O., and DUDLEY, W. R.

1892. *Catalogue of the Flowering Plants and Vascular Cryptogams Found in and near Lackawanna and Wyoming Valleys*, p. 14. Wilkes-barre, Pennsylvania.

THWAITES, R. G.

1904. *Early Western Travels*, III, 101. Cleveland.

TITFORD, W. J.

1812. *Sketches towards a Hortus Botanicus Americanus*, p. 51. London.

TORREY BOTANICAL CLUB.

1888. *Preliminary Catalogue of Anthophyta and Pteridophyta Reported as Growing Spontaneously within 100 Miles of New York*, p. 12. New York.

TORREY, JOHN.

1819. *Catalogue of Plants Growing Spontaneously within Thirty Miles of New York*, p. 33. Albany.

1843. *Flora of New York*, I, 130. Albany.

1845. "Catalogue of Plants Collected by Charles Geyer under the direction of J. N. Nicollet (in J. N. Nicollet, *Report, etc.*, Appendix B.), p. 147. Washington.

1856. "Report of the Botany of the Expedition," *Pacific Railroad Report Route near 35th Parallel Explored by Whipple in 1853–54*, Vol. IV.

1859. In W. H. Emory, *Report on the United States and Mexico Boundary*, II, 44. Washington.

1874. *Phanerogamia of Pacific North America*, in C. Wilkes, *United States Exploring Expedition*, XVII, 257. Philadelphia.

TORREY, J., and GRAY, A.

1838, 1843. *Flora of North America*, I, 217, 218, 681. New York and London.

TOURNEFORT, JOSEPH PITTON.

1700. *Institutiones Rei Herbariae*, I, 610–11. Paris.

TRACY, C. M.

1858. *Studies of the Essex Flora*, p. 26. Lynn.

TRACY, S. M.

1886. *Catalogue of the Phaenogamous and Vascular Cryptogamous Plants of Missouri*, p. 22. Jefferson City.

TRECUL, M. A.

1867. "Des Vaisseaux propres dans les térébinthanées," *Comptes Rendus*, LXV, 17.

TRELEASE, W.

1910. *Annual Report of the Missouri Botanical Gardens*, XX, 11. St. Louis.

TUCKERMAN, E., and FROST, C.

1875. *A Catalogue of Plants Growing without Cultivation within Thirty Miles of Amherst College*, p. 7. Amherst.

UPHAM, W.

1884. *Catalogue of the Flora of Minnesota*, p. 37. Minneapolis.

VAN DE POLDER, L.

1892. "L'Arbre a Laque du Japan et sa culture," *Bulletin van het Kolonial, Museum te Haarlem*, No. 3. Haarlem.

VASEY, G.

1876*a*. *Catalogue of the Forest Trees of the United States*, p. 11. Washington.

1876*b*. *Flora Columbiana*, p. 7. Washington.

VOIT.

1895. "Respiration," *Sitzungsb. Münch. Akad.*, XV, 51.

WALTER, T.

1788. *Flora Caroliniana*, p. 255. London.

WANGENHEIM, F. A.

1787. *Nood Amerikanischen Holzarten*, p. 92. Göttingen.

WARD, L. F.

1881. *Guide to the Flora of Washington and Vicinity* (United States National Museum, Bulletin No. 22), p. 73. Washington.

WARDER, J. A., and OTHERS.

1882. *Woody Plants of Ohio*, p. 14. Cincinnati.

WARMING, E.

1895. *A Handbook of Systematic Botany*, p. 439. London and New York.

WATSON, S.
1878. *Bibliographical Index to North American Botany*, pp. 181–84. Washington.

WATSON S., BREWER, W. H., and GRAY, A.
1876. *Botany*, p. 110 (In J. D. Whitney, *Geological Survey of California*, Vol. I). Cambridge.

WATSON, S., and COULTER, J. M.
1890. *Gray's Manual* (6th ed.), p. 119. New York and Chicago.

WATSON, S., EATON, D. C., and OTHERS.
1871. "Botany of the Fortieth Parallel," *United States Geological Exploration of the Fortieth Parallel*, p. 53. Washington.

WATSON, S., GRAY, A., and ROBINSON, B. L.
1897. *Synoptical Flora of North America* (2d ed.), I, Part 1, 383. New York.

WATSON, W., and THOMPSON, R. (editors).
1904. *Gardener's Assistant*, I, 317. London.

WATT, G.
1892. *A Dictionary of the Economic Products of India*, VI, 497–502. London and Calcutta.

WEATHERS, J.
1901. *A Practical Guide to Garden Plants*, pp. 319 ff. London, New York, and Bombay.

WHEELER, C. F., and SMITH, E. F.
1881. *Catalogue of the Phanogamous and Vascular Cryptogamous Plants of Michigan*, p. 21. Lansing.

WHEELER, LIEUT. G. M.
1878. *Report of the United States Geological Survey West of the Hundredth Meridian*, p. 42. Washington.

WIESNER, Julius.
1900. *Die Rohstoffe des Pflanzenreiches*, I, 299.

WILDENOW, C. L.
1797. *Species plantarum*, I, Part 2, 1479–81. Berlin.
1809. *Enumeratio plantarum hortii regii botanici berolinensis*, pp. 323, 324. Berlin.

WILLIAMS, S. W.
1849. "Report on the Indigenous Medical Botany of Massachusetts," *Transactions of the American Medical Association*, II, 911. Philadelphia.

WILLIS, A. R., and WOOD, A.
1889. *American Botanist and Florist*, p. 73. New York and Chicago.

WILLIS, O. R.
1874. *Catalogue of Plants Growing without Cultivation in the State of New Jersey*, p. 13. New York.
1893. *Flora of Westchester County*, p. 782. Westchester (?).

WILSON, J. M.
1852. *Rural Cyclopedia*, IV, 383. Edinburgh.
WOOD, A.
1869. *Class Book of Botany*, p. 284. Troy.
1879. *Flora atlantica*, p. 73. New York, Chicago, and New Orleans.
WOOD, A., and WILLIS, O. R.
1889. *American Botanist and Florist*, p. 73. New York and Chicago.
WOOD, T. F., and McCARTHY, G.
1887. *Wilmington (N.C.) Flora*, p. 18. Raleigh.
WOODVILLE, W.
1832. *Medical Botany* (3d ed.), V, 67. London.
WRIGHT, A. A.
1889. *Preliminary List of the Flowering and Fern Plants of Lorain County, Ohio*, p. 11. Oberlin.
WRIGHT, J., and HALL, J.
1836. *A Catalogue of Plants Growing without Cultivation in the Vicinity of Troy*, p. 33. Troy, New York.
WRIGHT, J., and EATON, A.
1840. *North American Botany*, p. 392. Troy, New York.
WRIGHT, J. S.
1906. "Indiana Plants Yielding Drugs," *Proceedings of the Indiana Academy of Science (1905)*. Indianapolis.
WRIGHT, MABEL O.
1901. *Flowers and Ferns in Their Haunts*, pp. 162 ff. New York.
YOUNG, H. W., and MILLER, E. S.
1874. *Catalogue of the Phaenogamous and Acrogenous Plants of Suffolk County, Long Island*, p. 6. Port Jefferson.

## CHEMICAL REFERENCES

### FAT FORMATIONS

#### CARBOHYDRATES TO FAT IN ANIMALS

BLEIBTREN.
1901. "Fettmast und respiratorischer Quotient," *Pflügers Archiv*, LXXV, 345.
BÖTTCHER.
*Landwirtschaftliche Versuchs-Stationen*, XLIV, 257.
CHANIEWSKI.
1884. *Zeitschrift für Biologie* (N.F.), II (or XX?), 179.
FISCHER.
1904. *Fühlings landwirtschaftliche Zeitung*, pp. 363, 412, 448.
GERHARD.
*Landw. Vers.-Stat.*, XLIV, 257.

GIERKE.
1906. "Stoffwechs. des Fettgewebes," *Verh. der pathol. Gesellschaft*, p. 182.

KELLNER.
*Landw. Vers-Stat.*, XLIV, 257.

KOCH.
*Landw. Vers.-Stat.*, XLIV, 257.

KÖHLER.
*Landw. Vers.-Stat.*, XLIV, 257.

KÖNIG.
*Landw. Vers.-Stat.*, XLIV, 257.

KÜHN.
*Landw. Vers.-Stat.*, XLIV, 257.

LANKISCH.
*Landw. Vers.-Stat.*, XLIV, 257.

LIEBIG.
1879–80. *Landwirtschaftliche Jahrbücher*, VIII, 701; IX, 651.

LÖSCHE.
*Landw. Vers.-Stat.*, XLIV, 257.

LYONS.
*Archiv für Hygiene*, XXVIII, 30.

MAGNUS-LEVY.
*Tierchemie*, XXXIII, 504.

MARTIN.
*Landw. Vers.-Stat.*, XLIV, 257.

MEISSL and STROHMER.
1883. *Sitzungsbericht der Wr. Akademie*, III, 88.

MEISSL, STROHMER, and LORENZ.
1886. *Zeitschrift für Biologie* (N.F.), IV, 63.

MIELTKE.
*Landw. Vers.-Stat.*, XLIV, 257.

MOHR.
*Landw. Vers.-Stat.*, XLIV, 257.

MUNK, I.
1885. *Virchows Archiv*, CI, 91.

PLOSZ.
1899*a*. *Malys Jahresberichte der Tierchemie*, 685.
1899*b*. *Tierchemie*, XXIX, 685.

REFERENTEN.
1884. *Landw. Vers.-Stat.*, XX, 82.

ROSENFELD, G.
1902. *Ergebn. der Physiol.*, I, 651.

ROSENFELD.
1904. "Bildung von Fett aus Kohlenhydraten," *Allg. Mediz. Zentr. Zeitung*, p. 50.
*Tierchemie*, XXII, 344.

SOXHLET, F.
1881. *Zeitschrift des landwirtschaftliche Vereins in Bayern*, p. 420.
THOMAS.
*Landw. Vers.-Stat.*, XLIV, 257.
TSCHERWINSKY, N.
1883. *Landw. Vers.-Stat.*, XXIX, 317.
VOIT.
1885. *Sitzungsbericht der Münchner Akademie*, p. 288.
*Tierchemie*, XV, 51.
WAAGE.
*Landw. Vers.-Stat.*, XLIV, 257.
WEISKE, H., and WILDT, E.
1874. *Zeitschrift für Biologie*, X, 1.
WOLFF.
*Tierchemie*, IX, 327.
ZEITSCKEK.
*Pflügers Archiv*, XCVIII, 614.

CARBOHYDRATES TO FAT IN PLANTS

BOUSILLE, A.
1878. "Recherches relatives à la maturation des olives," *Comptes Rendus*, LXXVI, 610.
CZAPEK, F.
1905. *Biochemie der Pflanzen*, I, 134. Jena.
DU SABLON, LE CLERC.
1893. *Comptes Rendus*, CXVII, 524.
1894. *Comptes Rendus*, CXIX, 610.
1895. *Rev. Gén. Bot.*, VII, 145.
1896. *Comptes Rendus*, CXXIII, 1048.
1897. *Rev. Gén. Bot.*, IX, 313.
FISCHER, A.
1890. *Jahrbuch für wissenschaftliche Botanik*, XXII, 73.
FUNARO, A.
1879. *Lavori del Labor. Chim. Pisa.*
1880. *Versuch-Stationen*, XXV, 52.
GERBER, C.
1897. *Comptes Rendus*, CXXV, 658, 732.
GLIKIN, W.
1912. *Chemie der Fette, u.s.w.*, I, 106–8. Leipzig.
GREEN.
1890. *Proceedings of the Royal Society of London*, XLVIII, 370.
HARTWICH, C., and UHLMANN, W.
1902. *Archiv der Pharmacie*, CCXL, 471.
JOLLES, ADOLF.
1912. *Chemie der Fette*, pp. 107–14. Strassburg.

LEATHES, J. B.
1910. *The Fats*, p. 107. London.
MESNARD.
1894a. *Bull. soc. bot.*, p. 14.
1894b. *Ann. sci. nat.*, Vol. XVIII.
MEIEN.
1888. *Neues System der Pflanzenphysiologie*, II, 293.
MILLER.
1910. *Ann. Bot.*, XXIV, 693.
MULDER.
1844–51. *Physiologische Chemie*, p. 269.
RECHENBERG.
1881. *Ber. Chem. Ges.*, XIV, 2216.
ROUSILLE, A.
1878. *Comptes Rendus*, LXXXVI, 610.
1879. *Biedermanns Centr.*, p. 131.
RUSSOW.
1882. *Dorpat. Naturforsch.-Gesellschaft*, VI, 492.
SCHMIDT.
1891. *Flora*, LXXIV, 300.
SPAMPANI, G.
1899. *Boll. soc. bot. Ital.*, p. 139.
VALLEE, C.
1903. "Anwesenheit von Rohrzucker in ölhaltigen Samen und seine Beziehung zur Bildung des Öles," *Jour. Pharm. Chem.*, XVII, 273.
1904. *Comptes Rendus*, CXXXVI, 114.
WAGNER, P.
1874. *Just*, II, 853.
ZAY, C. E.
1901. *Staz. sperim. agrar. Ital.*, p. 1080.

PROTEIN TO FAT IN ANIMALS

DRECHSEL, E.
1890. *Chem. Ber.*, XXIII, 3096.
DUCLAUX.
*Ann. de l'Inst. Pasteur*, LXXXIX, 413.
HENNEBERG, W.
1867. "Über das Fettbildungs äquivalent der Eiweisstoffe," *Landw. Vers.-Stat.*, X, 437.
1881. *Zeitschrift für Biologie*, XVII, 345.
JACOBSTHAL, H.
*Pflügers Archiv*, LIV, 484.
KERN, E., and WATTENBERG, H.
1878. *Journal für Landwirtschaft*, XXVI, 549.

NÄGELI and LÖW.
*Journal für praktische Chemie*, XVI, 97.
RUBNER.
1885. *Zeitschrift für Biologie*, XXI, 250.
1886. *Zeitschrift für Biologie* (N.F.), IV, 272.
SCHRÖDER, W.
*Archiv exp. Pathol. und Pharmak.*, XV, 364.
SCHULZE, B.
1882. *Landwirtschaftliche Jahrbücher*, I, 57.
STOHMANN.
*Journal für praktische Chemie*, XXI, 273.
WOLFFS, E. VON
1879. *Landwirtschaftliche Jahrbücher*, VIII (Supplement), 270.
ZUNTZ, N.
1879. *Landwirtschaftliche Jahrbücher*, VIII, 96.

JAPAN WAX

ALLEN.
1913. From W. Glikin, *Chemie der Fette*, II, 316. Leipzig.
ALLEN, A. H.
1886. *Analyst*, XI, 225. London.
ANONYMOUS.
1877. *American Journal of Pharmacy*, p. 451.
1894. "Veitch Collection of Japanese Vegetable Products," *Kew Bulletin*, pp. 14–17.
BAILLON, H. E.
1878. *The Natural History of Plants*, V, 299. London.
BARROWS, W. B.
1898. *The Common Crow of the United States* (U.S. Department of Agriculture, Division of Ornithology and Marmalogy, Bulletin No. 6), pp. 85–87. Washington.
BATKA, J. B.
1865. "Über das Wachs der Sumachineen," *Chemisches Central-Blatt* (N.F.), I, 12. Leipzig.
BECKE, VON DER.
1913. From W. Glikin, *Chemie der Fette*, II, 316. Leipzig.
BERG, R.
1903. "Einiges über die Untersuchung des Bienenwachses," *Chemiker-Zeitung*, XVII, 755. Cöthen.
BERTHELOT.
*Annales de chimie et de physique*, XLI, 242. Paris.
BRANDES.
*Archiv der Pharmacie* (2d ser.), XXVII, 288.
BRANNT, WILLIAM F.
1896. *Animal and Vegetable Fats and Oils*, pp. 138–41. London.

Brennheimer and Schiff.
1913. From W. Glikin, *Chemie der Fette*, p. 316. Leipzig.
Buchner.
*Buchner Repert*, XLIV, 513.
Bryant, H. C.
1916. "Habits and Food of the Roadrunner of California," *University of California Publication, Zoölogy*, XVII, 29.
Bührer, C.
1892. *Zeitschrift für Nahrungsmittel Untersuchungen, Hygiene und Waaren-Kunde*, VI, 303–6.
"The Vegetable Waxes," *American Druggist*, XXXI, 97–100.
Buignet, H.
1809. "Note sur la cire du Japon" (Editorial), *Journal de pharmacie et de chimie* (3d ser.), XXXVI, 368. Paris.
Buisine, A. and P.
1891. "Falsifications et essai de la cire des abeilles," *Bulletin de la société chimique de Paris* (3d ser.), V, 654 ff. Paris.
Buri, E.
1875. "Über den Japantalg, u.s.w.," *Archiv der Pharmacie* (3d ser.), XIV, 403. Halle.
Dietrich, K.
1913. From W. Glikin, *Chemie der Fette*, II, 316. Leipzig.
Du Sablon, Le Clerc.
1893. *Comptes Rendus*, CXVII, 524.
1894. *Comptes Rendus*, CXIX, 610.
1895. *Rev. Gén. Bot.*, VII, 145.
1896. *Comptes Rendus*, CXXIII, 1048.
1897. *Rev. Gén. Bot.*, IX, 313.
Eberhardt, L. A.
1888. *Über den Japantalg*, pp. 1–321 (Inaugural Dissertation, Strassburg). New York.
Editorial.
1859. *Pharmaceutical Journal and Transactions* (2d ser.), I, 176. London.
1877. *Journal of Applied Science*, VIII, 55. London.
Eichhorn, O.
1900. *Zeitschrift für analytische Chemie*, XXXIX, 642. Wiesbaden.
1901. Abstract in *Analyst*, XXVI, 47.
Eisenstein, A., Pastrovich P., and Ulzer, F.
1908. *Benedict-Ulzers Analyse der Fette und Wachsarten*, V, 840. Berlin.
Fawcett, W. (editor).
1900. *Bulletin of the Botanical Department, Jamaica* (new series), VII, 37. Kingston.
Frankforter, G. B., and Martin, A. W.
1904. "A Chemical Study of the Seed of Rhus glabra," *American Journal of Pharmacy*, LXXVI, 151–58.

GEITEL, A. C., and VAN DER WANT, G.
1900*a*. *Journal für praktische Chemie*, LXI, 151–56. Leipzig.
1900*b*. Abstract in *Analyst*, XXV, 214.

GMELIN, L.
1864. *Handbook of Chemistry*, XVI, 393. London.

HAGER, H.
1880*a*. *Chemisches Central-Blatt*, p. 367.
1880*b*. *Handbuch der pharmaceutischen Praxis*, I, 789. Berlin.
1913. From W. Glikin, *Chemie der Fette*, II, 316. Leipzig. "Untersuchung des Wachses," *Pharmaceutische Zentralhalle*, XXI, 119, 129.

HAGER, H., and HOLDERMANN, E.
1888. *Hagers Untersuchungen*, II, 658. Leipzig.

HANANSEK, E.
1877. "Chinensisches Wachs," *Zeitschrift der allg. österr. Apotheker-Vereins*, XV, 260.

HANBURY, D.
1853. *Pharmaceutical Journal and Transactions*, XII, 476. London.

HEFS.
*Poggendorphs Annalen der Physik und Chemie*, XLIII, 382.

HEHNER, O., and MITCHELL, C. A.
1896. *Analyst*, XXI, 330. London.
1897. *Journal of the American Chemical Society*, XIX, 32–51. Easton, Pennsylvania.

HEINTZ, W., and MATTHES, W.
1910. "Constants of Japan Wax," *Archiv der Pharmacie*, CCXLVII, 650.

HELL, C., and JORDANOFF.
1891. *Berichte der deutschen chemischen Gesellschaft*, XXIV, 936. Berlin.

HENRIQUES, R.
1896. *Zeitschrift für angewandte Chemie*, IX, 223. Berlin.

HILGER, A., HUSEMANN, T., and HUSEMANN, A.
1884. *Die Pflanzenstoffe in chemischer, physiologischer, pharmakologischer, und toxikologischer Hinsicht*, II, 867. Berlin.

HIRSCHSOHN, E.
"Contributions to the Chemistry of Several Varieties of Wax," *Pharmaceutical Journal and Transactions* (3d ser.), X, 749.

HÜBL, B.
1883. "Zur Prüfung des Bienenwachses," *Dinglers polytechnisches Journal*, CCXLIX, 338. Stuttgart.

HÜBL.
1913. From W. Glikin, *Chemie der Fette*, II, 316. Leipzig.

HUSEMANN, A., HILGER, A., and HUSEMANN, T.
1884. *Die Pflanzenstoffe in chemischer, physiologischer, pharmakologischer und toxikologischer Hinsicht*, II, 867. Berlin.

HUSEMANN, T., HUSEMANN, A., and HILGER, A.

1884. *Die Pflanzenstoffe in chemischer, physiologischer, pharmakologischer und toxikologischer Hinsicht*, II, 867. Berlin.

JOHNSON, C. T.

1859. *Proceedings of the Boston Society of Natural History*, VII, 54, 59, 149. Boston.

KEBLER, L. F.

1893. "Notes on the Examination of Beeswax," *American Journal of Pharmacy*, LXV, 585. Philadelphia.

1895. *American Druggist and Pharmaceutical Record*, XXVII, 3, 37. New York.

KLEINSTÜCK, O.

1888. *Archiv der Pharmacie*, XXVI, 166.

1890*a*. *Chemiker-Zeitung*, XIV, 1303.

1890*b*. *Journal of the Society of Chemical Industry*, p. 1072. London.

KRAFFT.

1888. *Berichte der deutschen chemischen Gesellschaft*, XXI, 2265.

LANDERER.

*Buchner Repert*, XLIV, 1–23.

LAWALL, C. H.

1897. *American Journal of Pharmacy*, LXIX, 18–21. Philadelphia.

LEWKOWITSCH, J.

1904. *Chemical Technology and Analysis of Oils, Fats and Waxes* (3d ed.), II, 755–59, 885, 898. London and New York.

1914. *Chemical Technology and Analysis of Oils, Fats and Waxes*, II, 650. London.

LOCK, C. G. W.

1882. *Spon's Encyclopaedia of the Industrial Arts, Manufacturers, and Raw Commercial Products*, II, 1621, 1692, 2045. London.

LUDWIG, H.

1872. "Über Pflanzenwachs," *Archiv der Pharmacie* (3d ser.), I, 193–213. Halle.

MCNAIR, JAMES B.

1917*a*. "Fats from Rhus Laurina and Rhus Diversiloba," *Botanical Gazette*, LXIV, 330–36.

MARPMANN.

1913. From W. Glikin, *Chemie der Fette*, II, 316. Leipzig.

MATTHES, H., and HEINTZ, W.

1910. "Constants of Japan Wax," *Archiv der Pharmacie*, CCXLVII, 650.

MENE, C.

1874. *Comptes Rendus*, LXXVIII, 1544. Paris.

MERCK & CO.

1907. *Index 1907* (3d ed.), pp. 461, 462. New York.

MEYER, A.

1879. "Über Japantalg," *Archiv der Pharmacie* (3d ser.), XV, 97, 128. Halle.

*Archiv der Pharmacie*, XXV, 120.

MITCHELL, C. A., and HEHNER, O.

1896. *Analyst*, XXI, 330. London.

1897. *Journal of the American Chemical Society*, XIX, 32–51. Easton, Pennsylvania.

MÖBIUS, M.

1897. "Über Wachsausscheidung in Innern von Zellen," *Berichte der deutschen botanischen Gesellschaft*, XV, 435–41.

MÜLLER.

*Buchner Repert*, XIV, 25; XLIV, 23–34.

NESENBECK.

*Repert*, XLVI, 283.

OPPERMAN, C.

1832. "Recherches sur la cire végétal et la cire des abeilles," *Annales de chimie et de physique*, XLIX, 240–44.

PASTROVICH, P., ULZER, F., and EISENSTEIN, A.

1908. *Benedict-Ulzers Analyse der Fette und Wachsarten*, V, 840. Berlin.

POSETTO.

1901. *Giornale di farmacia e di scienze affini*, L, 337. Torino.

1908. Abstract in *Benedict-Ulzers Analyse der Fette und Wachsarten*, V, 840.

PROCTON, B. S.

1863. *Chemist and Druggist*, IV, 214. London.

PROCTON, W., JR.

1860. "Note on Japanese Wax," *American Journal of Pharmacy*, XXXII, 311. Philadelphia.

PURCELL, R. C.

1899. *American Journal of Pharmacy*, LXXI, 217–22. Philadelphia.

PURSEL, R.

1899. *Bull. de Pharm. du Sud-Ect.*, p. 281.

REIN, J. J.

1889. *The Industries of Japan*, pp. 158–64, 342–76. London.

ROBERTSON (CONSUL).

1875. In "Report on the Trade of Kanagawa, Japan," reprinted in *Pharmaceutical Journal and Transactions* (3d ser.), V, 584. London.

ROGERS, W. B.

1859. *Proceedings of the Boston Society of Natural History*, VII, 55, 58. Boston.

ROUCHER, C.

1872. "Sur le double point de fusion d'une cire végétale originaire du Japon, et sur l'emploie de cette cire en pharmacie," *Journal de pharmacie et de chimie* (4th ser.), XVI, 20. Paris.

RUDORFF, F.
1872. *Poggendorphs Annalen der Physik und Chemie*, CXLV, 258. Leipzig.
SADTLER, S. P.
1906. *A Handbook of Industrial Organic Chemistry* (3d ed.), pp. 51, 100. Philadelphia and London.
SCHAAL.
1907. *Berichte*, XL, 4784.
SCHÄDLER.
1913. From W. Gliken, *Chemie der Fette*, II, 316. Leipzig.
SHERMAN, H. C.
1905. *Methods of Organic Analysis*, p. 146. New York.
SCHRANZ, W.
1900. *Zeitschrift für analytische Chemie*, XXXIX, 178. Wiesbaden.
STEVENS, A. B.
1908. "Poison Ivy Fruit," *American Journal of Pharmacy*, LXXX, 93. Philadelphia.
STEVENS, A. B., and WARREN, L. E.
1907. "Poison Sumac," *American Journal of Pharmacy*, LXXIX, 519–22. Philadelphia.
STHAMER, B.
1842*a*. *Journal de pharmacie et de chimie* (3d ser.), II, 528. Paris.
1842*b*. "Über die Zusammensetzung des japanischen Wachses, u.s.w.," *Liebig's Annalen der Chemie und Pharmacie*, XLIII, 335. Heidelberg.
THORP, F. H.
1907. *Outlines of Industrial Chemistry* (2d ed.), p. 333. New York and London.
TROMMSDORFF, J. B.
1834. *Journal für praktische Chemie*, I, 151. Leipzig.
ULZER, F., PASTROVICH, P., and EISENSTEIN, A.
1908. *Benedikt-Ulzers Analyse der Fette und Wachsarten*, V, 840. Berlin.
VALENTA.
1913. From W. Glikin, *Chemie der Fette*, II, 316. Leipzig.
VAN DER WANT, G., and GEITEL, A. C.
1900*a*. *Journal für praktische Chemie*, LXI, 151–56. Leipzig.
1900*b*. Abstract in *Analyst*, XXV, 214.
VISSER.
1913. From W. Gilkin, *Chemie der Fette*, II, 316. Leipzig.
VOGL, A. E. VON.
1900. *Bernatzik-Vogls Lehrbuch der Arzneimittellehre*, pp. 203, 549. Berlin and Wien.
WARREN, L. E.
1909. *Pharmaceutical Journal*, October 30 and November 6.

WEIGEL, G.
1908. *Pharmaceutische Centralhalle für Deutschland*, XLIX, 917. Dresden.

WERDER, J.
1898. *Chemiker-Zeitung*, XXII, 38, 59. Cöthen.

WILSON, G. F.
1859. *Pharmaceutical Journal and Transactions*, XVIII, 630. London.

WIMMEL.
1876. *Zeitschrift der allg. österr. Apotheker-Vereins*, p. 350.

YOSHIDA, HIKOROKURO.
1883*a*. "Chemistry of Lacquer (Urushi). Communication from the Chemical Society of Tokio," *Journal of the Chemical Society*, XLIII, 473–86. London.
1883*b*. Abstract in the *Pharmaceutical Journal and Transactions* (3d ser.), XIV, 377. Also in *Journal de pharmacie et de chimie*, IX, 320; *Jahresber. für Chemie*, p. 1768.

CHEMISTRY OF THE POISONOUS PRINCIPLE OF RHUS

ABBOTT, F.
1887. *Papers and Proceedings of the Royal Society of Tasmania for 1886*, p. 182. Hobart.

ACHARD, FRANZ KARL.
1786. *Nouv. Mém. de l'Acad. Royal de Sciences et Belles Lettres*, I, 48.
1787. "Nachricht von Versuchen, die über den Giftbaum (*Rhus Toxicodendron* Linn.) angestelltwurden zu Kennen, und die Art und Weise, wie sein Gift auf verschiedene Thiere wirkt, zu bestimmen," *Chemische Annalen von Lorenz Crell*, I, 387–95, 494–503.

ACKERMANN, JACOBUS FIDELIS.
1814. *Von der Natur des ansteckenden Typhus; dem Wesen des Ansteckungsstoffs, der Art sich gegen denselben zu sichern, und der Methode die Krankheit zu heilen.* Heidelberg.

ACREE, S. F.
1916*a*. "On the Constituents of Poison Ivy," *Journal of the American Chemical Society*, XXXVIII, 1421–25. Easton, Pennsylvania.
1916*b*. *Chemical News*, CXIV, 207–9. London.

ACREE, S. F., and SYME, W. A.
1906. "Some Constituents of the Poison Ivy Plant," *American Chemical Journal*, XXXVI, 301–21. Baltimore.
1906–7. "On the Composition of Toxicodendrol," *Journal of Biological Chemistry*, II, 547. New York.

ADELUNG, EDWARD VON.
1912. *An Experimental Study of Poison Oak.* M. A. Thesis, University of California, November, 1912. Published in *Archives of Internal Medicine*, XI, 184.

ANONYMOUS.

1802–5. *Archiv für die Pharmacie und ärztliche Naturkunde; hrsg. von Johann Schraub und Georg Heinrich Piepenbring.* Cassel and Gotha, Vols. I–III.

1809. *Nicholson's Journal of Natural Philosophy, Chemistry and the Arts,* XXIII, 234. London.

BEILSTEIN, F. K.

1903. *Handbuch der organischen Chemie.* Leipzig.

BENNETT, J. J.

1838–52. *Plantae Javanicae rariores descriptae iconibusque illustratae,* Part 1, p. 60. London.

BESSEY, C. D.

1914. "The Volatile Nature of the Toxic Constituent of Poison Ivy," *American Journal of Pharmacy,* pp. 86, 112.

BIDDLE, HENRY C.

1911. *Organic Chemistry,* p. 76. Berkeley, California.

BROWNE, C. A.

1912. *Handbook of Sugar Analysis* (1st ed.), p. 34. New York: John Wiley & Sons.

BROWNE, D. J.

1846. *Trees of America,* p. 186. New York.

BURACZYNSKI, A.

1902. "Dermatitis toxica, Nervorgerufen durch *Rhus vernicifera,*" *Wiener klinische Rundschau,* XVI, 955. Wien.

BURRILL, T. J.

1882*a*. "Some Vegetable Poisons," *American Monthly Microscopical Journal,* III, 192–96. New York.

1882*b*. "Some Vegetable Poisons," *Proceedings of the American Association for the Advancement of Science,* XXXI, 515, 518. Salem.

1895. "Rhus Poisoning," *Garden and Forest,* VIII, 368–69. New York.

CALDWELL, C.

1805. *Medical Theses,* containing Thomas Horsfield's Inaugural Dissertation, pp. 113 ff. Philadelphia.

CAPPELL (?).

1800. *Beitrag zur Beurtheilung des Brownischen Systems der Arzneikunde, u.s.w.* Göttingen.

CHESTNUT, V. K.

1902. "Problems in the Chemistry and Toxicology of Plant Substances," *Science* (new series), XV, 1016, 1019. New York.

CHESTNUT, V. K., and WILCOX, E. V.

1901. *The Stock Poisoning Plants of Montana,* p. 134. Washington.

CHEVALLIER, M., and FONTENELLE, J.

1825. Translation into French of M. Lavini, "Emanations délétères qui émanent du *Rhus Toxicodendron,*" *Journal de chimie médicale,* I, 249*a*–51*a*. Paris.

CHO, S., and MAJIMA, R.
1907. "Über einen Hauptbestandteil des japanischen Lackes," *Berichte der deutschen chemischen Gesellschaft*, XL, 4390–93. Berlin.

CHYSER, B.
1910. "Giftige Industrie-Pflanzen," *Vierteljahresschrift für gerichtliche Medizin und öffentliches Sanitätswesen* (3d ser.), XXXIX (Supp. II), 147–59. Berlin.

CLAISEN, L.
1894. "Bemerkung zu einer Mittheilung von A. Deninger: 'Über Darstellung von Benzoësäure-anhydrid,'" *Berichte der deutschen chemischen Gesellschaft*, XXVII, 3182–84.

CONRADI.
*Grundriss der Pathologie und Therapie*, I, 288.

CORNEVIN, C.
1893. *Des plantes vênêneuses et des empoisonnements qui elles dêterminent*, p. 275. Paris.

COTTON, ROBERT M.
1874. "*Rhus venenata*, or Poison Sumac—Description and Partial Analysis," *American Journal of Pharmacy*, XLVI, 355. Philadelphia.

CUTLER, M.
1785*a*. *An Account of the Vegetable Products Naturally Growing in This Part of America.*
1785*b*. *Memoirs of the American Academy of Arts and Sciences*, I, 427, 428, 429. Boston.
1903. Reprint in *Bulletin of the Lloyd Library of Botany, Pharmacy and Materia Medica*, pp. 422, 427–29. Cincinnati.

DILLENIUS, J. J.
1782. *Hortus eithamensis*, p. 390. London.

DUMOUTIER, G.
1892. *La laque et les huiles a laquer.* Hanoi.

EDITORIAL.
1893. *Medical News*, LXIII, 248. Philadelphia.
1911. *Journal of the American Medical Association*, LVI, 1501. Chicago.
1916. *Journal of the American Medical Association*, Vol. LXVII, No. 6, p. 441; No. 10, p. 763; No. 13, p. 970; No. 19, p. 1375.

FONTANA, F.
1787. *Trattato del veleno della vipera de veleni Americani*, I, 148; III, 114–17. Napoli. Translated by Joseph Skinner (2d ed.), II, 181–84. London, 1795.

FONTENELLE, J., and CHEVALLIER, M.
1825. Translation into French of M. Lavini, "Emanations délétère qui émanent du *Rhus Toxicodendron*," *Journal de chimie médicale*, I, 249*a*–51*a*.

Ford, W. W.
1908. *Science*, XXVII, 655. New York.
1909. "Note on *Rhus Toxicodendron*," *New York Medical Journal*, etc., XC, 215.
Frost, Lowell, C.
1916. "The Bacterial Etiology of Poison Oak Dermatitis (Rhus Poisoning)," *Medical Record*, XC, 1121–23, New York.
Gleditsch, Johann Gottlieb.
1777. "Nouvélles expériences concernant les dangereux effets que les exhalaisons d'une plantal de l'Amérique septentrionale produisent sur le corps humain," *Mém. de l'Acad. de Berlin*, pp. 61–80. Also in *Journal de physique*, XXI, 161–75.
Gleditsch.
"Verhandeling over de schadelyke gevolgen van een Nord-Americaansche Vergiftboom," *Algem. geneeskund. Jaarboeken*, V, 244–56; VI, 104–10.
"Nen vermehrte erläuterung über die schädlichen wirkungsfolgen des Nordamericanische Giftrebensstrauchs," *Beschäft. der Berlin. ges. Naturf. Fr.*, V, 263–313.
Gmelin.
*Pflanzengifte*, p. 176.
Halsted, B. D.
1895. "Notes on Poisonous Plants," *Garden and Forest*, VIII, 172. New York.
Hawley, J. W.
1890. "Rhus Roisoning," *Medical Advance*, XXIV, 257–62. Ann Arbor.
Hensinger, H.
1809. *Observata quaedam sistens circa Rhoa toxidocendron et radicantem*. Helmstadii.
Hitchcock, R.
1889. *Proceedings of the United States National Museum*, XI, 473. Washington.
1890. "Über japanischen Lack," *Druggists Circular*, XXXIV, 31.
Horsfield, Thomas.
1798. *An Inaugural Dissertation on Rhus vernix, R. radicans and R. glabrum, Commonly Known in Pennsylvania as Poison-Oak, Poison Vine, and Common Sumac*. Philadelphia.
1805. *Ibid.*, published in C. Caldwell's *Medical Theses*, pp. 113 ff. Philadelphia.
Hubbard, S.
1904. "Rhus Poisoning," *Medical Brief*, XXXII, 884.
Hunold.
*Piepenbrugs Archiv für die Pharmacie*, I, 279.

INCARVILLE (THE FATHER).
1760. "Mémoire sur la vernis de la Chine," *Mémoirs de mathêmatique et de physique*, III, 117–42. Paris.

INGENHOUSZ, JAN.
1779. *Experiments upon Vegetables, Discovering Their Great Power of Purifying Common Air in the Sunshine, and of Injuring in the Shade and at Night.* London.

ISHIMATSU, S.
1882. "On a Chemical Investigation of Japanese Lacquer or Urushi," *Memoirs of the Manchester Literary and Philosophical Society* (3d ser.), VII, 249. London and Paris.

JOHNSON, L.
1884. *Manual of Medical Botany of North America*, pp. 119–21. New York.

KHITTEL, J.
1858. "Chemische Untersuchung der Blätter des giftsumachs (*Rhus Toxicodendron*)," *Wittsteins Vierteljahresschrift für praktische Pharmacie*, VII, 348–59.

KIPLING, R.
1911. "The Female of the Species. A Study in Natural History," *Ladies' Home Journal*, XXVIII, 11.

KORSCHELT, O.
1884. "The Chemistry of Japanese Laquer," *Nature*, XXIX, 684. London.

KRAFT, F.
1888. "Über einige hochmoleculare Benzolderivate," *Berichte der deutschen chemischen Gesellschaft*, XXI, 2265.

KRAUSS, J. C.
1819. *Verhandeling over aard en de werking der geneesmiddelen, welke ter bestrijdung van Zenuwkwalen zu derzelver toevallen worden Aangewend*, pp. 1–208. Amsterdam.

KRÜGER.
*Archiv für die Pharmacie*, I, 261.

KRUNIZI.
In *Ökon., physical. Abhandl.*, Part XIX, p. 431.

LAVINI, M.
1825. "Emanations délétères qui émanent du *Rhus Toxicodendron*," *Journal de chimie médicale* I, 249*a*–51*a*. Paris. Translated by J. Fontenelle and M. Chevallier.

LIEBERMANN, C., and HÖRMANN, O.
1878. "Über die Formeln des Rhamnetins und Xanthorhamnins," *Berichte der deutschen chemischen Gesellschaft*, XI, 1619–22.

MCMASTER, J. B.
1918. *Life and Times of Stephen Girard.*

McNair, James B.

1916*a*. "The Poisonous Principle of Poison Oak," *Journal of the American Chemical Society*, XXXVIII, 1417–21. Easton, Pennsylvania. Reprinted in *Chemical News*, CXIV (1916), 185. London.

1917*b*. "The Poisonous Principle of Poison Oak, Non-Bacterial," *Medical Record*, XCI, 1042–43.

1921*c*. Lobinol—A Dermatitant from *Rhus diversiloba* (Poison Oak)," *Journal of the American Chemical Society*, XLIII, 159–64.

Maeda, M.

1878. "Les laques du Japan," *Revue scientifique* (2d ser.), XIV, 1173. Paris.

Maisch, J. M.

1858. *American Journal of Pharmacy*, XXX, 542. Philadelphia.

1866. "On the Active Principle of *Rhus Toxicodendron*," *American Journal of Pharmacy*, XXXVIII, 4–12.

1892. *A Manual of Organic Materia Medica* (5th ed.), p. 254. Philadelphia.

Majima, R.

1908. *Journal of the College of Engineering*, IV, 89–110. Tokyo.

1909*a*. "Über Urushiol und Urushioldimethyl Äther," *Berichte der deutschen chemischen Gesellschaft*, XLII, 1418–23. Berlin.

1909*b*. "Die oxydation des Urushiol-dimethyl Äthers mit Azon," *Berichte der deutschen chemischen Gesellschaft*, XLII, 3664. Berlin.

1912. "Die katalytische Reduktion von Urushiol," *Berichte der deutschen chemischen Gesellschaft*, XLV, 2727.

Majima, R., and Cho, S.

1907. "Über einen Hauptbestandteil des japanischen Lackes," *Berichte der deutschen chemischen Gesellschaft*, XL, 4390–93. Berlin.

Majima, R., and Nakamura, I.

1913. "Über den Hauptbestandteil des Japanlacks, "*Berichte der deutschen chemischen Gesellschaft*, XLVI, 4080. Berlin.

1914. *Science Reports*, Vol. III, No. 10, Imperial University. Tokyo.

Marcus.

*Prüfung des Brownschen Systems der Heilkunde durch Erfahrungen am Krankenbette*, Parts 1, 2.

Mazeas, W.

1756. *Philosophical Transactions*, XLIX, 157. London.

Meyer, A.

1880. "Über das Vorkommen von Krystallen in den Secreten einiger Rhusarten," *Archiv der Pharmacie* (3d ser.), XVII, 112. Halle.

Meyer, Victor, and Jacobson, Paul.

1893. *Lehrbuch der organischen Chemie*, II, 546. Leipzig: Veit & Co.

Millon.

1860–61. "Recherches sur le gui de chêne, et nouvelles observations sur le sumac vénéneux, ou Rhus toxicodendron," *Bull. Acad. de méd.*, XXVI, 501–5. Paris.

MILLON (DE REVEL).
1862. "Accidents-Constation d'immunité rapportie a la végétation," *Journal de médicine chirug. et pharm. de Toulouse* (November).

MONTI, GUISEPPE (JOSEPH).
1755. "De plantis venenatis," *Accademia delle scienze dell'Istituto di Bologna Commentarii* (2d ser.), III, 36, 160–68. Bologna.
*Ack. phys. Abhandl.*, Part 19, p. 446.
In *Überf. der Abhandl. des Bonon. Institutes*, Part II, p. 28.

MORBECK.
1798. *Medizinisch praktische Beobachtungen*, Vol. I. Heilbronn.

ORFILA, A. J. B.
1832. *Traité de Toxicologie*, II, 131.

ORR., S. S., and PFAFF F.
1895. *Science* (new series), I, 119. New York.

PECHMANN, H. VON
1892. "Über die Constitution des Acetessigäthers und des sogenannten Formylessigäthers," *Berichte der deutschen chemischen Gesellschaft*, XXV, 1040–54.

PERKIN, GEORGE ARTHUR.
1897. "Yellow Colouring Matters Obtained from *Rhus rhodanthema*, *Berberis oetnensis*, and *Rumex obtusifolius*," *Journal of the Chemical Society*, LXXI, 1194–1200. London.
1900. *Bulletin of the Botanical Department, Jamaica* (N.R.), VII, 19. Kingston.

PFAFF, FRANZ.
1897. "On the Active Principle of *Rhus Toxicodendron*," *Journal of Experimental Medicine*, II, 181–96. New York.
1903. *Kew Bulletin*, p. 15.

PFAFF, F., and ORR, S. S.
1895. *Science* (new series), I, 119. New York.

PICTET, AMÉ.
1913. *The Vegetable Alkaloids* (1st ed.), pp. 114–15 (Trans. by Henry C. Biddle). New York: J. Wiley & Sons.

PICTET, AMÉ, and ANKERSMIT, H. J.
1891. "Über das Phenanthridin," *Liebigs Annalen der Chemie*, CCLXV, 138–53.

PLENKI.
*Toxicologie*, p. 183.

PORNAI.
1783. *Giornale per servire alla storia ragionata della medicina di questo secolo*, I, 83. Venezia.

PRAAG, L. S. VON.
1820. *De rhoe-radicante sive rhoe-toxicodendro.* Lugd. Bot.

PRESCOTT, W. H.
1850. *Mexica and the Life of the Conqueror* (6th ed.), I, 109. London.

PRIESTLY, JOSEPH.

1774. *Experiments and Observations on Different Kinds of Airs*, pp. 1–324. London.

PURDY, C.

1896. *Garden and Forest*, VIII, 494. New York.

QUIN, J. J.

1882. *Report by Her Majesty's Acting Consulate at Hakodati, on the Laquer Industry of Japan*. London. Reprinted in *Pharmaceutical Journal and Transactions* (3d ser.), XIII, 266, 305, 326.

RAFINESQUE, C. S.

1830. *Medical Flora of the United States*, II, 256–57. Philadelphia.

REIN, J. J.

1882. "Das japanische Kunstgewerbe," *Öst. Monatsschrift für den Orient*, pp. 52–58. Vienna.

RIBAN, J.

1863. *Recherches ėxperimentales sur le principe toxique du redoul (Coriara myrtifolia)*. Paris.

ROBERTSON (CONSUL).

1875. In *Report on Trade of Kanagwa, Japan*, reprinted in the *Pharmaceutical Journal and Transactions* (3d ser.), VI, 487. London.

ROBINSON, B. L.

1897. "Pfaff's Observations on the Nature of Ivy Poisoning," *American Naturalist*, XXXI, 901–3. Philadelphia.

ROEMERI.

*Archiv für die Botanik*, I, Part 1, 115.

ROST, E.

1914. "Über die Giftwirkungen von *Rhus toxicodendron*, und der primula obconica, nebst Bemerkungen über *Rhus vernicifera*," *Med. Klin.*, X, 101, 155, 198–200. Berlin.

RYON, ANGIE, M.

"Habitat of *R. toxicodendron* and *R. venenata*," *American Botanist*, II, 87–89; IV, 86.

SANDO, C. E., and BARTLETT, H. H.

1918. "The Flavones of Rhus," *American Journal of Botany*, V, 112–19.

SCHMID, JAKOB.

1886. "Über das Fisetin, den Farbstoff des Fisetholzes," *Berichte der deutschen chemischen Gesellschaft*, XIX, 1736.

SMITH, A. B.

1905. *Poisonous Plants of All Countries*, pp. 66, 67. Bristol.

STEVENS, A. B.

1905*a*. "Nitrogen in Gums," *American Journal of Pharmacy*, LXXVII, 255. Philadelphia.

1905*b*. "Japanese Lac (Ki-Urushi)," *American Journal of Pharmacy*, LXVII, 53; LXVIII, 490.

1906. *Japanese Lac*. Inaugural Dissertation, Ann Arbor.

Stevens, A. B., and Tschirch, R.
1905. *Über den Japanlack* (*Kiruchi*), CCXLIII, 504. Berlin.
Stevens, A. B., and Warren, L. E.
1907. "Poison Sumac," *American Journal of Pharmacy*, LXXIX, 499. Philadelphia.
Strumpf.
1784. "Einladung an die Bienenliebhaber," *Leipz. Magaz.*, Part I, p. 79.
Syme, W. A.
1906. *Some Constituents of the Poison Ivy Plant.* (Johns Hopkins University Dissertation.) Baltimore.
Thompson, W.
1892. "Challenger Expedition," *Journal and Proceedings of the Hamilton Association*, VIII, 126.
Thomson, C. W.
1878. *The Voyage of the Challenger*, I, 305. New York.
Tschirch, A., and Stevens, A. B.
1905. *Über den Japanlack* (*Kiuruchi*), CCXLIII, 504. Berlin.
1906. "Japanese Lacquer," *Mon. Sci.*, pp. 731–60.
1907. Abstract in *Chemical Abstracts*, I, 491.
Van Mons, Jean Baptiste.
1797. "Mémoire sur le *Rhus radicans*," *Actes la sociêté de mêdecine, chirurgie et pharmacie*, I, Part 2, 136–67. Bruxelles.
1800. "Mémoire sur le *Rhus radicans*," *Journal de physique, de chimie, histoire naturelle et des arts, avec des planches en taille-douce*, LI, 193–213.
Wagener, G.
1875. "Japanischer Lack," *Dinglers polytechnisches Journal*, CCXVIII, 361–67, 452–56. Augsburg.
Warren, L. E.
1908. "Some Constituents of Poison Sumac and Poison Ivy," *Journal of the American Chemical Society*, XXX, 50. Easton, Pennsylvania.
1909. "The Poisonous Principle of *Rhus*," *Pharmaceutical Journal and Pharmacist* (4th ser.), XXIX, 531, 562. London.
1910*a*. "Contributions to the Bibliography of the Poisonous Species of *Rhus*," *Midland Druggist and Pharmaceutical Review*, XLIV, 149–50, 218–19, 288–90.
1910*b*. "*Rhus Michauxii*, a Non-Poisonous Plant," *American Journal of Pharmacy*, LXXXII, 499. Philadelphia.
1913. "Some Observations on the Pollen of Poison Sumac," *American Journal of Pharmacy*, LXXXV, 545–49. Philadelphia.
Warren, L. E., and Stevens, A. B.
1907. "Poison Sumac," *American Journal of Pharmacy*, LXXIX, 499. Philadelphia.

WIESNER, JULIUS.
1900. *Die Rohstoffe des Pflanzenreiches*, I, 299.
WILLMET, REMI (PATER).
1800. "Observations sur les effets du *Rhus radicans*," *Journal de physique de chimie, d'histoire naturelle et des planches en taille-douce*, LI, 369–70.
WILLMET, C.
1801. "Observations sur les effets du Rhus radicans," *Journal de méd. chir., pharm.*, I, 209–11. Paris.
WITTSTEIN, G. C.
1858. "Chemische Untersuchung der Blätter des Giftsumach," *Vierteljahresschrift für praktische Pharmacie*, VII, 348–59.

LACCASE

ANONYMOUS.
1895. *Pharmaceutical Journal and Transactions* (4th ser.), I, 89.
ASO.
1900. "On the Physiological Rôle of the Oxidases in Kaki-Fruit," *Botanical Magazine*, Vol. XIV, No. 166. Tokyo.
ATKINS.
1913. *Science Proceedings of the Royal Dublin Society*, XIV, 144.
BERTRAND, G.
1894*a*. "Recherches sur le suc laiteux de l'arbre à laque du Tonkin," *Bulletin de la société chimique de Paris* (3d ser.), XI, 674, 717. Paris.
1894*b*. "Sur le latex de l'arbre à laque," *Comptes Rendus Acad. Sci.* CXVIII, 1215–18. Paris.
1895*a*. "Recherches et présence de la laccase dans les végétaux," *Comptes Rendus Acad. Sci.*, CXXI, 166–68.
1895*b*. "Sur la laccase et le pouvoir oxydant de cette diastase," *Comptes Rendus Acad. Sci.*, CXX, 266–69.
1896*a*. "Sur les rapports qui existent entre la constitution chimique des composés organiques et leur oxydabilité sous l'influence de la laccase," *Bulletin de la Société Chimique* (3d ser.), XV, 791–93.
1896*b*. "Sur les rapports qui existent entre la constitution chimique des composés organiques et leur oxydabilité sous l'influence de la laccase," *Comptes Rendus Acad. Sci.*, CXXII, 1132.
1896*c*. "Sur une nouvelle oxydase, ou ferment soluble oxydant, d'origine végétale," *Journal de pharmacie et de chimie* (6th ser.), III, 607.
1896*d*. "Sur une nouvelle oxydase, ou ferment soluble oxydant, d'origine végétale," *Comptes Rendus Acad. Sci.*, CXXII, 1215–17.
1896*e*. "Sur une nouvelle oxydase, ou ferment soluble oxydant, d'origine végétale," *Bulletin de la Société de Chimie* (3d ser.), XV, 793–97. Paris.

1896*f*. *Comptes Rendus Soc. Biol.*, XLVIII, 811.

1896*g*. Sur la présence simultanée de la laccase et de la tyrosinase dans le suc de quelques champignons," *Comptes Rendus Acad. Sci.*, CXXIII, 463–65.

1897*a*. "Recherches sur la laccase, nouveau ferment soluble à propriétées oxydantes," *Annales de chimie et de physique* (7th ser.), XII, 115–40. Paris.

1897*b*. "Sur l'action oxydante des sels manganeux et sur la constitutins chimiques des oxydases," *Comptes Rendus Acad. Sci.*, CXXIV, 1355–58.

1897*c*. "Sur l'intervention du manganèse dans les oxydations provoquées par la laccase," *Journal de pharmacie et de chimie* (6th ser.), V, 545.

1897*d*. "Sur l'intervention du manganèse dans les ozydations provoquées par la laccase," *Comptes Rendus Acad. Sci.*, CXXIV, 1032–35.

1897*e*. "Sur le pouvoir oxydant des sels manganeux et sur la constitution chimique de la laccase," *Bulletin de la Société Chimique* (3d ser.), XVII, 753–56. Paris.

1897*f*. *Bulletin de la Société Chimique* (3d ser.), XVII, 577–78.

1897*g*. "Sur l'intervention du manganèse dans les oxydations provoquées par la laccase," *Arch. Agronom.*, XXIII, 285–399.

1902. "Sur le bleuissement de certains champignons du genre Boletus," *Ann. de l'Inst. Pasteur*, XVI, 179–84.

1904. *Chemiker-Zeitung*, XXVIII, 65. Cöthen.

1907. "Influence des acides sur l'action de la laccase," *Comptes Rendus Acad. Sci.*, CXLV, 340–43.

1908*a*. "Recherches sur le mélanogénèse; action de la tyrosinase sur divers corps voisins de la tyrosine," *Bulletin de la Société Chimique*, (4th ser.), III–IV, 335–43. Paris.

1908*b*. "Recherches sur le mélanogénèse; action de la tyrosinase sur divers corps voisins de la tyrosine," *Comptes Rendus Acad. Sci.*, CXLV, 1352–55.

BERTRAND, G., and BOURQUELOT.

1895. "Laccase dans les Champignons," *Comptes Rendus Soc. Biol.*, XLVII, 579–82.

1896. "Les ferments oxydants dans les Champignons," *Comptes Rendus Soc. Biol.*, XLVIII, 811–13.

BUNZEL.

1913. *United States Department of Agriculture, Bureau of Plant Industry Bulletin 277.*

EFFRONT, J. C.

1902. *Enzymes and Their Applications*, I, 272 ff. (Translated into English by S. C. Prescott.) New York.

EULER, H.

1909. *Grundlagen und Ergebruisse der Pflanzenchemie*, I, 73. Braunschweig.

FISCHER, EMIL.
1894. *Berichte der deutschen chemischen Gesellschaft*, pp. 2071, 2985, 1429, 3499.

FLETCHER and ALLEN.
*Chemical News*, XXIX, 167, 189.

GESSARD.
1903*a*. *Comptes Rendus Acad. Sci.*, CXXXVI, 631–32. Paris.
1903*b*. *Comptes Rendus Soc. de Biol.*, LV, 227–28, 637–39. Paris.

HEDIN.
1905. *Jour. Physiol.*, XXXII, 468.
1906. *Jour. Physiol.*, XXXIV, 370.
1908. *Hoppe, Seyler's Zeitschrift für physiologische Chemie*, LVII, 471.

HOLLEMAN, A. F.
1903. *Organic Chemistry*, p. 409. (Translated into English by A. J. Walker.) New York.

HUNGER.
1901. *Berichte der deutschen botanischen Gesellschaft*, XIX, 648.

MCNAIR, JAMES B.
1917*c*. "The Oxidase of Rhus diversiloba," *Journal of Infectious Diseases*, XX, 485–98. Chicago.

PRESCOTT, S. C.
1902. Translation of J. Effront, *Enzymes and Their Applications*, I, 272 ff. New York.

SARTHOU.
1900. "Sur une oxydase retirée du Schinus Molle, la schinoxydase," *Journal de pharmacie et de chimie* (6th ser.), XI, 482–88.
1901. "Contribution à l'étude de la nature des oxydase," *Journal de pharmacie et de chimie* (6th ser.), XIII, 464.
"Rôle que paraît jouer le fer dans le schinoxydase," *Journal de pharmacie et de chimie* (6th ser.), XII, 583–89.

SLOWTZOFF.
1900. "Zur Kenntniss der pflanzlichen oxydasen," *Zeitschrift für physiologische Chemie*, XXXI, 227–34.

STEVENS, A. B., and TSCHIRCH, A.
1905. Über die Gummi-Enzyme (Gummacen) speziell den Nachweis des Stickstoffes in ihnen," *Pharmaceutische Centralhalle für Deutschland*, XLVI, 501. Dresden.

SUZUKI.
1900. *Bulletin of the Agricultural College of Tokyo*, IV, 167.

TSCHIRCH, A., and STEVENS, A. B.
1905. "Über die Gummi-Enzyme (Gummacen) speziell den Nachweis des Stickstoffes in ihnen," *Pharmaceutische Centralhalle für Deutschland*, XLVI, 501. Dresden.

VAN SLYKE, D. D.
1912. *Journal of Biological Chemistry*, XII, 275.

WITTHAUS, R. A.
1906. *The Medical Student's Manual of Chemistry* (6th ed.), p. 606. New York.
WOLFF, J.
1909. *Comptes Rendus Ec.*, CXLVIII, 497. Paris.
WOODS.
1902. "On the Mosaic Disease of Tobacco," *United States Department of Agriculture Bulletin 18.*
YOSHIDA and KORSCHET.
*As. Soc. Japan*, XII, 182.

## PATHOLOGICAL REFERENCES

ALLEN.
1886. *Journal of Cutaneous Diseases, including Syphilis*, IV, 8.
ALUMBAUGH, W. E.
1903. *Medical World*, XXI, 176. Philadelphia.
ANONYMOUS.
1897. "Death from Ivy Poisoning," *Boston Medical and Surgical Journal*, CXXXVII, 302.
1906. Article, "Sumac," *American Encyclopedia*, Vol. XLV.
BABCOCK, H. H.
1875. *The Pharmacist*, VIII, 1. Chicago.
BARDEEN.
1898. *Johns Hopkins Hospital Reports*, Vol. VII.
BARTON, B. S.
1798 and 1804. *Collections for an Essay Towards a Materia Medica of the United States*, Part 1, p. 24; Part 2, pp. 31–36. Philadelphia.
BASCH, I. T.
1895. *Garden and Forest*, VIII, 239. New York.
BERENGUIER.
1874. *Thèse de Paris.*
BERINGER, G. M.
1896. *American Journal of Pharmacy*, LXVIII, 18–20. Philadelphia.
BLACKWOOD, W. R. D.
1880. "Some Thoughts on Rhus Poisoning," *Philadelphia Medical Times*, X, 618, 619. Philadelphia.
BOMMER, J.
1907. *Medical Brief*, XXXV, 877.
BROCHIN.
1879. *Gaz. du Hôpital*, LII, 99.
BROWN, E. D.
1922. "Experiments on the Variability in Susceptibility to Poison Ivy," *Archives of Dermatology and Syphilology*, V, 714–22.

BROWNE.
1885. *British Medical Journal*, II, 692.
BRUN.
1886. *Thèse de Paris.*
BUSEY, S. C.
1873. "Poisoning by *Rhus Toxicodendron*," *American Journal of Medical Sciences*, LXVI, 436–42. Philadelphia.
1891. "The Transmissions from One Person to Another of the Poison of *Rhus Toxicodendron*," *Medical News*, LIX, 555. Philadelphia.
CANTRELL, J. A.
1891. "Unusual Mode of Transmission in a Case of Dermatitis Venenata," *Medical News*, LIX, 484.
CHAUDRON, M.
1852. "Sur les propriétés du *Rhus radicans*," *Répertoire de pharmacie*, VIII, 223. Paris.
CLARUS, J.
1862. "Beiträge zur Pharmakologie und Toxikologie von *Rhus Toxikodendron*," *Wehnbl. d. k. k. Gesellsch. d. Ärzte in Wien*, pp. 137–42.
COQUILLET, D. W.
1895. "A Cecidomyiid that Lives on Poison-oak," *Insect Life*, VII, 348. Washington.
D. C. E.
1886. *Medical and Surgical Reporter*, LIV, 413. Philadelphia.
DAKIN, R.
1829. "Remarks on a Cutaneous Affection Produced by Certain Poisonous Vegetables," *American Journal of Medical Sciences*, IV, 98–100. Philadelphia.
DREYFOUS.
1885. Abstract in *L'Union méd. du Canada*, XIV, 226.
DUNMIRE, G. B.
1881–82. "A Case of Proctitis and Peritonitis from Rhus Poisoning of the Buttocks," *Philadelphia Medical Times*, XII, 636. Philadelphia.
EDITORIAL.
1876. *Canada Lancet*, VIII, 365. Toronto.
1921*a*. "Rhus Dermatitis," *Journal of the American Medical Association*, LXXVI, 1252.
1921*b*. "Rhus Dermatitis," *American Journal of Pharmacy*, XCIII, 346.
FARQUHAR, C.
1888–89. "Poisoning by *Rhus Toxicodendron* of Unusual Severity," *University Medical Magazine*, I, 640. Philadelphia.
FONTENELLE, J.
1828. "Empoisonnement par le redoul coriaria myrtifolia, corroyère à feuille de myrte sumac, rhus," *Journal de chimie médicale, de pharmacologie et de toxicologie*, IV, 551–53. Paris.

1832. "Des effets des *Rhus radicans* et *Rhus Toxicodendron*," *Journal de chimie médicale de pharmacologie et de toxologie*, VIII, 601. Paris.

FORNET, W.

1902. *Archiv für Dermatologie und Syphilis*, LX, 249. Wien and Leipzig.

FRANK, L. F.

1898. *Medical Record*, LIII, 551. New York.

FRIEDBURG, L. H.

1897. Translation into English of R. Kobert, *Practical Toxicology for Physicians and Students*, p. 108. New York.

FROST, J.

1826. "Remarks on the Erysipelatous Inflammation Produced by the Juice of *Rhus Toxicodendron*," *London Medical and Physical Journal*, LV, 116. London.

GARLAND.

1886. *Lancet*, I, 1005.

GILMORE, MELVIN RANDOLPH.

1911–12. "Uses of Plants by the Indians of the Missouri River Region," *Thirty-third Annual Report, Bureau of American Ethnology*, pp. 43–154.

GOTTHEIL, W. S.

1897. *Illustrated Skin Diseases*, p. 163. New York.

GOVAN, M. M.

1884. "Accident Divers—immunité," *Traité de botanique et de matière médicale*, p. 125. Montpellier.

GREEN, B. F.

1911. "Poison Ivy Causes Severe Eye Trouble," *Hillsdale Leader*, XXIX, No. 35, 8.

GUERNSEY, J. C.

1913. *Hahnemann Monthly*, XLVIII, 161–74.

HATCH, W. G.

1856–57. "Necrosis Following Poisoning by *Rhus Toxicodendron*—Amputation of Thigh, Recovery," *California State Medical Journal*, I, 465–67. Sacramento.

HORSCHELMANN.

1916. Quoted in Piersol, *Human Anatomy* (5th ed.), p. 1398. Philadelphia: Lippincott.

HUNT, JOSEPH H.

1897. *Brooklyn Medical Journal*, XI, 401.

JARISCH.

1878. *Wien med. Jahrb.*, No. 4.

JUNKER, F.

1883. *Lancet*, I, 892. London.

KOBERT, R.

1897. *Practical Toxicology for Physicians and Students*, p. 108. (Translated into English by L. H. Friedburg.) New York.

1906. *Lehrbuch der Intoxikationen*, II, 511. Stuttgart.

KOLMER, John A.

1917. *Infection, Immunity and Specific Therapy.* Philadelphia: W. B. Saunders Co.

KOSTER-SYKE.

1886. *Deutsch. Med. Zeitung*, XXXIV, 381.

KUNZE, R. E.

1878. *Botanical Gazette*, III, 53. Logansport.

LODEMAN, E. G.

1895. *Garden and Forest*, VIII, 398. New York.

MCATEE, W. L.

1920. "Account of Poisonous Sumachs, Rhus Poisoning, and Remedies Therefor," *Medical Record*, XCVII, 771–80.

MCNAIR, JAMES B.

1916*b*. "The Transmission of Rhus Poison from Plant to Person. *Rhus diversiloba* T. & G.," *Journal of Infectious Diseases*, XIX, 429–32. Chicago.

1916*c*. "Pathology of Dermatitis Venenata from *Rhus diversiloba*," *Journal of Infectious Diseases*, XIX, 419–28.

1921*d*. "Pathology of Rhus Dermatitis," *Archives of Dermatology and Syphilology*, III, 383–403.

1921*e*. "Susceptibility to Dermatitis from *Rhus Diversiloba*," *Archives of Dermatology and Syphilology*, III, 625–33.

1921*f*. "The Transmission of Rhus Poison from Plant to Person," *American Journal of Botany*, VIII, 238–50.

1921*g*. "Internal Poisoning from Rhus," *Archives of Dermatology and Syphilology*, IV, 62–66.

MOORMAN, J. W.

1866. "Poisoning by Eating the Fruit of *Rhus Toxicodendron;* Recovery," *American Journal of Medical Sciences*, LI, 560. Philadelphia.

MORROW, P. A.

1887. *Drug Eruptions*, pp. 167 ff. New York.

NICHOLSON, F.

1899. "A Case of Acute Dermatitis Caused by Handling the *Rhus Toxicodendron*," *British Medical Journal*, I, 530. London.

OVERTON and MEYER.

1899. *Archiv für experimentalische Pathologie und Pharmakologie*, XLII, 109.

1900. *Jahresber. für wissenschaftliche Botanik*, XXXIV, 669.

PAMMEL, L. H.
1921. "Poisoning from Western Poison Ivy," *Veterinary Medicine*, XVI, 47–48.
PARRISH, J.
1851. "Case of Annual Return of Cutaneous Poisoning," *New Jersey Medical Reporter*, IV, 55. Burlington.
PAYNE, G. F.
1894. *Proceedings of the American Pharmaceutical Association*, XLII, 135. Baltimore.
PENASSE.
1886. *Journal de méd. de Paris*, X, 760.
PIERSOL, GEORGE A.
1916. *Human Anatomy* (5th ed.). Philadelphia: Lippincott.
PRICHARD, A. W.
1891. *Bristol Medico-chirurgical Journal*, IX, 22. Bristol.
PUTNAM, B. L.
1895. *Garden and Forest*, VIII, 249.
ROBERTSON, T. B.
1908. *Journal of Biological Chemistry*, IV, 1.
ROSE.
1884. *Verhandlung der Gesellschaft der Ärzte.*
SCHAMBERG, J. F.
1919. "The Desensitization of Persons against Ivy Poisoning," *Journal of the American Medical Association*, LXXIII, No. 16, 1213.
1921. *A Compend of Diseases of the Skin* (6th ed.).
SPAIN, W. C.
1922. "Studies on Specific Hypersensitiveness. VI. Dermatitis Venenata," *Journal of Immunology*, VII, 179–92.
STILLE, A.
1874. *Therapeutics and Materia Medica* (4th ed.), 795. Philadelphia.
STIRLING, E. C.
1913. "An Eruption of the Skin Caused by the Poison Ivy (*Rhus Toxicodendron*)," *Australasian Medical Gazette*, 355–59. Sydney.
STRICKLER, ALBERT.
1921. "The Toxin Treatment of Dermatitis Venenata," *Journal of the American Medical Association*, LXXVII, 910–13.
TREILLE, G.
1904. "Un cas d'empoisonnement chronique causé par le contact des feuilles du *Rhus Toxicodendron*," *Marseille Méd.*, XI, 149, 161–79.
WALKER, J. B.
1891. "Poisoning by Ivy at Second Hand," *Medical News*, LIX, 556. Philadelphia.
WARREN, L. E.
1919. "Desensitization of Persons against Ivy Poisoning," *Journal of the American Medical Association*, LXXIII, 1382, 1543.

WELLS, H. G.
*Chemical Pathology*, p. 562.

WHITE, J. C.
1875. "Ivy Poisoning," *Boston Medical and Surgical Journal*, XCIII, 265–67. Boston.

## REMEDIES

A.
1837–38. "Erythema venenosa," *Boston Medical and Surgical Journal*, XVII, 347–50. Boston.

ABBOTT, F.
1887. "Notes on a Recent Case of Poisoning Caused by the Exhalation of *Rhus radicans*," *Papers and Proceedings of the Royal Society of Tasmania (1886)*, pp. 282–85.

ALBRIGHT, J. D.
1896–97. *Medical Summary*, XVIII, 242. Philadelphia.

ALDERSON, J.
1811. *An Essay on Rhus Toxicodendron with Cases of Its Effects in the Cure of Paralytic Affections and Other Diseases of Great Debility* (4th ed.). Hull. (Earlier editions appeared in 1793, 1798, and 1804.)

ALEXANDER, F. S.
1907. *Medical Brief*, XXXV, 878. St. Louis.

ALIBERT, J. L.
1817. *Nouveaux élémens de thérapeutique et de matière médicale* (4th ed.), p. 450. Paris.

ALLEN, H. N.
1887. *Journal of Cutaneous and Genito-urinary Diseases*, V, 26. New York.

ALLEN, T. F.
1878. *The Encyclopedia of Pure Materia Medica*, VIII, 330–400. New York and Philadelphia.

ALUMBAUGH, W. E.
1898. "How Not To Do It, and Why! *Rhus Toxicodendron* Poisoning," *Medical World*, XVI, 298. Philadelphia.

AMORY, R., and EMERSON, R. L.
1905. *Wharton and Stillé's Medical Jurisprudence* (5th ed.), II, 528. Rochester.

ANONYMOUS.
1810–11. "Bermerkungen über die Wirkung des *Rhus radicans* auf der Haut," *N. Jour. d. Erfind., etc.*, I, 400–412. Gotha.

1811*a*. Nouvelles expériences sur l'action du *Rhus radicans* sur la peau," *Annales génèrales de médicine d'Altembourg* (April).

1811*b*. "Nouvelles expériences sur l'efficacité du *Rhus Toxicodendron* ou *radicans* dans la paraplegie," *Annales génèrales de médecine d'Altembourg* (February).

1875. *Medical and Surgical Reporter*, XXXIII, 306. Philadelphia.
1880. "Discussion on Rhus Poisoning," *Proceedings of the Philadelphia County Medical Society*, II, 100. Philadelphia.
1886*a*. *Journal of Cutaneous and Venereal Diseases*, IV, 160.
1886*b*. "*Rhus diversiloba* Remedy," *Medical and Surgical Reporter*, LIV, 603.
1894. *Spatula Herb-Book*, p. 41. Boston.
1892. "Specific Suggestions," *Chicago Medical Times*, XXXIV, 44. Chicago.
1895*a*. "An Antidote for Poison Ivy," *Kansas Medical Journal*, VII, 633. Topeka.
1895*b*. *American Druggist and Pharmaceutical Record*, XXVII, 217. New York.
1897. *Bulletin of Pharmacy*, XI, 557. Detroit.
1905. *National Standard Dispensatory*, pp. 310, 1321 ff. Philadelphia and New York.
1906. *American Homeopathic Pharmacoepia*, pp. 390, 391, 392. Philadelphia.
1910. *British Medical Journal*, XI, 545.
1910–11. "Poison Ivy Rash," *Texas Medical News*, XX, 77. Dallas.
1912*a*. "Poisoning by *Rhus Toxicodendron*," *Pharm. Zeitung*, LVII, 313.
1912*b*. "Rhus Toxicodendron," *Forbes Medical Druggist*, XLVI, 239.
1916*a*. "Ivy-poisoning Remedies," *Country Gentleman*, LXXI, 1428.
1916*b*. "Poison Ivy: The Plant and Its Poison," *Rural New Yorker*, LXXV, 806.
1916*c*. "Treatment of Ivy Poisoning," *New York Medical Journal*, CIV, 416.
1917. "The Leucocyte Count as a Guide to Treatment of Wounds," *British Medical Journal*, I, 465–66.
"Observations sur les effets du *Rhus radicans*," *Annales de la société de médecine pratique de Montpellier*, Vol. VI (cahier de Nivôse an XIV).
*Bibliothèque médicale*, XXXVI, 396.

ANTHONY, E. C.
1903. *American Botanist*, IV, 36.

ARSCHAGOUNI, J., and JOURSET, P. (translation).
1901. *Practice of Medicine*, pp. 32, 40, 50, 95, 198, 204, 207, 228, 263, 284, 297, 309, 310, 312, 387, 427, 468, 601, 605, 640, 830, 1019, 1034, 1035, 1039, 1040, 1043, 1049, 1050, 1053, 1054, 1057, 1073, 1074. New York.

AULDE, J.
1889*a*. "Clinical Observations on *Rhus Toxicodendron*," *Therapeutic Gazette* (3d ser.), V, 676–82. Detroit.
1889*b*. *Medical News*, LIV, 446. Philadelphia.

1890. "The Therapeutic Uses of Rhus," *Medical and Surgical Reporter* LVIII, 360–65. Philadelphia.

AURAND, S. H.

1899. *Botanical Materia Medica and Pharmacology*, pp. 297–301. Chicago.

BAILEY, J. H.

1887. *Journal of Cutaneous and Genito-urinary Diseases*, V, 27. New York.

BAILEY, J. S.

1871. *Medical and Surgical Reporter*, XXIV, 322. Philadelphia.

BAILLON.

*Histoire des plantes.*

BAIRD, A. W.

1909. "Ivy Poisoning," *Medical Record*, LXXVI, 232. New York.

BALCH, A. W.

1906. "Poison Ivy," *Journal of the American Medical Association*, XLVI, 819–20. Chicago.

BALDWIN, A. E.

1887. "A Case of Poisoning by *Rhus Toxicodendron*," *Pacific Medical and Surgical Journal*, XXX, 509, 643. San Francisco.

BARNARD, H. C.

1879–80. "Rhus glabrum," *St. Louis Clinical Record*, VI, 132.

BARNES, EDWIN.

1886. *Medical Record*, pp. 157–58.

BARNEY, C. N.

1902. *Journal of the American Medical Association*, XXXIX, 441. Chicago.

BARTLEY, E. H.

1897. *Brooklyn Medical Journal*, XI, 405.

BARTRAM, WILLIAM.

1791. *Travels through North and South Carolina, Georgia, etc.* Philadelphia: James & Johnson.

BASINER, A.

1881. *Die Vergiftung mit Ranunkelöl, Anemorium und Cardol in Beziehung zu der Cantharidmin Vergiftung.* (Inaugural Dissertation.) Dorpat.

BATLETT, E., JR.

1838. "Use of Chloride of Soda in Cases of Poisoning with *Rhus radicans*," *Boston Medical and Surgical Journal*, XVIII, 303. Boston.

BAUDELOCQUE, N.

1837. *Journal de mêdecine et chirurgie pratiques*, VIII, 27. Paris.

BAZIN.

1862. *Lec. theor. et clin. sur les aff. cut. artif.*, p. 119. Paris.

BERNARD, E. H.
1876. "Poison-Oak Eruption," *Louisville Medical News,* II, 91. Louisville.
BIBB, L. B.
1914–15. "Experimental Rhus Poisoning," *Texas Medical Journal,* XXX, 162–63. Austin.
BIRKENHAUER, H. J.
1902. "Treatment for Rhus Poisoning," *Eclectic Review,* V, 279. New York.
BISSEL, G. P.
1904. *Medical Brief,* XXXII, 57. St. Louis.
BLACKWOOD, W. R. D.
1880. "Some Thoughts on Rhus Poisoning," *Philadelphia Medical Times,* X, 618.
1895. *Charlotte Medical Journal,* VI, 1398. Charlotte.
BLATCHLEY, W. D.
1891. "Lime Water in Rhus Poisoning," *Weekly Medical Review,* XXIII, 55. St. Louis.
BLODGETT, G. W.
1887. *Boston Medical and Surgical Journal,* CXVI, 622. Boston.
BOGUE, E. E.
1894. *Garden and Forest.*
BOMMER, J.
1907. *Medical Brief,* XXXV, 877. St. Louis.
BORDENER, H. H.
1879. *Michigan Medical News,* II, 178. Detroit.
BOWER, R. W.
1907. *Medical Brief,* XXXV, 877. St. Louis.
BOYER, J. A.
1903. *Medical World,* XXI, 83. Philadelphia.
BRAMAN, C. B.
1867. *Medical and Surgical Reporter,* XVII, 430. Philadelphia.
BRETONNEAU.
*Revue de thérap. médic-chirurgie,* I, 91.
BRANDT, W. E.
1879. "Poisoning by *Rhus radicans,*" *Medical Record,* XVI, 46–47. New York.
BROADNAX, B. H.
1887. *Journal of Cutaneous and Genito-urinary Diseases,* V, 27. New York.
BRONSON, B. D.
1904. *Medical Brief,* XXXIV, 590. St. Louis.
BROOKS, H.
1907. *Medical Brief,* XXXV, 877. St. Louis.

BROWN.
1899. "Dermatitis Due to Poison Oak," *Post Graduate*, XIV, 644. New York.

BROWN, A.
1886. *Medical and Surgical Reporter*, LIV, 762.

BROWN, C. A.
1897. "Poisoning by *Rhus Toxicodendron*," *Medical Brief*, XV, 704.

BROWN, F. N.
1889. *British Medical Journal*, II, 1332. London.

BROWN, S. A.
1878. "A Remedy for the Eruption of Poison Oak, Ivy, and Sumach," *Medical Record*, XIII, 320. New York.
1886. "The Treatment of Ivy Poisoning," *Medical Record*, XXX, 221. New York.

BROWNING, A. G.
1886. *Medical Record*, XXX, 222. New York.

BURSE.
1811. *Rhus Toxicodendron* (Inaugural Dissertation). Berlin.

BUSEY, S. C.
1873. "Poisoning by the *Rhus Toxicodendron*," *American Journal of Medical Sciences*, XVII, 436–42. Philadelphia.

BUSEY.
1891. *Medical News*, LIX, 555. Philadelphia.

BUTCHER, B. F.
1890. *American Journal of Pharmacy*, LXII, 540. Philadelphia.

BUTLER, B. H.
1916. "Permanganate of Potash for Ivy Poisoning," *Progressive Farmer*, XXXI, 987.

BUTLER, G. F., and JELLIFFE, S. E.
1906. *A Textbook of Materia Medica Therapeutics and Pharmacology*, (5th ed.), p. 329. Philadelphia and London.

C. M. C.
1903. "Dermatitis from Ivy Poisoning," *Alkaloidal Clinic*, X, 1485. Chicago.

CAMPBELL, J. C.
1879. *Michigan Medical News*, II, 178. Detroit.

CAMPBELL, J. F.
1879. *Michigan Medical News*, II, 178. Detroit.

CAMPBELL, W. R.
1894. *Louisville Medical Monthly*, I, 449. Louisville.

CANFIELD, C. A.
1859. "The Poison-Oak and Its Antidote," *American Journal of Pharmacy*, XXXII, 412.

1867. "Grindelia as an Andidote to Poison Oak," *Pacific Medical and Surgical Journal*, IX 294–98. San Francisco.

CANTRELL, J. A.

1894. "A Treatment for Ivy Poisoning," *Philadelphia Polyclinic*, III, 181. Philadelphia.

1895. *Philadelphia Polyclinic*, IV, 99, 450. Philadelphia.

1898*a*. "Relative Value of Certain Drugs in the Treatment of Ivy Poisoning," *New England Medical Monthly*, XVII, 270–72. Danbury, Connecticut.

1898*b*. *Philadelphia Polyclinic*, VII, 20. Philadelphia.

CARPENTER, C. R.

1890. "Rhus Toxicodendron," *Therapeutic Gazette* (3d ser.), VI, 93–95. Detroit.

CARRIÈRE.

"Deux observations intéressantes—constatation d'idiosyncrasie," *Le Journal de da Ferrne et des maisons de campagne*, p. 809.

CARVER, J.

1778. *Travels Through the Interior of North America in the Years, 1766, 1767, and 1768.*

1907. Reprinted in the *Bulletin of Lloyd Library*, No. 9, p. 504. Cincinnati.

CERNA, D.

1893. *Notes on the Newer Remedies*, p. 130. Philadelphia.

CHRISTY, A.

1829. "An Essay on the Poisonous Qualities of Some Species of the Genus *Rhus*, of Linnaeus," *New York Medical and Physical Journal* (new series), I, 21–30. New York.

CHRISTY, T., and LEONARD, C. H.

1892. *Dictionary of Materia Medica and Therapeutics*, p. 239. London.

CLARKE, T. H.

1897. "*Rhus Toxicodendron* Poisoning," *Medical Brief*, XXV, 1006. St. Louis.

CLARKE, T. W.

1856. *Boston Medical and Surgical Journal*, LIII, 163. Boston.

CLEVENGER, S. V.

1903. "Ammonia for Poison Ivy," *Medical Brief*, XXXI, 1359. St. Louis.

CLOYD, A. D.

1897. *Medical Brief*, XXV, 916.

COHEN, SOLOMON SOLIS.

1909. "The Analgetic Effect of Local Applications of Solutions of Magnesium Sulphate and Other Salts," *Journal of the American Medical Association*, LIII, 892.

CONLEY, C. W.
1897. *Medical World*, XV, 76. Philadelphia.
CONNER, J. J.
1907. "Poisoning by *Rhus Toxicodendron*," *American Journal of Dermatology and Genito-urinary Diseases*, XI, 368. St. Louis.
COUCH.
1887. *Montpellier Méd.* (2d ser.), IX, 219–26.
COUCH, L. B.
1887. "The Treatment of Rhus Poisoning," *Medical Record*, XXXII, 486. New York.
COXE, J. R.
1825. *American Dispensatory* (6th ed.), p. 527. Philadelphia.
CRAWFORD, A. C.
1908. *United States Department of Agriculture, Bureau of Plant Industry, Bulletin 121*, Part 1, p. 10. Washington.
CRAWFORD, J.
1893. *American Journal of Pharmacy*, LXV, 48. Philadelphia.
CROWLEY, T. J.
1902. *Medical World*, XX, 330. Philadelphia.
CUNDELL-JULLER, DR.
1883. "The Poison Vine," *Cincinnati Lancet and Clinic* (new series), XI, 73–76. Cincinnati.
DANIEL, T. J.
1903. *Medical Brief*, XXXI, 190. St. Louis.
1906. "A Specific for Rhus Poisoning," *Medical World*, XXIV, 299. Philadelphia.
DAVIDSON, A.
1897. *Southern California Practitioner*, XII, 94. Los Angeles.
DAVIS, W. B.
1886. *Medical World*, XXX, 222. New York.
DAVIS, W. T.
1897. "*Rhus Toxicodendron* Poisoning," *Medical Brief*, XXV, 938–40.
DENNIS, E. J.
1890. *Medical Brief*, XVIII, 603. St. Louis.
DENSTEN, J. C.
1904. *Medical Brief*, XXXIV, 781. St. Louis.
DESCOURTILZ, E.
1833. *Flore pittoresque et médicale des butilles* (2d ed.), I, 49, t. 79. Paris.
DE WITT, W. H.
1874. Poisoning by *Rhus Toxicodendron*," *American Journal of the Medical Sciences* (new series), LXVII, 116–18. Philadelphia.
DIEFFENBACH, W. H.
1917. "Treatment of Ivy Poisoning," *Southern California Practitioner*, XXXII, 91–92.

Doane, L. G.
1908–9. "A Serum for Ivy Poisoning," *Medical Summary*, XXX, 219. Philadelphia.

Double.
"Immunity," *Journal de méd. et de chir. pratiques*, III, 278.

Dudley, P.
1723. *Philosophical Transactions*, XXXI, 145. London.

Du Fresnoy (de Valenciennes).
*Des caractères, du traitement, et de la cure des dartes et de la paralysie, etc., par l'usage du rhus radicans* (1 vol. in 8 vo. an VII). Paris.

Duncan, C. H.
1916. "Autotherapy in Ivy Poisoning," *New York Medical Journal*, etc., CIV, 901.

Dunn, W. W.
1871. *Medical and Surgical Reporter*, XXIV, 195. Philadelphia.

Durodie, M.
1892. *Journal de médecine de Bordeaux*, XXII, 469. Paris.

Editorial.
1805. Caldwell's *Medical Theses* (c), p. 159. Philadelphia.
1870. *Boston Journal of Chemistry*, V, 87. Boston.
1881. *American Journal of Pharmacy*, LIII, 256. Philadelphia.
1882. *Therapeutic Gazette*, VI, 312. Detroit.
1886. *Medical Record*, XXX, 128. New York.
1893. *Medical Brief*, XXI, 1144. St. Louis.
1899. *Journal of Cutaneous and Genito-urinary Diseases*, XVII, 542. New York.
1900. *Medical Brief*, XXXVIII, 1050. St. Louis.
1903. *Medical Brief*, XXXI, 89. St. Louis.
1907. "Efficient Treatment by Ivy Poisoning," *Journal of the American Medical Association*, XLIX, 789. Chicago.
1908. *Journal of the American Medical Association*, L, 1549. Chicago.
1909. *Druggists Circular*, LIII, 525. New York.
*Garden and Forest*, VIII, 360.

Edson, B.
1882. "Gelsemium in Rhus Poisoning," *Medical Record*, XXII, 121. New York.

Ellingwood, F.
1898. *A Systematic Treatise on Materia Medica and Therapeutics*, p. 72. Chicago.

Ellis, R.
1910. "Poison Ivy Rash," *Medical Record*, LXXVIII, 160. New York.

Eltz, Carolus Fredericus Goltbob.
1800. *De Toxicodendro*. Vitebergae.

EMERSON, G. B.
1894. *A Report on the Trees and Shrubs Growing Naturally in the Forests of Massachusetts* (5th ed.), pp. 575, 577. Boston.
EMERSON, R. L., and AMORY, R.
1905. *Wharton and Stille's Medical Jurisprudence* (5th ed.), II, 528. Rochester.
ESCH, J. B.
1886. *Journal of Cutaneous and Venereal Diseases*, IV, 207. New York.
ESCAFET.
1847. "De l'action toxique des baies du Rhus coriaria, sumac des corroyeurs; empoisonnements avec terminaison funèste," *Journal de chimie méd., etc.* (3d ser.), III, 197–200. Paris.
EXCHANGE.
1886. *Journal of Cutaneous and Venereal Diseases*, IV, 160. New York.
1891. *Medical Brief*, XIX, 18. St. Louis.
EXTON, T. J.
1892. *Chicago Medical Times*, XXIV, 257. Chicago.
FARQUHARSON, R., and WOODBURY, F.
1889. *A Guide to Therapeutics and Materia Medica*, pp. 208, 314, 448. Philadelphia.
FELTER, H. W., and LLOYD, J. W.
1900. *King's American Dispensatory* (18th ed., rev. 3), II, 1666–1772. Cincinnati.
FINCH, A. T.
1897. *Medical Brief*, XXV, 410. St. Louis.
FISKE, H. M.
1875. *Pacific Medical and Surgical Journal*, XVIII, 124. San Francisco.
FLOWERS, J. R.
1886. *Medical Record*, XXX, 319. New York.
FORD, W. W.
1907. "Antibodies to Glucosides with Special Reference to *Rhus Toxicodendron*," *Journal of Infectious Diseases*, IV, 541. Chicago.
FOSTER, S. B.
1879. *Michigan Medical News*, II, 216. Detroit.
FOWLER, C. H., and DE PUY, W. H.
1880. *Home and Health and Home Economics*, p. 269. New York.
FOX, G. F.
1905. *Photographic Atlas of the Diseases of the Skin*, I, 56–61. Philadelphia and London.
FEARN, J.
1902. "Rhus Poisoning," *Chicago Medical Times*, XXXV, 560.
FRANK, L. F.
1898. *Medical Record*, LIII, 551–54.
1902. "A Case of Rhus Poisoning," *Chicago Medical Times*, XXXV, 512–15.

1903. "Rhus Toxicodendron and Rhus Poisoning," *Merck's Archives*, V, 223–25, 259–61. New York.

French, J. M.
1781. "Sur le toxicodendron," *Traité sur le venin de la vipère, etc.*, III, 158–61. Florence.
1787. "On Toxicodendron," *Treatise on the Venom of the Viper, etc.*, II, 181–84. London.

Friend, F. M.
1897. *Medical World*, XV, 35. Philadelphia.

Fritts, J. R.
1892. *Medical Brief*, XX, 1118. St. Louis.

Gans, E. S.
1899. "Dermatitis Venenata," *Medical Bulletin*, XXI, 291. Philadelphia.

German, W. H.
1886. *Medical Record*, XXX, 319. New York.

Gibson, G.
1804–5. "Observations on the Internal Use of *Rhus radicans*," *Philadelphia Medical and Physical Journal*, I, 33–35.

Gifford, T.
1883. "*Rhus Toxicodendron*," *Cincinnati Lancet and Clinic* (new series), XI, 162. Cincinnati.

Gilg, E., and Rost, E.
1912. "Der Giftsumach, Rhus toxicodendron L., und seine Giftwirkungen," *Berichte der deutschen pharmaceutischen Gesellschaft*, XXII, 296–358. Berlin.

Given, J. B.
1892. *North American Journal of Homeopathy*, XL, 568, 632. New York.

Gleanings.
1890. *Medical Brief*, XVIII, 1324. St. Louis.
1891. *Medical Brief*, XIX, 976. St. Louis.
1892. *Medical Brief*, XX, 382. St. Louis.

Gleditsch.
1782. "Nouvelles expériences concernant les dangereux effets des exhalaisons d'une plante de l'Amérique," *Journal de physique*.

Granville, J.
1882. *Therapeutic Gazette*, VI, 291. Detroit.

Griffin, C. H.
1879. *Medical Brief*, VII, 88. St. Louis.

Griffith, R. E.
1847. *Medical Botany*, pp. 184, 185. Philadelphia.

Grigsby, W. T.
1882. *Therapeutic Gazette*, VI, 291. Detroit.

GUÉRIN.
1832. "Observation d'accidents graves," *Journal de méd. et de chir. pratiques*, III, 278, 511.

GUERNSEY, JOSEPH COLBURN.
1913*a*. "Rhus Poisoning," *Hahnemann Monthly*, XLVIII, 162–74. Philadelphia.
1913*b*. *Rhus Poisoning*, pp. 19. Philadelphia.

GUIBOURT.
*Hist. natur. des drogues simple*, III, 487.

GUNDRUN, F.
1879. *Michigan Medical News*, II, 171. Detroit.

HADDEN, A.
1906. "Poison Ivy or *Rhus Toxicodendron*," *Medical Review of Reviews*, XII, 764–65. New York.

HAHN, L.
Article, "Sumac," in *Dictionaire encyclopédie de science médicale.*

HAINES, W. S., and PETERSEN, F.
1904. *Textbook of Legal Medicine and Toxicology*, II, 632. Philadelphia, New York, and London.

HALE, E. M.
1867. *Homeopathic Materia of the Newer Remedies* (2d ed.), pp. 874–94. Detroit.

HALE, W. L.
1902. *Journal of the American Medical Association*, XXXIX, 580. Chicago.

HALT, L.
1892. *Chicago Medical Times*, XXIV, 401. Chicago.

HARALSON, J. M.
1882. *Therapeutic Gazette*, VI, 211. Detroit.

HARDAWAY, W. A.
1881. "Rhus Poisoning," *St. Louis Courier of Medicine*, VI, 401. St. Louis.

HARE.
1892. *Medical World*, X, 464. Philadelphia.

HARRIMAN, W. E.
1897. "Rhus and Allied Poisons," *Medical Age*, XV, 295–98. Detroit.

HARRIS, N. M., and JORDAN, E. O.
1908. *Journal of the American Medical Association*, L, 1666. Chicago.

HART, K. M.
1903. *American Botanist*, IV, 55.

HAUPT, H.
1903. "Giftwirkung von *Rhus Toxicodendron*," *Pharmaceutische Centralhalle für Deutschland*, XLIV, 614. Dresden.

HAVARD, V.
1895. *Garden and Forest*, VIII, 203. New York.
1900. "Poison Ivy and Its Kindred; with Remarks on Other Skin Poisoning Plants," *Proceedings of the Association of Military Surgery of the United States*, VIII, 203–11. Columbus.

HAWLEY, J. W.
1890. "Rhus Poisoning," *Medical Advance*, XXIV, 257–62. Ann Arbor, Michigan.

HAYS, M. A., ACHARD, H. J., *et al.*
1916. "Treatment of Ivy Poisoning," *New York Medical Journal, etc.*, CIV, 902–4.

HEMMETER, J. C.
1911. *Journal of the American Medical Association*, LVII, 1152.

HENNING, DR.
1823. "Lähmung der oberen und unteren Extermitäten durch den wurzelenden Sumach (*Rhus radicans*) glücklich geheilt," *Archiv für medizinische Erfahrung im Gebiete der praktischen Medizin, Chirurgie Geburtschülfe und Staatsarzneikunde*, II, 391–98. Berlin.

HENNING, J. A.
1879. "*Rhus Toxicodendron*," *New Preparations*, III, 195. Detroit.

HENRY, A. F.
1893. *Michigan Medical News*, II, 178. Detroit.

HERING, C.
1879. *Condensed Materia Medica* (2d ed.), p. 734. New York and Philadelphia.

HEUSINGER, H.
1809. *Observata quaedam sistens circa Rhoa toxicodendron et radicantem.* Helmstadii.

HIGGINS, J. W.
1896–97. "Rhus Poisoning," *Medical Summary*, XVIII, 299. Philadelphia.

HINTON, R. L.
1882. *Therapeutic Gazette*, VI, 286. Detroit.
1883. "Sassafras in Rhus Poisoning," *Chicago Medical Review*, VII, 15.
1891. *Medical World*, IX, 302. Philadelphia.

HOARE, E. W.
1906–7. "Rhododendron Poisoning in a Cow," *Veterinary Record*, XIX, 630. London.

HOLM, T.
1910. *Merck's Report*, XIX, 95. New York.

HOLMES, H. P.
1910. *Medical Advance*, XXXVIII, 185. Batavia.

HOPKINS, I. D.
1871. *Medical and Surgical Reporter*, XXIV, 154. Philadelphia.

HOWARD, F. A.
1902. "Rhus Poisoning," *New York Medical Journal*, LXXVI, 1094.

HOWE, M.
1916. "Ivy Poisoning," *Ohio Farmer*, CXXXVII, 842.

HRDLICKA. ALES.
1908. "Physiological and Medical Observations Among Indians of Southwestern United States and Northern Mexico," *Bulletin of the Bureau of American Ethnology*, p. 34.

HUBBARD, R.
1886. *Medical Record*, XXX, 601. New York.

HUBBARD, S.
1885–86. "*Rhus Toxicodendron*," *Peoria Medical Monthly*, VI, 323. Peoria.
1891. *Medical Brief*, XIX, 1161. St. Louis.
1895. *Medical Brief*, XXIII, 1324. St. Louis.
1907. "Poison Oak or Ivy," *Medical Brief*, XXXV, 876–78. St. Louis.

HUBBARD, S. P.
1885. "Swamp Button-Bush in Rhus Poisoning," *Medical Record*, XXVIII, 258. New York.

HUDSON, A. T.
1898. "An Antidote to the Rhus Poison," *Medical Record*, LIV, 173. New York.

HUGHES.
1876. *A Manual of Pharmacodynamics*, p. 95. London.

HUGHES, G.
1750. *Natural History of Barbados*, p. 144. London.

HUGHSTON, W. L.
1905. "Poison Ivy," *Medical Brief*, XXXIII, 678. St. Louis.

HUMPHREYS, C. H.
1874. "Sulphate of Zinc in the Treatment of Poisoning by *R. radicans*," *American Journal of the Medical Sciences*, LXVIII, 160. Philadelphia.

HUNT, J. H.
1897. "Rhus Poisoning," *Brooklyn Medical Journal*, XI, 392, 406. Brooklyn.

HUNTINGTON, ANNIE OAKES.
1908. *Poison Ivy and Swamp Sumach*, pp. 1–57, Plates 6. Cambridge: University Press.

HURLBURT, E. T. M.
1869. "Antidote to Poison Oak (*Cypripedium*)," *California Homeopath*, VII, p. 235–39. San Francisco.

IMMERWAHR, R.
1900. "Ein neuer Fall von acuter Dermatitis durch Hantiren mit Rhus toxicodendron," *Dermat. Centralbl.*, III, 258. Berlin.

Inui, T.

1900. "Gummiharzgang des Lackbaumes, und seiner verwandten Arten" (abst.), *Bot. Centralbl.*, III, 352.

Jackson, J. R.

1872. *Pharmaceutical Journal and Transactions* (3d ser.), II, 985. London.

Jadin, F.

1893. "Observations sur quelques térébinthacées," *Journal de Bot.*, VII, 382–90.

James, F. L.

1876. *New Remedies*, V, 344. New York.

Jelliffe, S. E., and Butler, G. F.

1906. *A Textbook of Materia Medica Therapeutics and Pharmacology* (5th ed.), p. 329. Philadelphia and London.

Johnson, J. B.

1886. *Medical and Surgical Reporter*, LIV, 508. Philadelphia.

Johnston, D. M.

1879. *Michigan Medical News*, II, 154. Detroit.

Johnston, L.

1876. "Combat les conclusions de Bernard sur l'action du gelsemium," *New Remedies*, V, 305.

Jordan, E. O., and Harris, N. M.

1908. *Journal of the American Medical Association*, L, 1666. Chicago.

Jousset, P., and Arschagouni, J. (translation).

1901. *Practice of Medicine*, pp. 32, 40, 50, 95, 198, 204, 207, 228, 263, 284, 297, 309, 310, 312, 387, 427, 468, 601, 605, 640, 830, 1019, 1034, 1035, 1039, 1040, 1043, 1049, 1050, 1053, 1054, 1057, 1073, 1074. New York.

K., E. J.

1902. *Medical World*, XX, 442. Philadelphia.

Kahler, R.

1879. "Poisoning by Rhus (Tincture of Lobelia an Antidote)," *Medical Brief*, VII, 22. St. Louis.

Kell, J. B.

1886. *Medical Record*, XXX, 319. New York.

Kelley, K. M.

1897. *Medical World*, XV, 244. Philadelphia.

Kemper, G. G.

1891. *Medical World*, IX, 216. Philadelphia.

Kessler, J. B.

1898. *Medical Record*, LIV, 358. New York.

King, E.

1907. *Journal of the American Medical Association*, XLIX, 1042. Chicago.

KITE, J. A.
1891. *Medical News*, LVII, 556. Philadelphia.

KLOTZ, H. G.
1903. *Merck's Archiv*, V, 225.

KRAEMER, H.
1913. "Fruits of *Rhus glabra* Replaced by Fruits of *Rhus typhina*," *American Journal of Pharmacy*, LXXXV, 398–407. Philadelphia.

KUNZE, R. E.
1883. "Poison Rhus," *Medical Tribune*, V, 111–20. New York.

LADD, F. E.
1906. *Medical World*, XXIV, 398. Philadelphia.

LAMOTHE, BOURDOIS DE.
1832. *Journal de méd. et. de chir. pratique*, III, 278, 511.

LANE, J. E.
1915. "A Simple Treatment for Ivy Poisoning," *Medical Record*, LXXXVIII, 442. New York.

LATTA, J. M.
1888. *Journal of Cutaneous and Genito-urinary Diseases*, VI, 173. New York.

LAVINI, M.
1825. "Emanations délétères qui émanent du *Rhus Toxicodendron*," *Journal de chimie médic.*, 249–51. Paris.

LAYMAN, DR.
1893. *Medical Brief*, XXI, 152. St. Louis.

LEBLOIS, A.
1887. "Recherches sur l'origine et le développement des canaux sécréteurs et des poches sécrétrices," *Annales des sciences nat. botanique* (7th ser.), VI, 247–330 (p. 297).

LEFIVRE.
Article, "Sumac" in *Dict. encycl. de sc. médic.*

LEGGENHAGER, J.
1882. *Therapeutic Gazette*, VI, 291. Detroit.

LEONARD, C. H., and CHRISTY, T.
1892. *Dictionary of Materia Medica and Therapeutics*, p. 239. London.

LEONARD, W. W.
1884–85. "Rhus Poisoning," *Medical Chronicle*, III, 21. Baltimore.

LEPPER, R. M.
1899. *Popular Science*, XXXIII, 94. New York.

LESCHER, F. H.
1891. *Recent Materia Medica* (4th ed.), p. 93. London.

LEVICK, J. J.
1891. "A New Use for Aristol," *Medical News*, LIX, 105. Philadelphia.

LINCOLN, D. F.
Translation into English of A. Trousseau and H. Pidoux, *Treatise on Therapeutics* (9th ed.), II, 200, 201. New York.

LINDLEY, J. S.

1908. "Rhus Poisoning," *American Journal of Dermatology and Genito-urinary Diseases*, XII, 342–44. St. Louis.

LINNEL, E. H.

1892. *North American Journal of Homoeopathy*, XL, 260. New York.

LIVEZEY, A.

1857. *Boston Medical and Surgical Journal*, LV, 262. Boston.

LLOYD, J. W., and FELTER, H. W.

1900. *King's American Dispensatory* (18th ed., rev. 3), II, 1666–1772. Cincinnati.

LLOYD, J. U.

1894. *Proceedings of the American Pharmaceutical Association*, XLII, 135. Baltimore.

LOCKE, J. F.

1900. *Medical Brief*, XXVIII, 1813. St. Louis.

LONG, J. I. T.

1898. *Medical World*, XVI, 494. Philadelphia.

LUSK, T. G.

1899. *Journal of Cutaneous and Genito-urinary Diseases*, XVII, 398 f. New York.

LUTZ, L.

1905. "Accidents provoqués par la manipulation de la laque du Tonkin," *Bulletin de science pharmacologie Paris*, XI, 322–27. Paris.

LYLE, T. J.

1898. *Sanative Medicine*, abstract in *Medical World*, XVI, 494.

M. L. D.

1886. "Rhus Poisoning," *Medical and Surgical Reporter*, LIV, 603. Philadelphia.

MCATEE, W. L.

1920. "An Account of Poisonous Sumachs, Rhus Poisoning, and Remedies Therefor," *Medical Record*, XCVII, 771–80. New York.

MCCLANAHAN, J. T.

1879. "Rhus aromatica," *American Medical Journal*, VII, 183–86, 215–18. St. Louis.

MACKIE, W. W.

1903. "The Value of Oak Leaves for Forage," *California Experiment Station, Bulletin 150*. Berkeley.

MCKEE, E. S.

1905. "*Rhus Toxicodendron* Poisoning," *Wisconsin Medical Recorder*, VIII, 405–7. Janesville.

1905–6. *Therapeutic Record*, I, 31. Louisville.

1906a. "Poisoning by *Rhus Toxicodendron* or *Rhus radicans*," *Medical Herald* (new series), XXV, 98–100. St. Joseph.

1906*b*. "Poisoning by *Rhus Toxicodendron* and *Rhus radicans*," *Pacific Medical Journal*, XLIX, 129–34. San Francisco.

1906*c*. "Poisonous Plants," *Medical Age*, XXIV, 81–84. Detroit.

McNair, James B.

1921*h*. "A Contribution to the Chemotherapy of Rhus Dermatitis and Tentative Method for Treatment," *Archives of Dermatology and Syphilology*, III, 802–8.

1921*i*. "Remedies for Rhus Dermatitis," *Archives of Dermatology and Syphilology*, IV, 217–34.

McPhail, R. C.

1879. *Michigan Medical News*, II, 178. Detroit.

MacSwain, I. A.

1899. "Grindelia robusta in Rhus Poisoning," *Medical Progress*, XV, 242. Louisville.

Maiden, J. H.

*Agricultural Gazette of New South Wales*, XX, 111.

Maisch, J. M.

1865. *Proceedings of the American Pharmaceutical Association*, XIII, 166–74. Philadelphia.

1866. *Zeitschrift für Chemie*, p. 218.

1888. *American Journal of Pharmacy*, LVIII, 173. Philadelphia.

Majon, W.

1909. *Druggists Circular*, LIII, 291. New York.

Mammen, E.

1886. *Medical Record*, XXX, 252. New York.

Mann, A. J.

1904. *Medical Brief*, XXXII, 226. St. Louis.

Marchand, N. L.

1869. *Des Térébinthacées et ceux de leurs produits qui sont employés en pharmacie*. (Thèse d'agrégation à l'Ecole de Pharmacie.) Paris.

Matheson, A. C.

1874. "Treatment of Poisoning by Rhus Toxicodendron with Linseed Oil and Lime-Water," *American Journal of the Medical Sciences* (new series), LXVII, 118. Philadelphia.

Mathews, P.

1893. "Rhus Poisoning," *China Medical Miss. Journal*, VII, 184–87. Shanghai.

Mayraud, R.

1906–7. "Eruption érythémato-vesiculeuse causée par l'action toxique sur la peau du *Rhus Toxicodendron*," *Bulletin Méd. de Quebec*, VIII, 10–15.

Meltzer, S. J.

1918. "The Application of a Concentrated Solution of Magnesium Sulphate to Scalds and Burns," *Journal of Pharmacy and Experimental Therap.*, XII, 211–14.

MERAT.
1832. *Rapport sur l'action du Rhus Toxicodendron.*
MEYER, ARTHUR.
1880. "Des cristaux chez les Rhus," *Archiv der Pharmacie*, p. 112.
MICHALOWSKI.
1860. "Traitement de la paralysis," *Allg. Mediz. Centralzeitung*, No. 48.
MICHAUX.
1803. *Flora boreali Americana*, p. 183. Paris.
MILLS, M.
1896. *Medical World*, XIV, 428. Philadelphia.
MILLSPAUGH, C. F.
1892. *Medicinal Plants*, I, 37, 38. Philadelphia.
MILTON, R. L.
1906. *Medical World*, XXIV, 59–60. Philadelphia.
MITCHELL, S. C.
1907. *Medical Brief*, XXXV, 876. St. Louis.
MOREHOUSE, M. A.
1904. *Medical Brief*, XXXII, 399. St. Louis.
MORGAN, J. B. F.
1892. *Medical Brief*, XX, 55. St. Louis.
MORISON, J. L. D.
1896. *American Journal of Pharmacy*, LXVIII, 131. Philadelphia.
MORRIS, E. K.
1897. "Guaiacol in Rhus Poisoning," *Medical News*, LXX, 57. New York.
MORRISON, S. W.
1874–75. "Poisoning by *Rhus Radicans*," *Philadelphia Medical Times*, V, 629. Philadelphia.
MORROW, P. A.
1886. *Journal of Venereal and Cutaneous Diseases*, IV, 180. New York.
MORRUS, R. T.
1911. *Journal of the American Medical Association*, LVII, 1151.
MOSES, J. B.
1896. *Medical World*, XIV, 140. Philadelphia.
MURPHEY, C. W.
1896–97. *Medical Summary*, XVIII, 269. Philadelphia.
NEESON, H.
1881. *New Remedies*, X, 208. New York.
NELDON, C. M.
1904. *Medical Brief*, XXXIV, 784. St. Louis.
NOTT, H. W.
1910. "A Case of *Rhus Toxicodendron dermatitis*," *British Medical Journal*, No. 2591, p. 545. London.
ORFILA, A. J. B.
1832. *Traité de toxicologie* (5th ed.), II, 131 ff. Paris.

Osborn, T. C.

1879. "On Poison Vine Eruption," *American Medical Bi-Weekly*, X, 49. Louisville.

Panckoucke, C. L. F.

1812. "Sumac (Including *Rhus Toxicodendron*)," *Dictionaire des sciences médicales*, LIII, 409–14. Paris.

Park, R.

1879. "Dermatitis Venenata; or, *Rhus Toxicodendron* and Its Action," *Archives of Dermatology*, V, 227–34. Philadelphia.

Parke, Davis, & Co.

1901. *Physician's Manual of Therapeutics*, p. 419. Detroit.

Parsons, D. J.

1878. *Medical Brief*, Abstract in *Pharmacist*, XI, 214.

1879*a*. *Michigan Medical News*, II, 172. Detroit.

1879*b*. *Zeitschrift des Österreichischen Apotheker-Vereins*, p. 198.

Patterson, J. D.

1910. *Medical World*, XXVIII, 208. Philadelphia.

Patterson, R. L.

1890. *Medical Brief*, XVIII, 34. St. Louis.

1891. *Medical World*, IX, 250. Philadelphia.

1892. *Medical World*, X, 362. Philadelphia.

1896. *Medical Brief*, XXIV, 1664. St. Louis.

Penhallow, D. P.

1895. *Garden and Forest*, VIII, 359. New York.

Pereira, J.

1843. *The Elements of Materia Medica and Therapeutics* (2d ed.), II, 603. Philadelphia.

Perez, J.

1907. *Journal of the American Medical Association*, XLIX, 1042. Chicago.

Petersen, F., and Haines, W. S.

1904. *Textbook of Legal Medicine and Toxicology*, II, 632. Philadelphia, New York, and London.

Phelps, J. R.

1903. *Alkaloidal Clinic*, X, 586. Chicago.

Phillipps, C. D. F. (Piffard, H. G., editor).

1879. *Materia Medica and Therapeutics* (*Vegetable Kingdom*), pp. 158–62. New York.

Pickett, N. B.

1836–37. "Diervilla Canadensis [a specific for the erythemic inflammation of the Rhus toxicodendron]," *Boston Medical and Surgical Journal*, XV, 380.

Pidoux, H., and Trousseau, A.

1880. Article "Sumac" in *Treatise on Therapeutics* (9th ed.), II, 200, 201. (Translated into English by D. F. Lincoln.) New York.

Pierce, W. I.
1898. *North American Journal of Homeopathy* (3d ser.), XIII, 433. New York.
Piffard, H. G.
1881. *A Treatise on the Materia and Therapeutics of the Skin*, pp. 97–100. New York.
1883. *Journal of Cutaneous and Venereal Diseases*, I, 435. New York.
Piffard, H. G. (editor).
1879. C. D. F. Phillipps, *Materia Medica and Therapeutics* (*Vegetable Kingdom*), pp. 158–62. New York.
Planchon, G.
*Traité pratique de la détermination des drogues simple*, I, 165.
Planchon, L.
1887. "Accidents causés par le contact du *Rhus Toxicodendron* (térébinthacées anacardiées)," *Montpellier méd.* (2d ser.), IX, 61, 219.
Planck, E. A.
1896. *Medical World*, XIV, 391. Philadelphia.
Pollard, F.
1903. "Poison Oak," *Alkaloidal Clinic*, X, 599. Chicago.
Poynter, M. E.
1876. *Louisville Medical News*, II, 55. Louisville.
Praag, L. S. von.
1820. *De rhoe-radicante sive rhoe-toxicodendro*. Lugd. Bat.
Prentiss, D. W.
1889. "A Case of Poisoning by Japanese Laquer," *Therapeutic Gazette* (3d ser.), V, 447; "A Case of Poisoning from Homeopathic Rhus Pellets," *ibid.*, p. 448. Detroit.
Price, P. F.
1900. *Annual of Eclectic Medicine and Surgery*, VIII, 146. Cincinnati.
Prichard, A. W.
1891. "Case of Poisoning by Rhus Venenata," *Bristol Medical Chirurgical Journal*, IX, 22–26.
Proctor, W., Jr.
1863. *American Journal of Pharmacy*, XXXV, 506. Philadelphia.
Puy, W. H. de, and Fowler, C. H.
1880. *Home and Health and Home Economics*, p. 269. New York.
R. A.
1895. *Garden and Forest*, VIII, 389. New York.
Reagor, F. B.
1902. "Dermatitis Caused by Rhus Poison," *Transactions of the Medical Society of Tennessee*, LXIX, 109–12. Nashville.
Regensburger, A. E.
1886. "Treatment of Rhus Poisoning," *Journal of Cutaneous and Venereal Diseases*, IV, 244. New York.

Reid, T. J.
1886. *Journal of Cutaneous and Venereal Diseases*, IV, 345. New York.

Risk, J. B. A.
1871. "Poison Oak," *Cincinnati Medical Repertory*, IV, 316–18. Cincinnati.

Robinson, F. C.
1892. *Medical Brief*, XX, 960. St. Louis.

Rost, E., and Gilg, E.
"Der Giftsumach, Rhus toxicodendron L., und seine giftwirkungen," *Berichte der deutschen pharmaceutischen Gessellschaft*, XXII, 296–358. Berlin.

Rothrock, E. A.
1898. *Medical Brief*, XXVI, 124. St. Louis.

Rothrock, J. T.
1879. *New Remedies*, VIII, 232, 233. New York.

Saint-Philippe, R.
"De l'incontinence nocturne d'urine chez les enfants et de son traitement par la teinture de *Rhus radicans*," *Journal de mêdicine de Bourdeaux*, XX, 386, 389.
1892*a*. Abstract in *New York Medical Journal*, LVI, 553.
1892*b*. Abstract in *Journal de méd. et de chir.* (4th ser.), LXIII, 761.
1893. Abstract in *American Journal of Pharmacy*, LXV, 15.

Sajons, C. E. de M. (editor).
1899. "Dermatitis Venenata," *Annual and Analytical Cyclopaedia of Practical Medicine*, II, 367–69. Philadelphia, New York, and Chicago.

Salon, P.
1908. "Der Gefühlscharakter einiger rhythmischer Schallformen in seiner respiratorischen Ausserung," *Psychologische Studien*, IV, 1–75.

Sanders, W. R.
1867–68. "Case of Poisoning with the *Rhus Toxicodendron*," *Edinburgh Medical Journal*, XIII, Part 2, 714–19, 953. Edinburgh.

Sandfort, Barthe de.
1914. "De la kérithérapie (nouvelle application thermale des paraffines)," *Bulletin de l'Acadêmie de Médecine* (3d ser.), LXXI, 560–62.

Samuels, L.
1906. *Medical World*, XXIV, 148. Philadelphia.

Scharring-Hausen, R. L.
1918. "Poison Ivy: Curse of the Fields," *Rural New Yorker*, LXXVII, 743.

Schmiedeberg, O.
1895. *Grundriss der Arzneimittellehre* (3d ed.), pp. 213–24.

Schonberg.
1897. *Philadelphia Polyclinic* (October 16).

SCHWALBE, K.

1902. "Die giftigen Arten der Familie Rhus: *R. diversiloba, R. Toxicodendron* and *R. venenata*," *Münchener medicinische Wochenschrift*, XLIX, 1616. München.

1903. "On the Active Principle of *Rhus diversiloba* (Poison Oak)," *Medical Record*, LXIII, 855–56. New York.

SCOTT, J. A.

1899. "A Case of Poisoning by *Rhus Toxicodendron* Acquired in an Unusual Manner," *Philadelphia Medical Journal*, III, 902–4.

SEABROOK, H. H.

1891. "A Peculiar Case of Poisoning," *New York Medical Journal*, LIV, 51. New York.

SHADBOLT, L. P.

1916. "*Rhus Toxicodendron* Poisoning," *British Medical Journal*, II, 480. London.

SHEDD, P. W.

1903. *Medical World*, XXI, 75. Philadelphia.

SHERMAN, RUTH B.

1901–2. "Ivy Poisoning; with Report of a Case," *American Journal of Nursing*, II, 660–68. Philadelphia.

SHOEMAKER, J. V.

1891. *Materia Medica and Therapeutica*, II, 864. Philadelphia and London.

SHUTE, A. C.

1907. *Medical Brief*, XXXV, 877. St. Louis.

SIMMONS, C. L.

1895. *American Journal of Pharmacy*, LXVII, 412. Philadelphia.

SKILLERN, P. G.

1878–79. "Erysipelas Complicating *Rhus Toxicodendron* Poisoning," *Philadelphia Medical Times*, IX, 230.

SLAGLE, C. G.

1882. *Therapeutic Gazette*, VI, 291. Detroit.

SMITH, C. D.

1897. *Medical Brief*, XV, 1195.

SMITH, D. E.

1882. *Therapeutic Gazette*, VI, 287. Detroit.

SMITH, JOHN.

1812. "The General History of the Bermudas, now called the Summer Isles, from their beginning in the year of our Lord 1593, to this present 1624, etc.," in Book V of *The General History of Virginia, New England, and the Summer Isles by Captain John Smith*. In John Pinkerton, *A General Collection of the Best and Most Interesting Voyages and Travels*, XIII (1812), 172. London. 1808–14.

1882. *The Historye of the Bermudaes or Summer Islands* (edited by J. H. Lefroy), p. 2. London: The Hakluyt Society.

Smith, S. J.
1907. *Medical Brief*, XXXV, 876. St. Louis.

Smith, T.
1851. "Observations on the Treatment of External Poisoning by Vegetable Substances," *Western Lancet*, XII, 293–95. Cincinnati.

Smythe, A. G.
1878. *Archives of Dermatology*, IV, 320. Philadelphia.
1879. "Rhus-Poisoning," *Medical Record*, XVI, 284. New York.

Sollman, T.
1917. "Convenient Devices for Melting Paraffin for Burns," *Journal American Medical Association*, LXVIII, 1895–96.

Sonbeiran.
1875. *Traité de Pharmacie*, I, 687.

Southworth, S.
1892. *Medical Brief*, XX, 937. St. Louis.

Sprague, Dr.
1901. *Medical World*, XIX, 435. Philadelphia.

Spratt, A. W.
1895. *Garden and Forest*, VIII, 429. New York.

Squire, W. B.
1890. *Medical Brief*, XVIII, 601. St. Louis.

Steele, J. G.
1876. *Proceedings of the American Pharmaceutical Association*, XXIII, 637–43. Philadelphia.
1880. *Proceedings of the American Pharmaceutical Association*, XXVII, 610. Philadelphia.
*Pacific Medical and Surgical Journal*, XVIII, 297. San Francisco.

Stelwagon, H. W.
1905. *Treatise on Diseases of the Skin* (4th ed.), pp. 407 ff. Philadelphia and London.

Stephenson, J., and Churchill, J. M.
1836. *Medical Botany*, Vol. III, Nos. 167 ff. London.

Stevens, A. A.
1900. *Philadelphia Medical Journal*, V, 1415. Philadelphia.

Stickney.
1844. *Medical Examiner*, p. 133. Philadelphia.

Stille.
*Therapeutics and Materia Medica*, I, 683.

Stirling, E. C.
1913. "An Eruption of the Skin Caused by Poison Ivy," *Australasian Medical Gazette*. XXXIII, 355–59. Sydney.

STOCKARD, C. C.
1889. *Therapeutic Gazette* (3d ser.), V, 857. Detroit.

STOKES.
*Medical and Surgical Reporter*, XXX, 542.

STOKES, J.
1812. *Botanical Materia Medica*, II, 162. London.

STOKES, J. S.
1867. *Medical and Surgical Reporter*, XVII, 373. Philadelphia.

STONE, I. S.
1874. "Poisoning by *Rhus Toxicodendron*," *American Journal of the Medical Sciences* (new series), LXVII, 569. Philadelphia.

STRATTON, I.
1850. *Edinburgh Medical and Surgical Journal*, LXXIII, 327. Edinburgh.

STRICKLER, A.
1918. "Treatment of Dermatitis Venenata," *Journal of Cutaneous Diseases*, XXXVI, 327.

SUBSCRIBER, A CALIFORNIA.
1907. "An Inquiry for a Good Remedy in Rhus Poisoning," *Medical Brief*, XXXV, 760. St. Louis.

SUMMERLIN, D. C. M.
1879. *Michigan Medical News*, II, 216.

SWISHER, W. B.
1882. *Therapeutic Gazette*, VI, 291. Detroit.
*Medical Times*, IX, 230. Philadelphia.

TATE, W. H.
1885–86. "Cutaneous Poisoning with *Rhus Toxicodendron*," *Peoria Medical Monthly*, VI, 198. Peoria.

TAYLOR, R. W.
1882–83. "A Case of Poisoning from *Rhus Venenata*," *Journal of Cutaneous and Venereal Diseases*, I, 434, 1 plate. New York.
1889. *A Clinical Atlas of Venereal and Skin Diseases including Diagnosis, Prognosis and Treatment*, p. 274. Philadelphia.
1890. "A Case of Rhus Poisoning. II," *Medical News*, LVII, 424. Philadelphia.

THACKER, J.
1817. *American New Dispensatory* (3d ed.), pp. 334 ff. Boston.

THOMAS, F. W.
1893. "Clinical Notes on *Rhus Toxicodendron*," *Medical News*, LXIII, 390. Philadelphia.

THOMAS, J. J.
1906. *Medical Brief*, XXXIV, 292. St. Louis.

THOMPKINE, W. W.
1886. *Journal of Cutaneous and Venereal Diseases*, IV, 180. New York.

THUDICHUM, C. L.
1903. "*Rhus Toxicodendron*," *Alkaloidal Clinic*, X, 829–31; "Rhus, Skookum Chuck," *ibid.*, pp. 831–34. Chicago.

TILLAUX and GUERIN.
*Gazette Médicale de Paris*, III, 493.

TODD, J. B.
1909. "Rhus Poisoning," *New York Medical Journal, etc.*, LXXXIX, 251.

TODD, J. D.
1897. "*Rhus Toxicodendron* Poisoning," *Medical Brief*, XXV, 696.

TOOTHAKER, S. A.
1838–39. "*Rhus Toxicodendron* var. *radicans*," *Boston Medical and Surgical Journal*, XIX, 190–92. Boston.

TRAILL, CATHERINE P.
1885. *Studies of Plant Life in Canada*, pp. 110, 142, 143, 144. Ottawa.
1896. *Studies of Plant Life in Canada* (2d ed.), pp. 152, 200. Toronto.

TREAT, E. B. (publisher).
1891. *International Medical Annual*, IX, 48. New York and Chicago.

TROUSSEAU, A., and PIDOUX, H.
1880. Article "Sumac" in *Treatise on Therapeutics* (9th ed.), II, 200, 201. (Translated into English by D. F. Lincoln.) New York.

TUNMANN, P.
1908. *Pharmaceutische Zentralhalle*, XLIX, 457. Dresden.

USHER, J. D.
1892. *Medical Brief*, XX, 680. St. Louis.

UTZ, S. S.
1894. *Louisville Medical Monthly*, I, 257. Louisville.

WADE, J. W.
1896. *Medical World*, XIV, 471. Philadelphia.

WAGGAMAN, S.
1895. *A Compendium of Botanic Materia Medica*, p. 257. Washington.

WALLER, J. L.
1903. *Merck's Report*, XII, 218. New York.

WALLACE, C. K.
1876. *Louisville Medical Journal*, II, 57. Louisville.

WARD, J. M.
1879. "Poisoning by *Rhus radicans*," *Medical Record*, XVI, 117. New York.

WARD, RALPH F.
1908. "Severe Ivy Poisoning," *New York Medical Journal*, LXXXVIII, 1224–25.

WARREN, L. E.
1913. "Some Observations on the Pollen of Poison Sumac," *American Journal of Pharmacy*, LXXXV, 545–49. Philadelphia.

WATER, J. D.
1892. *Medical Brief*, XX, 958. St. Louis.
WAUGH, W. F.
1891. *Times and Register*, XXIII, 242. Philadelphia and New York.
WEATHERFORD, S. H.
1882. *Therapeutic Gazette*, VI, 291. Detroit.
WIERZBICKI, F. P.
1858. "Poison Oak (*Rhus Toxicodendron*)," *Transactions of the Medical Society of California*, II, 146–50. Sacramento.
WEISER, F. R.
1888. *American Journal of Pharmacy*, LX, 390. Philadelphia.
WERDER, M.
1906. *Medical World*, XXIV, 68. Philadelphia.
WHELPLEY, H. M.
1894. *Proceedings of the American Pharmaceutical Association*, XLII, 133. Baltimore.
WHITE.
1875. *Boston Medical and Surgical Journal*, XCIII, 265–67.
WHITE, C. J.
1912. "Rhus Poisoning," *Journal of Cutaneous Diseases including Syphilis*, XXX, 280. New York.
WHITE, G.
1886. "Is Rhus-Poisoning a Purely Local Affection?" *Medical Record*, XXX, 489. New York.
WHITE, J. B.
1886. *Journal of Cutaneous and Venereal Diseases*, IV, 207. New York.
WHITE, J. C.
1873. "On the Action of *Rhus Venenata* and *Rhus Toxicodendron* upon the Human Skin," *New York Medical Journal*, XVII, 225–49. New York.
1887. "*Dermatitis Venenata*." Boston.
1889. *Boston Medical and Surgical Journal*, CXXI, 583. Boston.
1897. *Boston Medical and Surgical Journal*, CXXXVI, 77. Boston.
1903. "Dermatitis Venenata—a Supplemental List," *Journal of Cutaneous Diseases*, XXI, 441. New York.
WICKHAM, W. H.
1879. *American Journal of Pharmacy*, XXVII, 610, 612. Philadelphia.
WIEGAND, F. S.
1884. "Remedy for Rhus Poisoning," *American Journal of Pharmacy*, LVI, 355. Philadelphia.
WILCOX, T. E.
1895. *Garden and Forest*, VIII, 478. New York.
1886. *Medical Record*, XXX, 222. New York.

WILLIAMS, R. G.
1886. *Medical Record*, XXX, 319. New York.
WILLIAMS, T. W.
1902. *Medical World*, XX, 482. Philadelphia.
WILMOT, E. T.
1879. *Michigan Medical News*, II, 178. Detroit.
WINFIELD, J. M.
1897. *Brooklyn Medical Journal*, XI, 404.
WINSOR, L. C.
1886. *Medical Record*, XXX, 320. New York.
WISEMAN, A. W.
1880–81. "Sulfate of Copper for the Eruption Caused by *Rhus Toxicodendron*, *Rhus radicans*, etc.," *Virginia Medical Monthly*, VII, 596–98. Richmond.
WITMER, A. F.
1895. "Mercuric Chlorid in the Treatment of Rhus Poisoning," *Philadelphia Polyclinic*, IV, 267. Philadelphia.
WOOD, GEORGE B.
1834. "Action du Rh. immunité de quelques personnes," *Dispensatory of the United States of America*, p. 669.
WOOD, H. C.
1890. *Therapeutic Gazette* (3d ser.), VI, 95. Detroit.
WOODBURY, F., and FARQUHARSON, R.
1889. *A Guide to Therapeutics and Materia Medica*, pp. 208, 314, 448. Philadelphia.
WRIGHT, P. B.
1900. "Medicine in Meter," *Annual of Eclectic Medicine and Surgery*, VIII, 505. Cincinnati.
WRIGHT, F. L.
1882. *Therapeutic Gazette*, VI, 382. Detroit.
YANDELL, L. P.
1876. "Poison Oak Eruption," *Louisville Medical News*, II, 32. Louisville.
YOUNG, A. H.
1878. "*Monotropa uniflora*," *Botanical Gazette*, III, 37, 38. Logansport.
YOUNG, W. H.
1898. *Medical World*, XVI, 298. Philadelphia.

# INDEX

PRINTED IN THE U.S.A.